project WILD

PRINCIPAL SPONSORS

Project WILD is principally sponsored by the Western Association of Fish and Wildlife Agencies and the Western Regional Environmental Education Council.

Participating Members

Alaska Department of Education
Alaska Department of Fish and Game
Arizona Department of Education
Arizona Game and Fish Department
California Department of Education
California Department of Fish and Game
Colorado Department of Education
Colorado Division of Wildlife
Idaho Department of Education
Idaho Department of Fish and Game
Montana Office of Public Instruction
Montana Department of Fish, Wildlife, and Parks
Nevada Department of Education
Nevada Department of Wildlife
New Mexico Department of Education
New Mexico Department of Game and Fish
Oregon Department of Fish and Wildlife
Oregon Department of Education
Utah Division of Wildlife Resources
Utah State Board of Education
Washington State Office of the Superintendent of Public Instruction
Washington Department of Game
Wyoming Department of Education
Wyoming Game and Fish Department

project WILD

Elementary Activity Guide

Project WILD is an interdisciplinary, supplementary environmental and conservation education program for educators of kindergarten through high school age young people.

These materials (1983 edition) have been endorsed by the National Council for the Social Studies
and are consistent with recommendations of the National Science Teachers Association.

Each of us alive today shares a commitment to the continuing health of this planet. It is not just our home—it is a home we share with all other living things.

Our future depends on our working to maintain and improve the quality of the environment for life on this earth.

We at Windstar—and I think each of us, everywhere—know that we have important choices to make.

One choice we each can make is to seek out and support quality education programs. Project WILD is one such program. Emphasizing wildlife as a way to understand our responsibilities to all living things, Project WILD takes young people "from awareness to action." Its goal is to develop awareness, knowledge, skills, and commitment which will result in informed decisions, responsible behavior, and constructive actions...for wildlife, and the environment upon which all life depends.

Project WILD is sponsored principally by state wildlife agencies, and state departments of education, working in cooperation with diverse organizations and caring, hard-working people throughout the United States and Canada.

We hope you get involved. Thanks for what you are doing—each of you, in your own way—to contribute to a healthy, peaceful planet earth... now, and in the future.

Peace,

John Denver
Founder and President
Windstar

Project WILD Steering Committee
Kerry Baldwin, Arizona Game and Fish Department, Chairman
William F. Hammond, Lee County Schools, Florida
William R. "Bob" Hernbrode, Oracle Education Project, Arizona
Dr. Richard Kay, Idaho Department of Education
Joanna P. Lackey, New Mexico Department of Game and Fish
Dolores Moulton Larson, Alaska Department of Fish and Game
Dr. Don Lundstrom, Pajaro Valley School District, California

Ex-Officio: Cliff Hamilton, Fiscal Manager,
  Western Regional Environmental Education Council; former member.

Former Members: Edward Eschler, Montana Office of Public Instruction,
  former Chairman;
Dr. Lewis Nelson, Jr., University of Idaho, former member;
Rudolph J. H. Schafer, California Department of Education,
  former Chairman.

Project Staff
Dr. Cheryl Charles, Director
Judy Dawson, Administrative Assistant

Project WILD, Salina Star Route, Boulder, Colorado 80302.
                                    (303) 444-2390

Independent Research and Evaluation
Dr. Ben Peyton, Michigan State University,
  Research and Evaluation Advisor
Lyn Fleming, Director, Project WILD Field Test

PREFACE

Project WILD is an interdisciplinary, supplementary environmental and conservation education program emphasizing wildlife.

For instructional purposes in Project WILD, wildlife is defined as any non-domesticated animal. Wildlife may be small organisms only visible to people if seen through a microscope, or as large as a great blue whale. Wildlife includes, but is not limited to, insects, spiders, birds, reptiles, fish, amphibians, and mammals, if non-domesticated.

Project WILD's primary audience is teachers of kindergarten through high school students. This does not limit the usefulness of the Project to formal educational settings, however. Volunteers working with young people in pre-school and after-school programs; representatives of private conservation, industry, and other community groups who are interested in providing instructional programs for young people or their teachers; and personnel involved in preparation of future teachers are all among those who effectively use the instructional resources of this program.

Project WILD is based on the premise that young people and their teachers have a vital interest in learning about the earth as home for people and wildlife. The program emphasizes wildlife—because of its intrinsic, ecological, and other values, as well as its importance as a basis for understanding the fragile grounds upon which all life rests. Project WILD is designed to prepare young people for decisions affecting people, wildlife, and their shared home, earth. In the face of pressures of all kinds affecting the quality and sustainability of life on earth as we know it, Project WILD addresses the need for human beings to develop as responsible members of the ecosystem.

The goal of Project WILD is to assist learners of any age in developing awareness, knowledge, skills, and commitment to result in informed decisions, responsible behavior, and constructive actions concerning wildlife and the environment upon which all life depends.

Project WILD is a joint project of the Western Association of Fish and Wildlife Agencies (WAFWA) and the Western Regional Environmental Education Council (WREEC). These two organizations are the primary sponsoring agencies.

The Western Association is a group comprised of the directors of the state agencies in 13 western states who are responsible for management of wildlife in their respective states.

The Western Regional Environmental Education Council is a not-for-profit corporation comprised of representatives of the state departments of education and state resource agencies in 13 western states.

Agreements between these two sponsoring organizations allow for additional sponsorship by other interested organizations and agencies.

The WILD Steering Committee, staff, WREEC, WAFWA members, and all associate organizational and state sponsors as well as others associated with the program are dedicated to achieving the highest possible standards of professional quality, factual accuracy, and objectivity in all programs, activities and materials bearing the WILD name. The Project WILD Steering Committee has adopted policies and guidelines which state Project WILD's commitment to neutrality on controversial issues, treating such issues fairly and honestly without advocating any one particular point of view, recognizing that people need information from a variety of sources to make their own informed decisions. Project WILD programs, activities, and materials are not to be used to promote agency or organizational policies or political points of view.

Associate and Contributing Sponsorship

It is possible for an agency or organization to become an associate or contributing sponsor of Project WILD, with appropriate credit given for that organization's involvement in the program. Each revision of the project materials will reflect the complete list of sponsors.

For Additional Information

For additional information about participation in Project WILD as an associate or contributing sponsor, please contact the Project WILD Steering Committee or the Project Director.

For information about Project WILD's availability in Canada, please contact the Canadian Wildlife Federation, 1673 Carling Avenue, Ottawa, Ontario, Canada T5K 2G6.

INTRODUCTION

A concern for the land and its resources is basic to our survival, both as individuals and as a nation, for we cannot live apart from our planetary home. Environmental quality and human health and well-being are interdependent.

What will our land be like 20, 40, or 100 years from now? No one can really be certain, but the trends are there, and we are gaining in our knowledge of environmental cause and effect. We can be sure, however, that our environmental future is to a large degree in our hands. We have our technologies, and we are gaining in our ability to manipulate the physical environment and its resources—for better or for worse. The directions we take with our technologies are very much dependent upon the values we hold and the choices we make, individually and socially.

Two elements of society play key roles in shaping future environments: resource management and education. Both are concerned with the future. The goal of education is the highest and best use—or conservation—of the human resource. The goal of resource management is the highest and best use—or conservation—of natural resources. These goals are interdependent.

Project WILD is a joint effort involving representatives of these two key elements of society to do something together which might have a beneficial effect on future environments as well as on the lives and well-being of humans and wildlife who will share them. Much has been accomplished thus far; much remains to be done. The commitment is there, however, and steady progress is being made. How might we describe what has been accomplished thus far?

Some might say that Project WILD is an excellent set of teaching materials bound in an attractive format. Professional educators could describe these materials as a supplementary, interdisciplinary, educational program directed at providing learning experiences for students in kindergarten through grade twelve.

WILD is these things, and more. These descriptions fall short of capturing the essence of the program. Quite simply, Project WILD is people—educators, resource managers, citizen conservationists, and others—doing something together which they believe is important for children, and for the land and its resources, now and for the future.

The prime movers in Project WILD were resource management professionals and education administrators with state-level responsibilities from 13 western states working through the Western Regional Environmental Education Council (WREEC) and the Western Association of Fish and Wildlife Agencies. These people put together the basic concept and plan of action for the program and secured the necessary resources to get it underway. Organizationally, WREEC is responsible for the materials and program development, while the Western Association provides technical expertise and program resources and is responsible for state-level implementation. Other agencies and organizations have since joined as cosponsors, and have an input into the direction of the program through the joint WREEC/Western Association Steering Committee for Project WILD.

WREEC has provided a means for its members to develop and coordinate state-level conservation and environmental education programs on a regional basis for the last 12 years. The organization began as a federal project through a U.S. Office of Education grant in 1970, and became an independent nonprofit educational corporation in 1976.

One of the most visible accomplishments of WREEC is Project Learning Tree (PLT), also a supplementary, interdisciplinary educational program for educators working with students in kindergarten through grade twelve. Project Learning Tree was produced through a grant from the American Forest Institute, and is cosponsored by WREEC and the American Forest

Institute. Now in use in more than 30 states and two Canadian provinces, Project Learning Tree provides materials and support services. The Project to date has provided instruction and materials for more than 60,000 teachers and youth leaders—with an emphasis on effectively teaching youngsters about forest resources and our interdependence with the natural world.

The experience gained over ten years of working with Project Learning Tree proved to be of great value in developing Project WILD. The same general procedure was followed in developing the materials. A content outline or framework was developed cooperatively with input from a great number of people—educators, preservationists, conservationists, wildlife managers, business and industry representatives, and others. The basic materials to teach the concepts in the outline were developed by teachers in five writing workshops held in western states, and were extensively field-tested and edited before being assembled in final form. As with Project Learning Tree, the materials will be available to those who attend instructional workshops to be offered by staff-trained leaders. In the sponsoring states, the fish and wildlife agencies typically will be responsible for the statewide implementation program, working with the state education agency, citizens groups, local school personnel, and others. Follow-up activities, evaluation, revision of the materials, and other staff services will be offered through WREEC for the forseeable future.

As with all good teaching materials, Project WILD is concerned with providing information and helping students evaluate choices and thereby make reasonable decisions. In short, our mission is to help youngsters learn **how** to think, not **what** to think.

In order to assure objectivity, WREEC retained editorial control over the entire project. Decisions are made by a Steering Committee chaired by the President of WREEC, with representation from both WREEC and the Western Association of Fish and Wildlife Agencies. Associate sponsors may attend and participate in all Steering Committee meetings, but have no vote. We are proud of the fact that our strict efforts at balance and objectivity, as well as the technical validity and educational value of the materials, have gained sponsors for the project from a number of organizations representing a wide range of views on wildlife and its management.

As noted, Project WILD is a people program. Its overall purpose is to motivate youngsters to take intelligent and constructive action to conserve wildlife and natural resources. Much has been accomplished so far: framework and materials produced, field testing and evaluation completed, implementation plans developed and initiated. However, the process will not be complete until the learning activities reach a significant number of youngsters—in classrooms, through youth groups, and as individuals.

That is why we consider you—the person now reading this volume—to be so important. You are a key part of the people process, and it is you who must take WILD on the next step in its journey to the youngsters. We will help you all we can, but the final success of the program depends upon your skill in using these materials and resources. And, in so doing, you become part of us—and we become part of you: people who care about children, about our land and its resources, about the present and the future, and who are willing to do something about it.

Welcome to Project WILD!

Rudolph J.H. Schafer

Western Regional
Environmental Education Council

HOW TO USE THIS BOOK

Thanks for your interest in Project WILD! Project WILD has been designed to be an instructional resource for people who care about natural resources and the environment—beginning with the recognition that the earth is home for people and wildlife.

A Supplement to Existing Courses and Programs

Instructional activities within the Project WILD materials are designed for easy integration into school subject and skill areas—especially science, social studies, language arts, mathematics, and art—so that classroom teachers may use the materials as a means by which to teach required concepts and skills. . .at the same time teaching about people, wildlife, and the environment. Educators in non-school settings, such as scout leaders, outdoor education camp personnel, park naturalists, and others also find the materials of use.

Instructors may use one or many Project WILD activities. The activities may be integrated into existing courses of study, or the entire set of activities may serve quite effectively as the basis for a course of study.

Organization of the Materials

Because these materials are supplementary—designed for integration into existing courses of study—instructors may pick and choose from the activities. Each activity is designed to stand alone, without other Project WILD activities. There is no need to do the activities in order, nor to do all activities, even for a given grade level. However, the activities have been placed in a thematic and developmental order that can serve as an aid to their use. They are organized to allow students to acquire knowledge, information, and skills to assist them in making informed and responsible decisions affecting wildlife, people, and our shared environments.

The activities are organized into seven major sections, corresponding to the Conceptual Framework which can be found in the back of this guide. By looking at the Table of Contents—or reading the Conceptual Framework—you can see the conceptual development: from awareness and appreciation. . .to responsible human actions. The sections are:

Section One: Awareness and Appreciation

Activities in this section are introductory. They are designed to establish a foundation for most of the activities which follow. For example, beginning the school year or an instructional unit involving wildlife with either "What's Wild" or "Animal Charades" establishes a definition of wildlife, and distinguishes between wild and domesticated animals. Other activities in this section examine similar survival needs of people, domesticated animals, and wildlife, including a basic introduction into the components of habitat.

Section Two: Diversity of Wildlife Values

Activities in this section provide students an opportunity to consider the range of contributions by wildlife to people and the environment—including aesthetic, ecological, scientific, political, commercial, economic, recreational, and intrinsic values.

Section Three: Ecological Principles

Activities in this section provide a good foundation for understanding the characteristics of environments, how they work, who and what inhabits them, and specific implications for understanding these principles as they affect wildlife. If the students have limited or no background in ecological principles, it is best to select a few introductory activities from Sections One and Three before tackling some of the more complex activities found in later sections of the Project WILD materials.

Section Four: Management and Conservation

This section builds on the general principles established in Sections One and Three, and provides an opportunity for more depth in understanding how wildlife and other natural resources can be managed and conserved.

Section Five: People, Culture, and Wildlife

The major emphasis of activities in this section is to examine the influence of ways that human cultures affect people's attitudes toward and treatment of wildlife and other natural resources—from music to advertisements to cartoons and bumper stickers.

Section Six: Trends, Issues, and Consequences

Activities in this section are most effective when students have some background in wildlife and ecological principles. A range of difficult issues is addressed. Students are given opportunities to apply knowledge they have gained in earlier activities by consideration of difficult issues and their consequences.

Section Seven: Responsible Human Actions

Activities in this section are designed to serve as a way for students to recognize, evaluate, and make responsible choices in their own lives—reflecting the knowledge and skills they have acquired in earlier activities. Solutions are not prescribed for students. Instead, students are provided opportunities to consider and take constructive actions as thoughtful, informed, and responsible inhabitants of our shared home.

Organization of Each Activity

Each activity includes a statement of the instructional objective; a brief description of the instructional method employed; background information for the instructor; a list of any materials needed; step by step procedures; a few limited examples of ways in which to evaluate student learning; indication of recommended grade level, subjects from which concepts are drawn, skills, duration; recommended group size; setting (indoors or outdoors); and key vocabulary. In every case, an instructor is encouraged to adapt activities for different ages, subjects, skills, group sizes, etc. Finally, each activity includes a listing of points in the Conceptual

Framework outline to which the activity either corresponds directly, i.e., the activity is designed to teach the concepts specifically; or, indirectly, i.e., the points noted are useful additional background information for the instructor.

Appendices

The Appendices include a list of agencies and organizations which are referenced in one or more Project WILD activities; a glossary of terms for use by the instructor; a complete listing of the Conceptual Framework in outline form; an alphabetical listing of activities by title; a set of guidelines for study of live animals in classrooms; and cross references by subject area, skills, grade levels, and topics for use in creating instructional units.

We hope you find these materials of use. Let us hear from you at any time with suggestions as to how to improve them, requests for additional information and assistance—and any news of your experiences and those of your students as you "do something WILD!"

The time is overdue in developing a long-term approach to the problems of people, wildlife, and habitat . . . The earth is home to us all.

TABLE OF CONTENTS

SECTION ONE:
AWARENESS AND APPRECIATION

SECTION TWO:
DIVERSITY OF WILDLIFE VALUES

SECTION THREE: ECOLOGICAL PRINCIPLES

SECTION FOUR: MANAGEMENT AND CONSERVATION

SECTION FIVE: PEOPLE, CULTURE, AND WILDLIFE

SECTION SIX:
TRENDS, ISSUES, AND CONSEQUENCES

SECTION SEVEN:
RESPONSIBLE HUMAN ACTIONS

APPENDICES

AWARENESS AND APPRECIATION

WHAT'S WILD?

Objectives

Students will be able to: 1) distinguish between wildlife and domesticated animals; and 2) recognize that wildlife occurs in a variety of forms.

Method

Students find and classify pictures of wild and domesticated animals, and construct collages.

Background

An animal is generally referred to as any living organism other than a plant. Wildlife is any animal that lives in a basically free condition, providing for its own food, shelter, and other needs in an environment that serves as a suitable habitat. Wildlife refers to animals that are not tamed or domesticated. Wildlife may be small organisms only visible to humans if seen through a microscope, or as large as a whale. Wildlife includes, but is not limited to, insects, spiders, birds, reptiles, fish, amphibians, and mammals, if non-domesticated. Domesticated animals are those which humans have tamed, kept in captivity, and bred for special purposes. The process of domestication takes place over a long period of time and has involved genetic manipulation through selective breeding. All domesticated animals have their origins in wild ancestors. Cattle used for food and other products; sheep for wool and other products, as well as dogs, cats, birds, and fish commonly kept as pets are all examples of domesticated animals.

Confusion can arise about animals that sometimes may be wild, sometimes may be tamed, and sometimes may be domesticated. If the animal, or population of animals, can live on its own, survive, and even reproduce, it is probably wild. Individual animals may be tamed—like some animals in zoos—while most of their numbers remain wild. A wild animal may appear to be tame, but still should be considered wild unless it is both tamed and domesticated. Some animals that are usually considered domesticated—like dogs, cats, horses, and goats—may become wild. When they do, the term "feral" is used. For example, there are feral goats on Catalina Isle, and feral horses and burros in some areas of western states in the U.S.

Where it is difficult to distinguish whether an animal is wild or domesticated, encourage the students to think in terms of what is **usually** the case. Remember that wild animals basically take care of themselves, as long as they have a suitable environment or habitat in which to live. Domesticated or tamed animals basically depend on people to feed and take care of them, and are typically used by people; for example, as a source of products and as pets. Whereas domesticated animals like cats and dogs are normally considered suitable pets, wild animals—even if tamed—are nearly always unsuitable, inappropriate, and frequently illegal pets.

The major purpose of this activity is for students to be able to distinguish between wild and domesticated animals.

Materials

magazine or newspaper pictures of a wide variety of animals, poster board or heavy construction paper, glue

Age: Grades K-3
Subjects: Science, Language Arts, Art
Skills: classification, media construction, observation
Duration: 60 minutes
Group Size: any
Setting: indoors
Conceptual Framework Reference: I., I.B.3., I.B.4., V.A.1
Key Vocabulary: animal, wild, domesticated

Procedure

1. Ask students to bring pictures to class of as many animals as they can find in magazines or newspapers at home (or get them from magazines and newspapers available in school, if any). Ask the students to look for pictures of as many different animals as they can, telling them that animals are any living things except plants.

2. Once the students have assembled a collection of animal pictures, it is time to classify them. Students may work alone or in small groups. Talk with the students about wild animals and domesticated animals (like pets, farm animals, etc.) before they get started with their classifying.

3. Once the students have put their animals into two categories—either wild or domesticated—get out the poster board or construction paper and glue and ask the students to make two collages. . .one of wildlife, and one of domesticated animals. You can make a classroom gallery out of the products.

Extensions

1. Make a master list of the wildlife and domesticated animals. Use the words for spelling, and talk about the variety of animals found.

2. Younger students can take cut-outs of animals and put them where they fit—like birds in the sky, whales in the ocean, a deer in the forest.

3. Make mobiles that show "layers" of animals—in the sea, on land, and in the air. Build one huge mobile with an animal for each student that shows deserts, forests, mountains, seas, and the skies. Different colors of brightly-colored yarn can be used to hang the different animals in the mobile according to the ecosystem in which they live.

Evaluation

Which animals have been domesticated: goldfish, horses, cows, ducks, boa constrictors, mosquitoes, bats, chickens, lions, eagles?

ANIMAL CHARADES

Objective

Students will be able to define wildlife, as well as to distinguish between domesticated and non-domesticated animals.

Background

An animal is generally referred to as any living organism other than a plant. Wildlife is any animal that lives in a basically free condition, providing for its own food, shelter, and other needs in an environment that serves as a suitable habitat. Wildlife refers to animals that are not tamed or domesticated. Wildlife may be small organisms only visible to humans if seen through a microscope, or as large as a whale. Wildlife includes, but is not limited to, insects, spiders, birds, reptiles, fish, amphibians, and mammals, if non-domesticated. Domesticated animals are those which humans have tamed, kept in captivity, and bred for special purposes. The process of domestication takes place over a long period of time and has involved genetic manipulation through selective breeding. All domesticated animals have their origins in wild ancestors. Cattle used for food and other products; sheep for wool and other products, as well as dogs, cats, birds, and fish commonly kept as pets are all examples of domesticated animals.

Confusion can arise about animals that sometimes may be wild, sometimes may be tamed, and sometimes may be domesticated. If the animal, or population of animals, can live on its

Age: Grades 4—12
Subjects: Language Arts, Science, Drama
Skills: physical interpretation of concepts, observation, analysis
Duration: 30 minutes
Group Size: 30—40 students, or fewer
Setting: indoors or outdoors
Conceptual Framework Reference: I.B.4., V.A.1
Key Vocabulary: animal, wild, domesticated

own, survive, and even reproduce, it is probably wild. Individual animals may be tamed—like some animals in zoos—while most of their numbers remain wild. A wild animal may appear to be tame, but still should be considered wild unless it is both tamed and domesticated. Some animals that are usually considered domesticated—like dogs, cats, horses, and goats—may become wild. When they do, the term "feral" is used. For example, there are feral goats on Catalina Isle, and feral horses and burros in some areas of western states in the U.S.

Where it is difficult to distinguish whether an animal is wild or domesticated, encourage the students to think in terms of what is **usually** the case. Remember that wild animals basically take care of themselves, as long as they have a suitable environment or habitat in which to live. Domesticated or tamed animals basically depend on people to feed and take care of them, and are typically used by people; for example, as a source of products and as pets. Whereas domesticated animals like cats and dogs are normally considered suitable pets, wild animals—even if tamed—are nearly always unsuitable, inappropriate, and frequently illegal pets.

The primary purpose of this activity is for students to be able to distinguish between wildlife and domesticated animals.

Method
Students use "charades" to distinguish between wild and domesticated animals.

Materials
chalkboard for use by scorekeeper, small pieces of writing paper, container (e.g., box, hat, wastebasket)

Procedure

1. This is charades—with an instructional purpose! In order to begin this activity, first create a space in the classroom that provides room for individual students to act out an animal; and room for the other students to observe the charade and guess which animal is being portrayed.

2. Once the stage and audience areas have been established, each student should take a small piece of paper. On this paper, the student should write **his or her name, the name of the animal the student is going to portray, and whether the animal is domesticated or wild.** (Or, don't have the students identify themselves. Have each student write the name of an animal on a slip of paper, indicate whether it is wild or domesticated, and then take turns randomly selecting and portraying the animals.) These slips of paper should be given to the teacher before the charades begin.

3. The teacher drops the slips of paper into a container. The charades will be played in the order the teacher pulls the names from the container, or simply by letting the students take turns. The student goes to the area of the room that is the "stage." A timekeeper (designated from among the students) says, "Begin," and the student on stage dramatizes the animal chosen. A charade should be guessed by the audience—who may call out their guesses—within a ten-second time limit.

4. Follow the charades with a summary discussion, asking the students to clarify their definitions of **wildlife** and **domesticated animals.** Encourage their identification of the range of forms found in wild and domesticated species. For example, they should recognize that wildlife may be microscopic in size, like an amoeba, or longer than most houses, like some whales.

Determining whether an animal is wild or domesticated can sometimes be difficult. Students may recognize that animals in zoos might fit the definition of domesticated animals. Taking lions, for example, you might note two things: most lions are not in zoos, therefore the species is still found most commonly in the wild; and, lions are not commonly bred for special purposes in zoos, nor usually tamed, and thus might fit only one of the three criteria within the definition of domesticated—that of being captive. Raising trout for stocking and food is an example of another confusing issue. Such trout are captive and bred for special purposes. However, most species of trout exist in the wild, and even those captive are not considered tame. In assisting students to establish definitions for what may be considered wild and domesticated species, both lions and trout can be considered wild. However, it is useful and important for the students to consider what appear to be and may be exceptions, as they refine their understanding of distinctions between wild and domesticated animals.

Extensions

1. One or more "animals" which coexist can mime together, representing the animals, their relationships, and the ecosystem within which they live.

2. Classify animals into appropriate and inappropriate pets, with reasons for the classifications.

Evaluation
Define wildlife.

Explain, using examples, how a species can be considered "wild" and "domesticated."

BEARLY BORN

Objective
Students will be able to identify similar survival needs of both black bears and human babies.

Method
Students illustrate, compute, and graph differences between people and black bears at various stages of maturity.

Background
There are similarities in basic survival needs of black bear cubs and human babies. Both are mammals, born from their mother's body. Although humans sometimes substitute soy or other products for mother's milk, bear cubs and most humans survive solely on mother's milk in the first months of life.

This activity is designed for students to recognize similarities between bear cubs and human babies, as well as to develop mathematics skills.

The following additional information about bear cubs and their families may be of assistance.

Age: Grades 4—7
Subjects: Mathematics, Science
Skills: analysis, comparing similarities and differences, graphing, estimation, prediction with ratio and averaging optional, discussion, drawing, generalization, media construction, reading, writing
Duration: two 30-minute periods
Group Size: any
Setting: indoors
Conceptual Framework Reference: I.A.
Key Vocabulary: similarities, differences, survival needs, omnivore

BLACK BEAR CUBS AND THEIR FAMILIES

A baby bear is called a cub. An adult female bear is called a sow. An adult male bear is called a boar. A sow is usually impregnated by a boar in May or June. Interestingly, the fertile egg does not begin active development until around October. In this way, the mother bear's body naturally slows down the development process so that birth can take place around January 1. Contrasted with human fetal development of nine months, the mother bear is pregnant for about seven months, with the fetus actively developing only for about three months.

The sow has her cub or cubs in the shelter or den where she spends the winter months. A mother black bear usually has one or two cubs, although she may have as many as four. However, she won't have any cubs until she is four or five years of age, and then only every other year. From the time of birth, the mother's milk is the first food source for the young animals. At birth, a young cub has hair and weighs about eight ounces—about the size of a guinea pig. The bear cubs stay in the den with their mother until they are able to move around very actively. The bear cubs and their mother usually stay in the den until late April or early May. Boars and sows without cubs usually leave their dens a month earlier.

At the time the cubs leave the den with their mother, they are extremely dependent upon her. They still nurse, depending on mother's milk as a food source until the middle of summer, around six months. However, once out of the den, they quickly learn about additional food sources.

Black bears are omnivores. That means they eat plant and animal material. They tend to eat grass, nuts, berries in late summer, insects, grubs—and fish and rodents when they can catch them! Although they do not normally eat carrion, they will turn over dead and decaying animals to find and eat the protein-rich maggots.

When black bear cubs reach one year in age, female cubs weigh about 30 to 50 pounds. Males weigh about 50 to 70 pounds. A mature female bear will weigh about 150 to 185 pounds, and a male will weigh about 275 pounds.

NOTE: Your students may ask where the male, or father, bears are during the time the young cubs are growing. Male bears will kill cubs, so the mother bear keeps the cubs out of contact with males, and will fight to protect them if provoked. Under good conditions, a bear may live as long as 30 or more years.

Materials
graph paper and drawing paper (Optional, for extension: yardsticks, 36 inch sewing tapes)

Procedure
1. Begin a discussion with the students about black bears. Ask them to guess how much a cub (baby bear) might weigh when it is born. Every student can write down a guess on a piece of paper. Call for their guesses. Ask for their ideas about how long mother bears are pregnant, what baby bears eat when they are born, how much they might weigh when they are a year old, how many brothers and sisters they might have who are their same age, how much they weigh when they are full grown, and how long they live.

2. Following the discussion, post this information, or provide it as a "hand-out:"

WEIGHT AND AGE RELATIONSHIPS
FOR BLACK BEAR

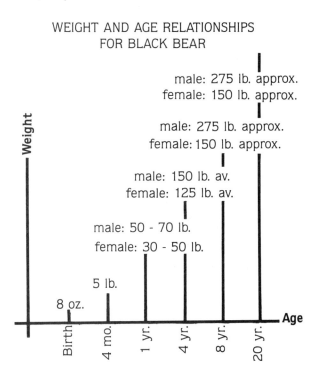

male: 275 lb. approx.
female: 150 lb. approx.

male: 275 lb. approx.
female: 150 lb. approx.

male: 150 lb. av.
female: 125 lb. av.

male: 50 - 70 lb.
female: 30 - 50 lb.

5 lb.

8 oz.

(Data are characteristic of black bear in the southwestern United States. There will be regional variation.)

3. Ask students to "fill in the blanks" with their own weight at the same ages as the information shows for the black bears. They will be required to estimate for years past their present age. Ask the students to:
a. graph both sets of data
b. draw a picture of the bear at each age
c. draw a picture of themselves at each age
One student's comparative data might look like this:

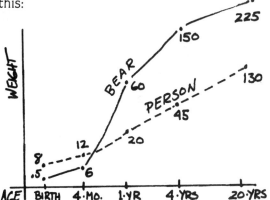

4. Ask the students to compute the following, and include their results with their graph and drawing:
a. How much weight did the black bear gain at each interval; that is, from birth to four months, four months to one year, etc.?
b. How much weight did you gain during the same intervals?
c. How many times more weight did the bear gain during each period?
5. In discussion, ask the students to comment on similarities and differences between bears and people. (For example, both are mammals. Describe their characteristics.) Ask students to identify clearly similarities in basic survival needs of bear cubs and babies.

Extensions

1. Get out your measuring tape! Researchers can estimate the weight of a bear by measuring the bear's girth (the distance around a bear's chest). Given the following data, students can measure the girth of their own chests and estimate how much they would weigh if they were black bears!

22'' girth: weight of 50 pounds
30'' girth: weight of 100 pounds
35'' girth: weight of 150 pounds
39'' girth: weight of 200 pounds
45'' girth: weight of 300 pounds
52'' girth: weight of 400 pounds

Or: Have the students weigh themselves and measure their chest girth. Graph or chart their weight and girth. Graph or chart the weight and girth of black bears. Compare! Weigh and measure girth of older students, teachers, and family members. Graph or chart the results. Possible questions:

a. How much does a four-year-old bear weigh per inch of girth? Ten-year-old? Twenty-year-old?
b. How much do various age groups of children weigh per inch of girth?
c. Are bears or children heavier per inch? How about adults versus bears?

2. Calculate how fast a given bear population, if unchecked by limiting factors, can increase over a specific period of time, assuming that: a sow will have two cubs (one of each sex) in her fifth year of life; the total time frame is ten years, from July 1 to June 30; the initial bear population is one five-year-old boar and two six-year-old sows, one with two cubs. Graph or chart the results.

Evaluation

List three survival needs which are similar for bears and humans.

Use the following data to construct a graph which compares the growth of catfish from Lake Erie and the growth of catfish from the Ohio River.

AGE IN YEARS

	1	2	3	4	5	6	7	8	9	
Lake Erie Catfish	69	115	160	205	244	278	305	336	366	
Ohio River Catfish	56	101	161	227	285	340	386	433	482	SIZE (in mm)

a. Which catfish grew the most between the ages of four and five years?
b. How many times larger is the Ohio catfish at nine years of age than at one year of age?

ANTS ON A TWIG

Objectives
Students will be able to: 1) identify similarities and differences in basic needs of ants and humans; and 2) generalize that humans and wildlife have similar basic needs.

Method
Students go outside to observe and demonstrate ant behavior.

Background
Humans, domesticated animals, and wildlife have similar basic needs. All depend upon the appropriate distribution (or arrangement) of food, water, shelter, and space.

Sometimes we forget that all living things share the same environment and basic needs. We don't always remember that every creature—from ants to people—needs food, water, shelter, and space to survive.

The major purpose of this activity is to remind students that humans are not the only species with these basic survival needs.

Materials
note pads and pens or pencils

Procedure
1. Go outside and find some ants—or even inside, if you can find some in school buildings. Check sidewalks, near the cafeteria, around windows. Look on trees, in flower beds, in vacant lots. Working in teams of three to six, ask the students to observe the ants' behavior. At least one student in each group should serve as a recorder, noting the students' observations. Included in their observations should be: evidence of how ants take care of their basic needs; description of what their basic needs are; and description of ant behavior, **including how ants move in a line.** (This is important for a later phase of the activity!) **Caution: Remind the students to make their observations without harming the ants or their habitat.**

2. After approximately 20 minutes of observation time, bring the teams of students to a central location outside. Ask the students to report their findings. Close the discussion with a sharing of descriptions of ant behavior.

3. Now it's time to demonstrate ant behavior. The students need to get into two lines of equal length facing each other in a narrow area—like on top of a fallen log, between two lines drawn with chalk on a sidewalk, or on a low wall about one foot wide. The two lines of ants must pass each other without falling off! The students should simulate ant behavior based on their earlier observations. Their arms and hands can serve as antennae; for example, touching as they pass each other. **Note to Teacher:** Physical dramatization of concepts—in this case, ant behavior—is an excellent way to facilitate retention of concept understanding.

Age: Grades 3—9
Subjects: Science (Modified: English, Drama)
Skills: analysis, classification, comparing similarities and differences, description, discussion, generalization, kinesthetic concept development, observation, small group work, writing
Duration: two 30-minute class periods; one 50—60-minute class period
Group Size: teams of three to six; approximately 30 students total
Setting: outdoors
Conceptual Framework Reference: I.A., I.A.4., I.C.1, I.C.2
Key Vocabulary: basic or survival needs, observation, evidence

---

4. The log or wall can now serve as a seating space. Having investigated the ways that ants meet their basic needs for **food, water, shelter,** and **space,** in a suitable arrangement, ask the students to describe similarities and differences between basic needs of ants and humans. Assist the students in generalizing that humans, ants, and other animals—both wild and tame—have similar basic needs. Summarize the discussion by noting that, although humans and ants are obviously different, both species share the same basic needs shared by all animal species—the fundamental needs for food, water, shelter, space, and the appropriate arrangement of these.

Extensions

1. Find resources for ant information. Do the student observations match the printed references? Verify accuracy of observations and check any discrepancies.

2. Commercial ant farms are available. One can be established in the classroom for additional observation.

3. Various humane experiments, stressing scientific observation, can be undertaken by the students. For example:

a. Map the space used by an ant colony—from their shelter, through their travels, and back to their shelter again.

b. Observe how ants find and use water. (Ants get most of their water from their food.) Put water out in various forms for a colony of ants; e.g., in a dish, in chunks of bread soaked in water, in smaller chunks. Observe and record what happens.

c. Find ants moving in a line. Drop a small piece of food near the line. Record whether the ants will move off the line to get the food. Repeat this process several times, varying the distance from the ant line and the food that is dropped.

Evaluation

Describe three ant behaviors you have observed.

For one of these behaviors, describe why the ants behaved that way. How does the behavior help the ant to survive?

What five basic needs do humans and ants share?

COLOR CRAZY

Objective
Students will be able to generalize that wildlife occurs in a wide variety of colors.

Method
Students create representations of colorful wild animals.

Background
Color is used as both protection and decoration. All life forms are colorful. This color is sometimes distinctive—like on zebras—and sometimes changeable, like on chameleons. Nature is the first, and ultimate, source of color.

The major purpose of this activity is for students to recognize that wildlife exists in a variety of colors.

Materials
crayons, paint, chalk, construction paper, scissors, glue are necessary; other brightly colored art construction materials, like artificial feathers, tissue paper, acorn shells, uncooked noodles are useful, but optional

Age: Grades K—6
Subjects: Science, Language Arts, Art
Skills: description, drawing, generalization, invention, media construction, observation, reading, writing
Duration: 45 minutes
Group Size: any
Setting: indoors
Conceptual Framework Reference: I.B.4.
Key Vocabulary: color, wildlife

Procedure

1. This is a "**Make A Colorful Wild Animal**" project! Get out brightly colored crayons, paint, chalk, construction paper, scissors, and glue. Other brightly colored materials would also be helpful. With these materials, ask the students to draw, paint, or construct a colorful creature—but one that could be a real, wild animal. This is not a monster-making project—but a project in which students create a colorful animal that could be real. They can make birds, reptiles, amphibians, insects, fish, mammals—whatever real, wild animal they would like.

2. Make a "**Colorful Wildlife Gallery.**" Display the animal creations in the classroom.

3. Develop a vocabulary list based on the children's descriptions of the animals.

4. Optional: Bring in wildlife reference books. Let the students look to see if they can find **real** animals like those they created.

5. Ask the students what they have learned about wild animals. Encourage the generalization that wild animals occur in a wide variety of colors.

Extensions

1. Make a "**Museum of Color.**" Match the students' invented animals with pictures of real animals. Find the primary colors of red, yellow, and blue. Look for "rainbow" animals that have three or more distinct colors on their bodies.

2. Make a "**Colors from Nature**" exhibit, and include colors from plants, rocks, and soil—as well as wildlife.

3. Put the pictures of animals with pictures of their natural surroundings. Look for animals that blend and those that stand out brightly.

Evaluation

Name a wild animal that has red for a color. Name two wild animals that have brown for a color. Name one that has yellow, one that has blue, and two that have green for a color.

INTERVIEW A SPIDER

Objective
Students will be able to generalize that wildlife ranges from microscopic forms to those many tons in size, and occurs in a variety of forms, colors, and adaptations.

Method
Students become reporters and use interview techniques to research and write about wild animals.

Background
Wildlife is surprisingly diverse. Insects, spiders, reptiles, worms, and most species of fish, birds, and mammals may be considered wildlife.

The major purpose of this activity is for students to establish a working definition of wildlife which recognizes that wildlife ranges from microscopic forms, like amoebas, to species many tons in size, like whales, and occurs in a variety of forms, colors, and adaptations.

CAUTION: Students may have a tendency to project inapplicable human characteristics to animals, especially because the "interview" format puts the "animals" in a human situation. Assist the students in avoiding anthropomorphism. Stress that they should try to see the world from the animals' perspective.

Materials
writing materials

Procedure
1. OPTIONAL: Invite a local newspaper reporter to talk with your students. Ask him or her to describe what a reporter does, and especially about the techniques of interviewing and writing used.
2. Work with the students to establish a research, interview, and reporting format for their use as reporters. For example:

Research
Each team of two students should:
Decide what animal to "interview." (You can assist by providing a diverse list of animals from which to choose—from microscopic to huge!)
Write a list of questions to ask.
Use reference materials to take notes for appropriate responses to the questions.

Interview
It's time to conduct the interview! Each team of reporters needs to find its animal. The students can go outside and find the real animal; or work in partners with roles changing (first one student asks the questions as the reporter and the other answers as the wild animal, and then switch roles). They may take notes, use a tape recorder, and even take photos! Remind the students to convey the perspective of the animal being interviewed and avoid projecting inapplicable human characteristics.

Age: Grades 5—8
Subjects: Language Arts, Science
Skills: description, discussion, generalization, interview, reading, research, writing (creative writing, grammar, punctuation, vocabulary development)
Duration: three classroom periods of 30 minutes each or longer; some research and writing done by students at home
Group Size: any
Setting: indoors and outdoors
Conceptual Framework Reference: I.B.4.
Key Vocabulary: interview, reporting, anthropomorphism

Reporting

Now it's time to organize the information gathered through the process of researching and interviewing the animal. Each team should use its notes as the basis for writing a newspaper article about the wild animal they interviewed.

3. Talk about the diversity of wildlife. Finally, ask each student to define wildlife in some way that shows his or her understanding of the term—including that wildlife ranges from microscopic forms to those many tons in size, and occurs in a variety of forms, colors, and adaptations.

Variation

Each team can conduct its interview in front of the other students, emphasizing public-speaking skills.

Extension

With the newspaper articles complete, either:
a) work with the students to publish a wildlife newspaper, for everyone to read and keep a copy; or
b) ask the students to read their articles aloud for everyone to hear.

Evaluation

Name one wild animal for each category:

Mammals that are very large.
Mammals that are very small.
Reptiles which have dull colors.
Reptiles which are colorful.
Fish that eat plants.
Fish that eat animals.
Birds that eat plants.
Birds that eat animals.
Fish which have dull colors.
Fish which are colorful.
Amphibians that are very large.
Amphibians that are very small.
Amphibians that run.
Amphibians that hop.
Insects that run.
Insects that hop.
Reptiles that are very large.
Reptiles that are very small.
Birds which have dull colors.
Birds which are colorful.
Mammals that run.
Mammals that hop.
Insects that eat plants.
Insects that eat animals.

GRASSHOPPER GRAVITY!

Objectives
Students will be able to: 1) describe a relationship between structure and function; 2) generalize that wildlife ranges from small to large, and occurs in a variety of forms; and 3) recognize that people have power to affect other animals, and with that power comes responsibility.

Method
Students observe, handle, and describe live grasshoppers or crickets.

Background
The major purpose of this activity is for students to recognize that wildlife occurs in a variety of forms and that people have power to affect animals. In the process, they develop important observation skills—and an increased appreciation of grasshoppers!

Materials
one plastic container, hand lens, live grasshopper or cricket for every two students, chalkboard

Procedure
1. People don't often think of insects as animals, and they hardly ever think of grasshoppers as wildlife. But a grasshopper is wildlife, too! Either send a small group of students out to collect grasshoppers in plastic jars, or send pairs of students out with a plastic jar. (A clear, plastic sheet pulled to the ground by two students usually traps grasshoppers safely!) You need one grasshopper for every two students. (Crickets can also be studied and can sometimes be purchased from pet and sporting goods stores.) Caution the students not to harm the grasshoppers. When you are through studying the grasshoppers, please release them. Tell the students they are going to be like some scientists—carefully observing wildlife, with as little impact as possible. Be prepared, however, for an accidental mishap that a grasshopper doesn't survive. Deal with such accidents on a case-by-case basis, encouraging the students to be careful—but also not to feel guilt if a grasshopper accidentally dies.

2. The following questions may be written out in some form for the students to use in observing their grasshoppers, or you might offer questions to the students aloud as they examine their grasshoppers. (This list can be shortened, and different questions used.) You may want to define some of the vocabulary before using the questions—like antennae, appendage. (For older students, see "Wild Words" for a journal-making activity that could precede this activity.)

Age: Grades 2—7 (and older)
Subjects: Science, Language Arts, Social Studies
Skills: analysis, classification, comparing similarities and differences, computation, description, discussion, generalization, listing, observation, reading, writing
Duration: 45 minutes, or longer if all questions are used; can serve as basis for two-week unit of study
Group Size: any
Setting: outdoors and indoors
Conceptual Framework Reference: I.B.4., I.D., II.A.3., II.B., II.F.
Key Vocabulary: wildlife, compound, antennae, appendage, estimate, habitat, responsibility

GRASSHOPPERS!

INTERESTING FEATURES What are some of the most outstanding features of the grasshopper?

LEGS How many legs does it have? Are they alike or different? Which legs are the jumping legs? Notice where the legs are attached to the grasshopper's body.

WINGS Look at the wings, if they are present. (Adults have wings. Immature grasshoppers show pads or stumps.) How many wings are there? Notice where they attach to the body.

HEAD Look at the head. How many eyes do you see? Why do you think they have so many eyes? Do they look like your eyes? Check carefully in front and below the large, compound eyes for three smaller, simpler eyes. These eyes probably see light but may not be able to see shapes, sizes, and colors.

MOUTH Do you see a mouth? Does the grasshopper have lips? Try to feed the grasshopper a leaf to watch the mouth parts move. Try to describe the mouth parts and how they move.

ANTENNAE Where are the antennae? Are they each a long, string-like, single appendage, or are they made up of many parts? Can you count the parts? Do they all look alike in size, shape, and color? Why do you think a grasshopper needs the antennae? For what? Think about radio and television antennae.

MOTION We usually think that grasshoppers "hop." Do they also walk? How do they walk on the ground or floor? If possible, watch the grasshopper climb a small stick, weed stem, or blade of grass. Does it use all of its legs? Without hurting your grasshopper, place it on the ground and make it jump. (If it is an adult with wings, it may fly instead!) Follow your insect and make it hop or jump several times (at least five times). Does it hop the same distance each time? Measure or estimate the distance of each hop of flight. Does the grasshopper seem to get tired? What makes you think so?

NOISE Do grasshoppers make noises? If your grasshopper makes a noise, try to learn if it does it with its mouth or with some other part of its body.

COLORS Look at the whole grasshopper carefully. Is it the same color all over? Are the colors, shapes, and sizes the same on both sides? What is attractive about your grasshopper? Is it clean? Watch to see what the grasshopper does to clean or groom itself.

HABITAT Where does the grasshopper live? What does it eat? Do grasshoppers live in your neighborhood year-round? Suggest two reasons that grasshoppers might not be seen where winters are cold (freezing temperatures, not enough food).

CONCLUSIONS Did you think there were so many interesting things about a grasshopper? Do you think other insects might be as interesting? What other insects or small animals might be interesting to look at and learn more about?

3. Finally, remind the students that a grasshopper is only one kind of animal—that animals, including wildlife, are all sizes and shapes. Some are smaller than a grasshopper, and some—like the whale—are much, much bigger.

4. Ask the students to take their grasshoppers outside and let them go. Some of the students may want to keep the grasshoppers as pets. Talk with the students about how difficult it is for a grasshopper to live very long in a captive state. How much space does a grasshopper need to live? Can you supply that in captivity? Tell the students that by studying grasshoppers, they have done what some scientists do: they have studied something very carefully to learn more about it. People have power over other animals in a lot of circumstances. The students exercised power over the grasshoppers while they studied them. With that power comes important responsibility. In this case, the students exercised their power by making an effort to be careful in handling the grasshopper and releasing it safely. Ask the students about other situations in which they feel a responsibility for their actions affecting animals. Examples: taking care of pets, not leaving litter outside that can hurt wild animals. (See "Litter We Know.")

Extensions

1. Find out what contributions grasshoppers make to ecological systems. What animals use grasshoppers as a food source?

2. Some farmers and gardeners consider grasshoppers a nuisance. Find out why. Find out what actions, if any, are taken to reduce crop damage from grasshoppers in your region. Do the actions seem appropriate? Why or why not? See "Deadly Links" for a related activity about pesticides in the environment.

Evaluation

If you were a biologist studying wildlife, which of these could you study and call it wildlife: tigers in India, deer in the forest, cows on a farm, foxes in Iowa, sparrows in the city, spiders in the forest, ants in a building, rats in a garbage dump, white mice in a laboratory cage? (probably all except the cows on a farm and the white mice in a laboratory cage)

Name three wild animals that are smaller than a grasshopper.

Name three wild animals that are larger than a grasshopper.

Name three types of wildlife that have one of the same colors as your grasshoppers but aren't insects.

Many animals must protect themselves from being eaten. Describe something about the grasshopper's body that would help the grasshopper protect itself from being caught and eaten.

How do you feel about this statement: "It is all right when a person is careless and kills or damages wildlife, as long as that person is studying the animal and finding out important information."

WILDLIFE IS EVERYWHERE!

Objectives
Students will be able to: 1) state that humans and wildlife share environments; and 2) generalize that wildlife is present in areas all over the earth.

Method
Students search their environment for evidence of wildlife.

Background
People often think of wildlife only as large animals like those they see in pictures of Africa, with lions and elephants. They might think of creatures of the North American forests that they have seen themselves, like deer and elk. But wildlife includes all animals that have not been domesticated by people.

Domesticated animals are those which have been tamed, made captive and bred for special purposes. Farm animals and pets are considered domesticated animals. (See "What's Wild?" and "Animal Charades.")

Wild animals are all the rest. What may be surprising is that wildlife includes the smallest animal organisms—even those that can be seen only through a microscope. Spiders, insects, reptiles, worms, and most species of fish, birds, and mammals may be considered wildlife. Wildlife occurs in a tremendous variety of forms and colors. And wildlife can be found all around us. Even when we think we can see or hear no animals at all—they exist somewhere around us—maybe even under our feet! There are even tens of thousands of life forms on our skin, in our hair, and inside our bodies! In fact, each of us would die if all the organisms that inhabit our bodies were to disappear. People are never truly alone in an environment. Some form of wildlife is near.

The major purpose of this activity is for students to understand that people and wildlife share environments. By investigating microenvironments or microhabitats, the students should be encouraged to generalize from the information they acquire to the entire planet, coming to the understanding that wildlife exists in some form in all areas of the planet. In the deserts of the southern hemisphere; the oceans, tropical jungles, and cities of the earth; from the Antarctic snow fields to the glaciers of the Arctic region, wildlife exists in a variety of forms.

Materials
string (optional)

Age: Grades K-3 (and older)
Subjects: Science, Language Arts
Skills: analysis, discussion, generalization, observation
Duration: 30 to 45 minutes
Group Size: any
Setting: indoors and outdoors
Conceptual Framework Reference: I.B., I.B.1, I.B.3.
Key Vocabulary: wildlife, wild, domesticated, environment, evidence

Procedure

CAUTION: Ask students to observe but not touch or disturb animals they see.

1. Invite your students to explore the classroom, looking for signs of wildlife. Even in the most cleanly-swept classrooms, you can usually find some signs of life—either past or present. It might be a spider web, dead insects near lights, or insect holes along baseboards and behind books. After the search and a discussion with the students about what—if anything—they found, introduce the idea that people and other animals share environments. Sometimes we don't even notice that we are sharing our environment with other living things, but we are.

2. Expand the search for other animals to the out-of-doors. Take the students on the school grounds and give everyone, working in pairs, five minutes to find an animal or some sign that an animal had been there. Look for indirect evidence, such as tracks, webs, droppings, feathers, and nests. (Be sure not to harm or seriously disturb anything.) After five minutes, sit down and talk about what everyone found.

Or, in advance, create a wildlife trail for your students to follow—looking for signs of animals along the way—by placing a long piece of string around an area of the school grounds and "salting" the path along the string with evidence of animals: bones, feathers, etc. The students can explore the trail in a "follow the leader" fashion. The students should remain quiet, observing to themselves. At the end of the trail, everyone should sit and discuss what they saw.

3. Talk with the children about what they learned. Emphasize that they have seen that people and wildlife share environments. They have seen evidence of wildlife at their school. Ask the children to guess whether they think different kinds of animals are found all over the earth—in the deserts, oceans, mountains, and cities. They may harvest their own experiences and talk about places they have been and have seen animals. Encourage the students to make the generalization that wildlife is present all over the earth.

Extensions

1. Survey your yard, kitchen, neighborhood, or city park . . . looking for wildlife.
2. Search magazines and books for wildlife from all over the planet.
3. "Invent" names and describe the wildlife found outside during searches. Older students can observe the animals, write a written description —and then check their invented names and descriptions against the scientific names and information found in reference materials.

Evaluation

In which of the following places would you be likely to find animals living? in a forest; in a hot, dry, desert; in a lake; at the top of a mountain; at the North Pole; in New York City. What kinds of animals might you find in these places? Name any areas on earth where you couldn't find any animals.

Name the things you saw, heard, or smelled which showed you that wildlife lives in the classroom and on the schoolgrounds.

MICROTREK SCAVENGER HUNT

Objectives
Students will be able to: 1) state that humans and wildlife share environments; 2) demonstrate that humans do not have exclusive use of environments; and 3) generalize that wildlife can be all around us even if we do not actually see or hear it.

Method
Students go outside on a "scavenger hunt" for wildlife.

Background
See "Wildlife Is Everywhere." The major purpose of this activity is for students to understand that people and wildlife do share environments. By investigating microenvironments or microhabitats, the students should be encouraged to generalize from the information they acquire to the whole of the planet, coming to the understanding in general terms that wildlife exists in all areas of the planet, in some form. In the deserts of the southern hemisphere, the oceans, tropical jungles, and cities of the earth; from the Antarctic snow fields to the glaciers of the Arctic region, wildlife exists in a variety of forms.

Materials
hand lens, digging tool, pencil and mimeographed instruction sheet for each group of two to five students

Procedure
1. This is a wildlife scavenger hunt! The students will be given a list of things to find, and then will go outside and find different kinds of evidence that wildlife exists—even at school! (This activity can be done almost anywhere, with supervision—from city centers to parks to outdoor education sites. It is especially effective where students would not expect to find much wildlife.)

2. Divide the students into groups of two to five. Provide each group with a small hand lens, small digging tool, pencil, and instruction sheet. The instruction sheet could look something like the following:

Age: Grades 4—6 (and older)
Subjects: Science, Language Arts, Social Studies
Skills: analysis, application, classification, description, discussion, generalization, listing, observation, problem solving, reading, small group work, writing
Duration: 30 minutes to two hours
Group Size: small groups working simultaneously; any number
Setting: outdoors and indoors
Conceptual Framework Reference: I.B., I.B.1., I.B.2., I.B.3., I.B.4.
Key Vocabulary: evidence, environments, wildlife

WILDLIFE SCAVENGER HUNT

This is a scavenger hunt to look for evidence of wildlife!

CAUTION: Be careful not to kill any animals or damage their homes!

Find evidence that:

1. Humans and wildlife share environments.
2. Humans and wildlife must adjust to their environment, move to a more suitable environment, or perish.
3. Wildlife is all around us, even if we don't see or hear it.
4. Wildlife ranges from small in size, to very big.
5. People and wildlife experience some of the same problems.
6. People and wildlife both need a place to live.

3. Establish a length of time the students may be outside. This depends on how many things they are asked to look for. Go outside with them to supervise. You can use 15-minute blocks of time, with 15 minutes for every one or two things the students are looking for. For example, the six-item scavenger hunt used in the sample given in this activity could take anywhere from 15 to 45 minutes for the students to find their evidence. You could ask all of the students to find evidence for all of the items. Or, especially with younger students, you could assign each group just one of the things to find. Every group should return with some evidence. Evidence can be such things as small drawings on the mimeographed sheet or on extra paper the students take along. It can be word descriptions of what they see. It can be small samples they bring back to class, if they can bring samples without doing significant damage to the environment. You should provide paper sacks for evidence if they are going to bring things back.
4. Before sending the students outside, make sure the instructions are clear. Talk with the students about what wildlife is, contrasted with other animals like pets. Go through the list of things they are "scavenging" for, to make sure they have an understanding of what they will be looking for. Don't be too specific with your examples. (The most creative and conceptually solid solutions often come up in the face of ambiguity. The students are apt to find delightfully inventive and appropriate evidence, if allowed to be responsibly resourceful!) With the time limits established, open the door and begin "trekking."
5. At the end of the designated time period,

everyone should meet back at the classroom. Ask each of the groups to report on what they found.
6. What are some of the most interesting things the students felt they learned? Encourage the students to come to the generalizations that people and wildlife share environments, that wildlife is all around us, and in fact that wildlife in some form is in areas all over the planet.

Extensions
1. Creative writing!
2. Classify the types of wildlife found.
3. Tally the types of wildlife found, and the numbers of each kind of wildlife. (You can develop this tally into a pyramid of numbers to demonstrate that such a concept is real.)
4. Do microscope work with some of the samples found; for example, the underside of leaves with insect eggs, soil with a lot of plant matter, water, larvae, the inside of insect galls, bark, and a hollow plant stem.
5. See "Wild Words" and add drawings and descriptions to personal journals!

Evaluation
Name three things you saw, heard, or smelled which showed you that wildlife lives in the school area.

Name at least five different kinds of wildlife from five different areas on the earth.

In which areas on earth would you not be able to find any animals?

STORMY WEATHER

Objective
Students will be able to generalize that humans and wildlife share environments and experience some of the same natural phenomena.

Method
Students go on a "guided imagery" to experience a storm.

Background
This activity is designed for students to experience feelings associated with the recognition that people and wildlife co-exist, and sometimes experience the same natural phenomena. During a storm, for example, most people, pets, and wildlife need to seek shelter.

Materials
none needed

Procedure
Note to Teacher: This activity makes use of an instructional technique called visualization or guided imagery. Brain researchers and learning theorists tell us that the technique provides access to ways of processing information that facilitate long-term memory and comprehension of concepts. As a teacher using this technique, you read or describe in your own words a series of images for your students, with their eyes closed, to conjure in their minds. Leave time between the phrasing of your words for the students to visualize the images you are suggesting. Some teachers use guided imagery techniques as a regular part of each teaching day. It is not necessary to use the technique frequently; however, it is a powerful and helpful instructional tool for both teachers and students.

Age: Grades 4—9 (and older)
Subjects: Language Arts, Science, Social Studies
Skills: comparing similarities and differences, description, generalization, visualization
Duration: 20—40 minutes
Group Size: any
Setting: indoors or outdoors
Conceptual Framework Reference: I.A., I.A.2., I.B., I.B.3., I.C., I.C.4
Key Vocabulary: environment

1. Provide the students with the following instructions:

"You are to try to imagine the things you will hear me describing. I won't put in all the details—so you must try to see and feel as clearly as you can the things that I describe. Before we begin, I want you to decide *who* you will be during this activity. You may either be yourself, or an animal. If you are an animal, you may either be a wild animal, a pet, or a farm animal. You don't have to *do* anything special if you choose to be an animal. It is just that you will be visualizing things from the point of view of the animal you pick. Any questions? Okay, let's see by a show of hands how many people and how many animals we will have for this activity. How many of you are going to be farm animals? Pets? Wild animals? Yourselves?"

Note to Teacher: You don't want to find out *which* animals the students have selected to be. You only want to be sure that you have some variety—some of them seeing things from their own perspective, some from the perspective of a domesticated animal, and some from the perspective of a wild animal.

Optional: *Grand Canyon Suite* might be played at this point to set the mood and get an idea of the storm, or other music with a "storm" or natural environment theme.

"Now, we are ready to begin. Get yourselves in a comfortable place. Don't worry about who is sitting next to you. All of you will have your eyes closed. Just be comfortable, and do your best to imagine the things I will describe. Okay, close your eyes, and imagine what you hear . . .
It is a late summer's night. There is a coolness in the air . . . You hear the sounds of summer . . . Somehow, you can feel some changes coming in the weather . . . In the distance, the dark sky is broken by bright flashes of lightning . . . The light is far away . . . After a long wait, a rolling rumble is heard . . . The lightning gets closer . . . The rumbles are louder . . . Suddenly, the lightning flashes and lights up the whole sky . . . You need to find shelter, to find a safe place.
The brilliant flashes of lightning pop and crackle all around you. The noise of thunder is crashing so that the earth seems to shake . . . There are no longer times of quiet between the rumbles of thunder and flashes of lightning . . .
It becomes still . . . You notice scents in the air, things you can smell and feel . . . You begin to hear a new sound . . . You are not sure what it is . . . You again have to find shelter, if you had come out thinking the storm was gone . . . You need to find a place to stay dry . . . Suddenly, the rain is pouring down with a loud, rich sound . . . It rains, and rains . . . and rains . . . And then stillness . . . The storm has passed."

Note to Teacher: Wait a few seconds, and then tell the students, "Open your eyes."

2. Now it is time to find out what the students saw and felt during the guided imagery. There is no need to hear from every student, nor any reason for them to feel pressured to share. Most often, they are eager to describe what they experienced. Let the students volunteer, being sure to include who they were—that is, wild or domesticated animal of some kind, or themselves. Find out what shelter they found, and where, and what happened to them throughout the storm.

3. After the students have shared their descriptions, turn the discussion to the idea that many creatures—including people, pets, and wildlife—share a common environment. Whether we live in the cities, in the country, in the desert, or on a mountaintop, people are not the only living creatures who live in those environments. Even if we don't see many animals where we live, they are there in some form—from the ant on the sidewalk to the spider in the garden. It is useful to remember that we are not the only inhabitants of our environment. Events like summer storms, a strong wind, and a light or heavy snowfall can all serve as special reminders. Every creature who experienced this imaginary storm experienced some of the same things, although not in exactly the same ways. Any creatures who were out that night likely had to find some kind of protection. Remind the students next time they see the lightning, hear the thunder, and feel the rain . . . to wonder where the birds are, the spiders, the cats and dogs, the fox, and the bear. Where are the other creatures who might be feeling this storm?

Extensions
1. Draw pictures of what you imagined.
2. Pantomime the actions the animals took during the storm.

Evaluation
Write a story that compares the ways a child and an animal might experience any of these: drought, snowstorm, flood, tornado, fire, earthquake.

THE BEAUTIFUL BASICS

Objective
Students will be able to identify five basic survival needs shared by people and animals, including pets and wildlife.

Method
Students list and organize needs of people, pets, and wildlife.

Background
All animals, either directly or indirectly, depend upon plants, sunlight, water, soil, and air.

All animals—including people, pets, and wildlife—need food, water, shelter, and space in which to live. These must be in the quality and quantity required by the particular animal. Because animals need food, water, shelter, and space to be available in a way that is suitable to their needs, we say that these things must be available in a suitable "arrangement."

The major purpose of this activity is for students to identify the basic survival needs of all living things and to recognize that people and all animals—including pets—have similar basic needs.

Materials
chalkboard

Procedure
1. Put three words on a chalkboard, so that a column of words can be listed under each: People—Pets—Wildlife. Ask the students, "What do people need in order to be able to live?" List the students' ideas in a column under the word, "People." Do the same for pets and wildlife. (Remember to do the activity, "What's Wild?" before this one, so that students know the major differences between pets and wildlife.)

2. After the lists are made, ask the students to look to see which ideas seem to go together into larger ideas. For example, warmth might be combined with physical comfort and both might fit within the concept of shelter. See if the students can narrow down the lists and come up with the **essential** survival needs for people, pets, and wildlife. The most basic survival needs will be the same for each of the three groups. The lists, when reduced, could include and be limited to:

All Organisms	People	Pets	Wildlife
food	food	food	food
water	water	water	water
shelter	shelter	shelter	shelter
space	space	space	space
arrangement	arrangement	arrangement	arrangement
sunlight	sunlight	sunlight	sunlight
soil	soil	soil	soil
air	air	air	air

Evaluation
List at least four things plants and animals need for survival.

Which of these are needed by animals but not by plants: soil, water, air, food, shelter, arrangement, sunlight?

Age: Grade 2 (and older)
Subjects: Science, Language Arts, Health
Skills: analysis, classification, comparing similarities and differences, discussion, listing, reading
Duration: 20 minutes
Group Size: any
Setting: indoors
Conceptual Framework Reference: I.A., I.A.1., I.A.4., I.C.1., I.C.2.
Key Vocabulary: pets, wildlife, survival needs

EVERYBODY NEEDS A HOME

Objective
Students will be able to generalize that people and other animals share a basic need to have a home.

Method
Students draw pictures of homes and compare their needs with those of other animals.

Background
Humans and other animals—including pets, farm animals, and wildlife—have some of the same basic needs. Every animal needs a home. But that home is not just a "house" like people live in. Home, for many animals, is a much bigger place—and it's outdoors. The scientific term for an animal's home is "habitat." An animal's habitat includes **food, water, shelter** or cover, and **space**. Because animals need the food, water, shelter, and space to be available in a way that is suitable to the animals' needs, we say that these things must be available in a suitable **arrangement**.

The major purpose of this activity is for students to generalize that animals need a home. Homes are not just houses. A house may be considered shelter. People build houses, apartments, trailers, houseboats, and other kinds of shelter in which to live. Animals don't need a home that looks like a house—but they do need some kind of shelter. The shelter might be underground, in a bush, in the bark of a tree, or in some rocks.

Everybody needs a home! And "home" is bigger than a "house." Home is more like a "neighborhood" that has everything in it that is needed for survival.

Age: Grades K—3
Subjects: Science, Language Arts, Art
Skills: analysis, comparing similarities and differences, discussion, drawing, generalization, visualization
Duration: 30 minutes or longer
Group Size: any; however, no more than 25 students is recommended
Setting: indoors or outdoors
Conceptual Framework Reference: I.A., I.A.4., I.C.1., I.C.2.
Key Vocabulary: differences, similarities, survival needs, habitat

Materials
drawing paper, crayons or chalk

Procedure
1. Ask each student to draw a picture of where he or she lives—or to draw a picture of the place where a person they know lives. Ask the students to include pictures in their drawing of the things they need to live where they do; for example, a place to cook and keep food, a place to sleep, a neighborhood.

2. Once the drawings are finished, have a discussion with the students about what they drew. Ask the students to point out the things they need to live that they included in their drawings.

3. Make a "gallery of homes" out of the drawings. Point out to the students that everyone has a home.

4. Ask the students to close their eyes and imagine: a bird's home, an ant's home, a beaver's home, the President's home, their home. OPTIONAL: Show the students pictures of different places that animals live.

5. Discuss the differences and similarities among the different homes with the students. Talk about the things every animal needs in its home: food, water, shelter, and space in which to live, arranged in a way that the animal can survive. Summarize the discussion by emphasizing that although the homes are different, every animal—people, pets, farm animals, and wildlife—needs a home. Talk about the idea that a home is actually bigger than a house. In some ways, it is more like a neighborhood. For animals, we can call that neighborhood where all the survival needs are met a "habitat." People go outside their homes to get food at a store, for example. Birds, ants, beavers, and other animals have to go out of their "houses" (places of shelter) to get the things they need to live.

Extensions
1. Draw animal homes. Compare them to places where people live.

2. Go outside and look for animal homes. Be sure not to bother the animals—or the homes—in the process!

Evaluation
Name three reasons why people need homes, and three reasons why animals need homes.

HABITAT LAP SIT

Objectives

Students will be able to: 1) identify the components of habitat; 2) recognize how humans and other animals depend upon habitat; and 3) interpret the significance of loss or change in habitat in terms of people and wildlife.

Method

Students physically form an interconnected circle to demonstrate components of habitat.

Background

See "The Beautiful Basics," "Everybody Needs A Home," "What's That, Habitat?," "Habitracks," and "Habitat Rummy" for activities with similar purposes.

People and other animals share some basic needs. Every animal needs a place in which to live. The environment in which an animal lives is called "habitat." An animal's habitat includes **food, water, shelter,** and **adequate space** in an **arrangement** appropriate to the animal's needs.

If any of these components of habitat are missing or are affected significantly so that the arrangement for the individual animal or population of animals is no longer suitable, there will be an impact. The impact will not necessarily be catastrophic, but can be. There are a great many additional limiting factors beyond those of suitable food, water, shelter, and space. For example, disease, predation, pollution, accidents, and climatic conditions are among other factors which can have impact.

All things are interrelated. When we look at a biological community, we find interrelationships and interdependencies between plants and plants, plants and animals, as well as animals and animals. These interrelationships and interdependencies are important.

The major purpose of this activity is for students to become familiar with the **components of habitat**, and to recognize that it is not sufficient for there to be **food, water, shelter,** and **space** in order for animals to survive—those components of habitat must be in a suitable **arrangement.**

NOTE: This activity was inspired by a "New Game," and adapted to teach concepts related to wildlife.

Materials

none needed

Procedure

1. This activity takes very little time—but has a lot of impact! Ask the students to number off from "one" to "four." All the "ones" go to one corner of the room, the "twos" to another, etc.

2. As the students move to their corners, clear a space in the center of the room. Better still, go outside to a clear, grassy area. The "ones" should sit or stand together, "twos" together, etc.

3. Assign each group a concept as follows: "ones"=food, "twos"=water, "threes"=shelter, "fours"=space.

4. Now, it's time to form a circle! This is done by building the circle in chains of food, water, shelter, and space. A student from each of the four groups walks toward the cleared area. The four students stand next to each other, facing in toward what will be the center of the circle. Four more students—one from each group—join the circle. Keep adding to the circle in sets of four until all the students are in the circle.

5. All students should now be standing shoulder to shoulder, facing the center of the circle.

6. Ask the students to turn toward their **right,** at the same time taking one step toward the center of the circle. They should be standing close together, with each student looking at the back of the head of the student in front of him or her.

7. Don't panic—this **will** work! **Ask everyone to listen carefully.** Everyone should place their hands on the waist of the person in front of them. At the count of three, you want the students to **sit down . . .on the knees of the person behind them,** keeping their own knees together to support the person in front of them.

Age: Grades 4—9 (also younger and older)
Subjects: Science, Physical Education
Skills: discussion, generalization, kinesthetic concept development, small group work
Duration: 20 minutes
Group Size: 15 to 45 students
Setting: outdoors preferred; indoors possible
Conceptual Framework Reference: I.A., I.A.2., I.A.4., I.C., I.C.1., I.C.2., I.C.3., I.C.4., I.D., III.B.
Key Vocabulary: habitat, food, water, shelter, space, arrangement

You then say, "Food, water, shelter, and space—in the proper **arrangement** (represented by the students' intact, "lap-sit" circle)—are what is needed to have a suitable (good) habitat."

8. The students at this point may either fall or sit down. When their laughter has subsided, talk with them about the necessary components of suitable habitat for people and wildlife.

9. After the students understand the major point—that food, water, shelter, and space are necessary for any animal's survival, and in their appropriate arrangement comprise a suitable habitat—let the students try the circle activity again! This time ask them to hold their lap sit posture. As the students lap-sit—still representing food, water, shelter, and space in their appropriate arrangement—identify a student who represents "water." Then say, "It is a drought year. The water supply is reduced by the drought conditions." At this point, have the student who was identified as representing "water" remove himself or herself from the lap-sit circle—and watch the circle collapse, or at least suffer some disruption in arrangement. You could try this in several ways—removing one or more students from the circle. Conditions could vary: pollution of water supply, urban sprawl limiting availability of all components, soil erosion impacting food and water supplies, etc. Since animals' habitat needs depend upon food, water, shelter, and space, in their appropriate arrangement, "removal" of any will have an impact.

10. Ask the students to talk about what this activity means to them. Ask the students to summarize the main ideas they have learned. They could include: a) food, water, shelter, and space, in their appropriate arrangement, can be called habitat; b) humans and other animals depend upon habitat; c) loss of any of these elements of habitat will have impact on the animals living there; and d) the components of habitat must be in an arrangement suitable to the needs of the individual animals or populations of animals in order for the animals to survive.

Variation

Have students form a circle, holding hands. Walk around the circle, first naming one student as an animal of a particular ecosystem. Name the next four students in the circle as food, water, shelter, and space for that animal. Repeat the process until all the students are involved. Any "extras" can be identified as elements of habitat, e.g., resulting from a particularly good year for habitat needs for the last animal named. When all of the students have been designated as an animal or as components of an animal's habitat, comment on the fact that they are holding hands. This represents the idea that all things in an ecosystem are interrelated. Briefly discuss the idea of interrelationships. Then move the students into position to do the "lap sit" described in the Procedure above. Remind the students that they noticed all elements of the ecosystem were interrelated when they were holding hands. Now they are going to find out that they all are dependent upon one another as well. Do the "lap sit." Discuss interrelationships and interdependencies in ecological systems.

Evaluation

What are the five essential components of habitat?

Explain how the arrangement of food, water, shelter, and space is important to humans and other animals.

What would probably have the greater long-term impact on the wildlife living on a farm in Iowa? A severe winter which killed many animals or the development of part of the farm into a commercial shopping center?

HABITRACKS

Objectives
Students will be able to: 1) identify the basic components of habitat as food, water, shelter, and space in a suitable arrangement; and 2) generalize that these components of habitat are needed by all animals—including people and wildlife.

Method
Students identify the components of habitat by using a map and exploring their school grounds.

Background
People and other animals share some basic needs. Every animal needs a place in which to live. The environment in which an animal lives is called "habitat." An animal's habitat includes food, water, shelter, and adequate space in an arrangement appropriate to the animal's needs.

The major purpose of this activity is for students to understand that all animals—including people—share some of the same basic needs.

NOTE: This activity may serve as an extension to "Everybody Needs A Home" for students in Grades 2 and 3.

Materials
habitat maps, task cards, and habitat components (see below); glue or tape, scissors, pencils, chalkboard, small paper bags

Age: Grades 2—5
Subjects: Science, Language Arts, Social Studies
Skills: analysis, classification, comparing similarities and differences, discussion, math (shape recognition and matching), generalization, mapping, observation, reading, small group work, synthesis
Duration: 30 to 60 minutes
Group Size: three to ten groups of three students in each group
Setting: outdoors and indoors
Conceptual Framework Reference: I.A., I.A.4., I.C.1., I.C.2.
Key Vocabulary: habitat, track, survival needs, food, water, shelter, space, arrangement

Procedure

ADVANCE PREPARATION BY TEACHER

1. Draw a simple map of the school grounds, including sidewalk, buildings, and playgrounds. Make enough copies of the map—saving your original to use another time—so that you have a map for every group of three students.

2. Choose different animals for which you can draw "tracks." For example: bird, cat, dog, bear, mouse, child, deer, and horse.

3. On each map, mark the travels of the animal you have chosen for that map. Try to map the travel as realistically as possible—however, you can begin from the classroom and end back at the classroom. Write the name of the animal, with the word "HABITAT," at the top of each map. For example: "BIRD HABITAT: WHAT BIRDS NEED TO SURVIVE."

4. Make one task card for each animal whose tracks you have mapped. Each task card should look the same, but be a different color. Each card needs to have a shape drawn to represent "food," "water," "shelter," and "space." For example:

5. Make a set of food, water, shelter, and space pieces which will fit over the shapes on each task card. Again, these "habitat component" pieces need to be the same color as the task card they go with. For example, if you chose brown for the bear task card, the habitat pieces should also be brown. Just before the activity begins, go outside on the school grounds and place the habitat component pieces along the trail for the appropriate animals. (Be certain to tell other teachers and students about the trail, and ask their cooperation in not disturbing it.) For example, food in the "BEAR HABITAT" might be found at a bush, water in a puddle near the drinking fountain, and space on the playground. Several habitat pieces for different animals will need to be in the same general area—for safety and convenience as you watch the children. The color-coding works well to minimize confusion—since each group of children with a map and a task card is only looking for the color that matches their task cards.

PROCEDURES WITH STUDENTS

1. Divide the class into teams of three students each.

2. Give each team a "habitat map" that indicates the name of the animal they are tracking. Tell the students that they have ten minutes to track the animal they have been given, looking for the things their animal needs to survive. Give each team the task card for their animal. Also give each team a paper sack to put their habitat pieces in as they find them.

3. Tell the students that to track the animals, they have to be quiet. Being very quiet, all the teams are to go outside and—using their maps—track their animals. To share responsibilities, one student could hold the map, another the task card, and another the sack for the habitat pieces. Tell the students that they are going to find things that represent what their animals need to survive. When they find something that is the color of the task card they are holding, they should put it in their sack. They should find pieces that match what they see on their task cards.

4. Within ten minutes, the students should all follow their maps back to class.

5. Once back in class, give the students tape or glue so that they can affix their habitat pieces to their task cards.

6. Once the habitat task cards are completed, invite the student groups to report on what they found and where they found it. Ask the students if everyone found "food." When they say, "Yes," write food on the chalkboard. Do the same with "water," "space," and "shelter." Ask one of the students in each group to draw a line connecting the four habitat pieces. For example:

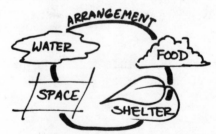

Tell the students that the food, water, space, and shelter have to go together in a suitable **arrangement** in order for an animal to live. For example, animals need the right amount of space to survive. A bear needs more space than a small insect. Animals must have the right amount and the right kind of food. Food, water, and shelter must be available when needed, etc. (The line connecting food, water, space, and shelter represents the idea of a **suitable arrangement** for the animal in its habitat.)

Extensions

1. Take a brightly-colored ball of yarn. Each child is labeled either food, water, shelter, or space. Connect the "food," "water," "shelter," and "space" by having the children each take hold of part of one long string of the yarn. The children all connected by the yarn represent a suitable arrangement of food, water, shelter, and space to meet an animal's needs. First, use a very long piece of yarn that leaves the children standing a distance from each other. This can represent some animals' need for a large habitat in which to live—like a bear or mountain lion. A short length of yarn that has the children standing close to each other can represent some animals' smaller habitat—like an insect.

2. If possible, show the students real animal tracks! See "Tracks!"

Evaluation

Draw a picture of an animal in a suitable habitat. Identify and describe what the animal needs to survive, and show where and how its needs are met in the habitat.

Whitetail Deer

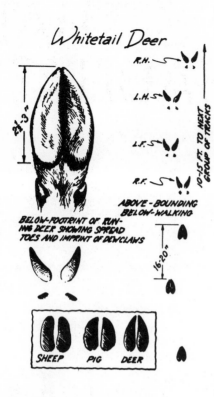

R.H.

L.H.

L.F.

R.F.

ABOVE-BOUNDING
BELOW-WALKING

10-15 FT. TO NEXT GROUP OF TRACKS

2"-3"

16-20"

BELOW-FOOTPRINT OF RUNNING DEER SHOWING SPREAD TOES AND IMPRINT OF DEWCLAWS

SHEEP   PIG   DEER

Gray Squirrel

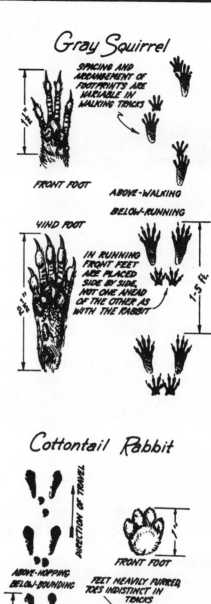

SPACING AND ARRANGEMENT OF FOOTPRINTS ARE VARIABLE IN WALKING TRACKS

FRONT FOOT

ABOVE-WALKING

BELOW-RUNNING

HIND FOOT

IN RUNNING FRONT FEET ARE PLACED SIDE BY SIDE, NOT ONE AHEAD OF THE OTHER AS WITH THE RABBIT

1½"

2½"

1-5 ft.

Black Bear

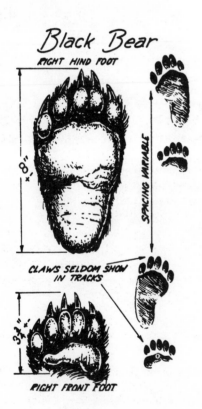

RIGHT HIND FOOT

SPACING VARIABLE

8"

CLAWS SELDOM SHOW IN TRACKS

3½" +-

RIGHT FRONT FOOT

Cottontail Rabbit

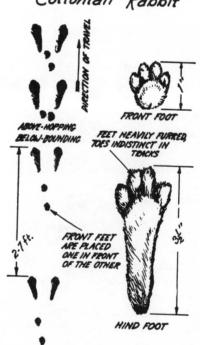

DIRECTION OF TRAVEL

ABOVE-HOPPING
BELOW-BOUNDING

FRONT FOOT

1"

FEET HEAVILY FURRED, TOES INDISTINCT IN TRACKS

FRONT FEET ARE PLACED ONE IN FRONT OF THE OTHER

2-7 ft.

3½"

HIND FOOT

J. J. SHOMON

Reprinted from December, 1953 Virginia Wildlife Magazine

WHAT'S THAT, HABITAT?

Objectives
Students will be able to: 1) identify their own basic needs for food, water, shelter, and space in a suitable arrangement; and 2) generalize that wildlife and other animals have similar basic needs.

Method
Students draw pictures of people's and animal's homes, comparing basic needs.

Background
This activity is similar to "Habitracks." One option is to use "Habitracks" with 4th and 5th grade students, and "What's That, Habitat?" with 2nd and 3rd grade students. Use either activity after "The Beautiful Basics" and "Everybody Needs A Home," especially with 2nd grade students and older. The same drawing used in "Everybody Needs A Home" can be used to start "What's That, Habitat?"

See "The Beautiful Basics" and "Everybody Needs A Home" for more background.

The major purpose of this activity is for students to understand that animals—including people, pets, and wildlife—have some of the same basic needs.

Materials
drawing paper, crayons or chalk

Procedure
1. List the following words on a chalkboard: **food, water, shelter, space.**
2. Read each word aloud, asking the students to repeat the words after you. (They may say the letters of the words and use for spelling.)
3. Food and water will be easy concepts for the students to understand. They are familiar needs for themselves each day. Shelter and space will be more difficult. Ask the students to explain what shelter and space are. Make sure the meaning of all four words is clear before you proceed.

4. Give the students drawing paper and chalks or crayons. Ask the students to draw a picture of where they live, including pictures of where they find food, water, shelter, and space. (NOTE: If the students have made drawings in "Everybody Needs A Home," use those same drawings instead of making new ones!) Ask the students to label the parts of their drawings where they find their **food, water, shelter,** and **space.** For example:

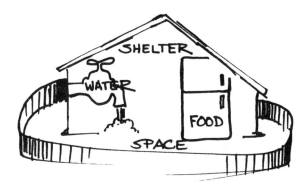

NOTE: Food and water will not be difficult to identify. Shelter could be shown in a number of ways. Here, for example, it is shown by labeling the roof. Space can be shown as the area outside and inside the house or apartment. Shown here, it includes the house and yard. Space can also include the neighborhood. (Space actually includes all the areas used for survival.)

5. Once the drawings are complete, write two more words on the chalkboard: **arrangement, habitat.** Say the words aloud, asking the children to repeat them after you. (Again, these words may be used for spelling.)

Age: Grades 2—3
Subjects: Science, Language Arts, Art, Social Studies
Skills: analysis, comparing similarities and differences, discussion, drawing, generalization, reading, writing
Duration: two 20-minute sessions, or one 40-minute session
Group Size: any
Setting: indoors
Conceptual Framework Reference: I.A., I.A.4., I.C.1., I.C.2
Key Vocabulary: habitat, survival needs, food, water, shelter, space, arrangement

6. Tell the students that when food, water, shelter, and space go together in a special way, so that animals—including people—can live, we call that place a **habitat.** The food, water, shelter, and space are in an **arrangement** that makes it possible for animals to live. (Optional: Ask the children if they could live in a home where the bathroom was four miles north, the kitchen was 12 miles west, and the bedroom was nine miles east. The answer, of course, is likely, "No," since the "arrangement" is not suitable for a person. Some animals, do travel great distances in their habitat, however.)

7. Ask the students to write the word "habitat" in big letters at the top of their drawings. Talk with them about the meaning of habitat.

8. Give the students another piece of drawing paper. Ask them to think of an animal—any animal. Ask a few students what animal they are thinking of. Identify whether the animals they named are "wild" or "domesticated." You will probably get both. If you don't get both, ask the students to think of the kinds of animals that are missing. It is important to make sure the students are thinking about both wild and domesticated animals.

9. Ask the students to draw a picture of their animal in a place where it lives. Ask the students to make sure they include: food, water, shelter, and space in an arrangement that they think would make it possible for the animal to survive.

10. Ask the students to talk about their drawings, pointing out the habitat components they have included.

11. Ask the students to write "habitat" in big letters on the top of their drawing. Talk with the students about how humans and other animals need food, water, shelter, and space. The arrangement is different for each, but all have similar basic needs. When food, water, shelter, and space are arranged in a way that is suitable for an animal to survive, we call that place where these things are available a habitat. When the students have an understanding of "habitat," write a few sentences on the chalkboard defining habitat. As much as possible, make use of the ideas the students suggest. For example: **Habitat is a place. It has food, water, shelter, and space. These are things that animals need to live.**

Possible sentences for older students: **Food, water, and shelter must be within a useable range for each animal. Different kinds of animals need different kinds of food, water, and shelter and different amounts of space.**

12. The students may now write these sentences on the back of one of their drawings or on a piece of writing paper. They may also read the words in the sentences you have put on the board, after you. They may also write their own sentences about what habitat is, drawing pictures to go along with their words.

Evaluation

Choose which things wildlife need to survive: food, water, shelter, space, arrangement.

Choose which things people need to survive: food, water, shelter, space, arrangement.

HABITAT RUMMY

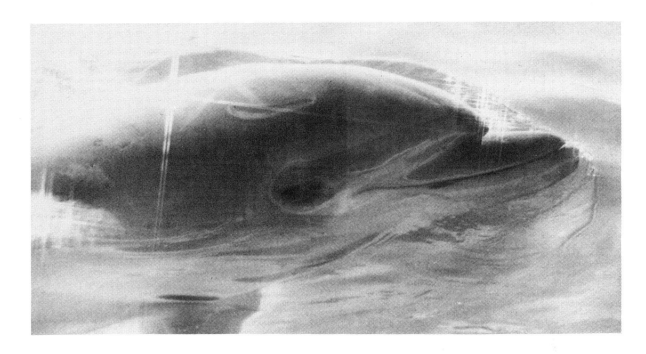

Objectives
Students will be able to: 1) identify components of habitat as food, water, shelter, and space in a suitable arrangement; and 2) apply knowledge of these components to habitat requirements of various species of animals.

Method
Students make cards and play a card game.

Background
NOTE: See "The Beautiful Basics," "Everybody Needs A Home," What's That, Habitat?," or "Habitracks." Any one of these activities would be a good introduction to "Habitat Rummy," even though all except "Habitracks" are written for younger students.

The major purpose of this activity is for students to acquire a working understanding of the components of habitat.

Materials
writing paper and pencils, drawing paper, construction paper, scissors, glue, chalkboard (card masters have been included for those who want to eliminate research phase)

Procedure
PREPARATION OF CARDS FOR GAME (Skip this if you use card masters.)

1. Assign students to groups of two or three. Ask each group to pick one animal they will research. Encourage a wide range of animals, including both wild and domesticated.

Age: Grades 4-7 (and older)
Subject: Science
Skills: analysis, application, classification, comparing similarities and differences, media construction, reading, small group work, writing
Duration: two 40-minute periods
Group Size: groups of two to three students
Setting: indoors or outdoors
Conceptual Framework Reference: I.C.2.
Key Vocabulary: habitat, survival needs, food, water, shelter, space, arrangement

2. Ask each group of students to use reference materials to research their animal. (You may need to instruct students in the use of the library. If library skills or references are a problem, students might be asked to choose from a list of animals for which you have classroom references.) Included in their findings should be a listing of what each animal uses to meet the following needs: **food, water, shelter,** and **space**. They should also find out where the animal lives. For example, if a group of students picks a lizard, they might determine that most lizards eat insects for food; use insects as a water source because of their high moisture content; rest in rock crevices or trees for shelter; and use a hillside or sandy wash as a space in which to find food. The lizard might live in a desert environment.

3. Either you or the students make a large, master "Habitat Information Chart" which includes the major categories of information found by the students as follows:

HABITAT COMPONENTS ↓ / ANIMAL →	LIZARD	SEAGULL	BEAR	CHIPMUNK	GOSHAWK
FOOD	INSECTS	FISH	INSECTS, FISH BERRIES, BIRDS, EGGS MAMMALS	SEEDS BERRIES	SMALL MAMMALS BIRDS
WATER	WATER	WATER	WATER	WATER	WATER
SHELTER	ROCK CREVICES	CLIFFS – SAND DUNES	CAVES	BURROW	TREES
SPACE	HILLSIDES	OCEAN – COAST	HILLS VALLEYS	HILLSIDES	FIELDS HILLSIDES
ARRANGEMENT	DESERTS	AQUATIC	WOODLAND	MEADOW WOODLOT	WOODLANDS MEADOWS

4. Once this information is on the master chart, make a smaller version on mimeograph or ditto stencils. You can make six, equal-sized rectangles on each stencil, with each stencil including the habitat components needed for one animal. Once printed, these rectangles will serve as playing cards. Or, the students can transfer the information to 3x5 cards for use to play. For example, the stencil for one animal could look like this:

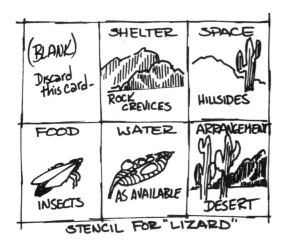

5. Make a copy of the stencil for every two to three students. (If you want every student to have a complete deck of cards to keep, print a copy of each stencil for every student.)

6. Pass out a complete set of the card sheets to every group of students, along with heavy construction paper and glue. They can glue the printed sheets onto the five individual habitat cards per animal according to the printed stencil. Once cut, each set of five habitat cards makes a "book." For example:

Blank on one side; habitat components on the other side.

With the deck of cards complete, it is time to play "HABITAT RUMMY!"

TO PLAY HABITAT RUMMY

1. The object of the game is for a player to get five cards from one vertical column—or a complete set of habitat components for an animal—as listed on the master "Habitat Information Chart." The game ends when all "books" or complete sets of habitat components have been made, with the student having the most complete sets the "winner" of the game. Every group of two to three students playing the game uses one complete set of habitat cards and each group has a "winner." The game is based on luck, but the students become familiar with the habitat components for the animals involved as the game is played. The "Habitat Information Chart" must be in plain sight of the players.

2. The game begins as one student deals five cards to each of the players in his or her group. This happens simultaneously around the room, as all groups begin play. The first player—after dealing is complete—may discard an unwanted card and select another from the remaining deck, situated in the center of the circle of play. Play progresses around the circle with discarded cards being added to the leftover cards in the center (either face-up or face-down) and new cards being drawn, until one player gets a book—a complete set of five habitat components for an animal. (The master "Habitat Information Chart" serves as a reference in this process.) When a player does get a book, he or she yells "HABITAT!" This process continues until all "habitats" are complete, and the student in each group with the most "books" or complete habitats is the "winner." "Winners" could play "winners" with class champion given the title, "Wildlife Biologist!"

3. Ask the students to summarize what they have learned.

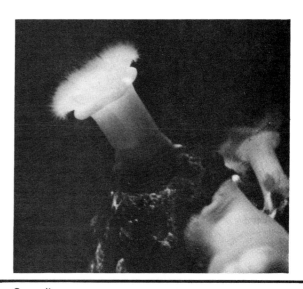

Variations or Extensions

1. Showdown Challenge: Deal out all cards to players. Players showdown with the player to their left, starting at the dealer's left. Players challenge other players according to predator/prey relationships—with predators winning the challenge. The player with the most cards wins. Play for a specified time, using a time limit to end the game.

2. Food Chain Rummy: Play as in rummy. Players get a point for each component of every complete food chain. Cards may be added to either end of a food chain by any other player, acquiring points for every card involved each time. High score wins. Cards remaining in hand at the end of the game must be subtracted from the player's score.

Evaluation

Identify habitat needs (what kinds of food, water, shelter, and space, in what arrangement) for any five wild animals.

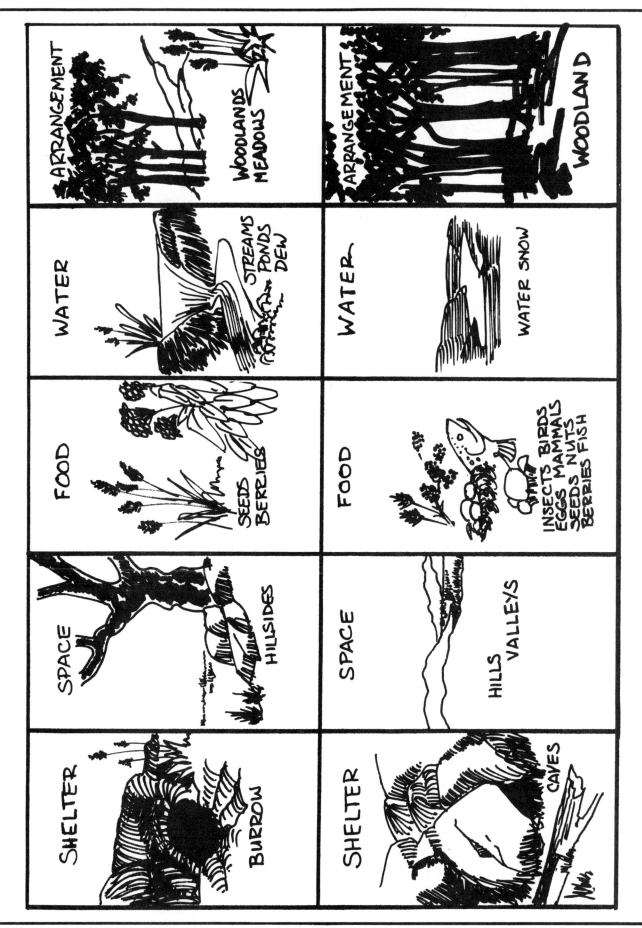

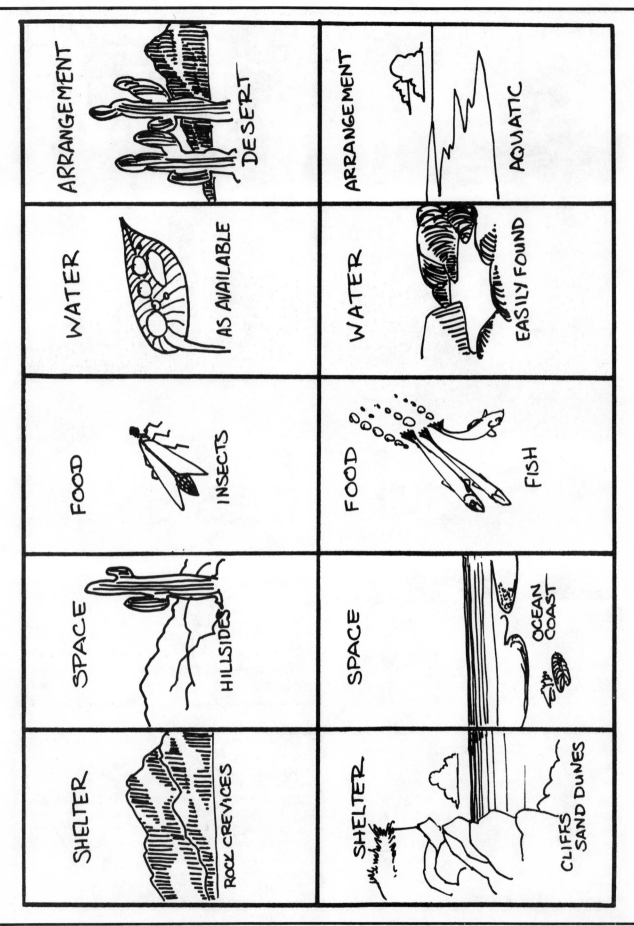

ARRANGEMENT — DESERT

WATER — AS AVAILABLE

FOOD — INSECTS

SPACE — HILLSIDES

SHELTER — ROCK CREVICES

ARRANGEMENT — AQUATIC

WATER — EASILY FOUND

FOOD — FISH

SPACE — OCEAN COAST

SHELTER — CLIFFS SAND DUNES

MY KINGDOM FOR A SHELTER

Objectives

Students will be able to: 1) identify the materials and techniques used by at least one animal to construct its shelter; and 2) construct a model of an animal using materials collected from the natural environment.

Method

Students create replicas of wildlife shelters.

Background

This activity emphasizes one habitat need of animals—shelter. The activity is most useful following an introductory activity which teaches all of the components of habitat. For example, see elementary activities, "The Beautiful Basics," "Everybody Needs A Home," "What's That, Habitat?," "Habitracks," and "Habitat Rummy," and secondary activities, "Ants On A Twig," "Habitat Lap Sit," and "Habitrekking."

Animals must use materials in their habitat to create shelters. Need for shelter is characteristic of animals—including people, farm animals, pets, and wildlife.

The major purpose of this activity is for students to recognize the importance of shelter to animals.

Materials

natural materials **CAUTION: Do no damage to animals or their habitats while gathering materials.**

Age: Grades 5—9
Subjects: Science, Art (emphasis is on shelter design and construction)
Skills: application, description, media construction, observation, research
Duration: minimum of two 45-minute periods (recommended 45 minutes to introduce activity and begin research; additional research and model construction as independent and at-home work; 45 minutes for reports and discussion)
Group Size: any
Setting: indoors, outdoors for observation
Conceptual Framework Reference: I.C.2.
Key Vocabulary: shelter, habitat, design

Procedure

1. This can be an individual or small group project. Each student or group should choose an animal to investigate its shelter. Some animals with architecturally interesting shelters are: beavers, termites, muddaubers, caddis flies, spiders, cliff and barn swallows, chimney swifts, prairie dogs, siamese fighting fish, underwater bubble spiders, osprey.

2. Go outside if possible, as well as use reference materials, to learn what the animals use to construct their shelters (nests, dens, etc.)—paying attention to **how** the shelters are constructed. (If observing animal shelters, do not harm. Do not conduct this activity during mating and reproducing seasons.)

3. Ask the students to collect representative materials from the environment, similar or comparable to those their animals would use in constructing their shelters. Caution the students to be careful in collecting materials, doing no harm to the environment.

4. Build facsimiles of models of each animal's shelter.

5. Display the completed shelters, asking the students to describe the shelter and identify the animal that uses it. Contrast how much time it took to replicate the shelters with how much time it would take the animal. Contrast techniques the students use with those the animals would use. Compare similarities and differences in the shelters and animal habitats. Discuss consequences of habitat loss for each of the animals. Which animals are most vulnerable to loss of materials for creating shelter?

Extensions

1. Create a diorama, putting the shelter within a model of the habitat in which the animal lives.

2. Follow this activity with one on animal adaptation.

Evaluation

What would you look at in a library to discover the materials and techniques used by a yellow jacket hornet to construct its shelter?

Select an animal. Describe the materials and techniques it uses to build its shelter.

WHAT'S FOR DINNER?

Objective
Students will be able to generalize that all animals, including people, depend on plants as a food source, either directly or indirectly.

Method
Students list and analyze the sources of foods.

Background
Plants ultimately support all forms of animal life, including people, either directly or indirectly. Most people are omnivores, which means that they eat both plants and animals in some form. Some people include a lot of meat in their diets, others much less, and some people none at all. It is easy to see that people who are vegetarians—who eat only plants and plant products—are supported directly by plants. It may not be as easy for children to see that even when they are eating animal products, they are indirectly relying on plant sources. For example, cows from which milk and other products are derived, and chickens which provide eggs and meat, are animals which depend upon plants for some or all of their food. Every animal, including people, either eats plants directly—or depends for food upon other species which in turn depend upon plants.

The primary purpose of this activity is for students to trace human and other animals' dependence upon plants for food.

Materials
writing materials, chalkboard; poster board and drawing materials optional

Procedure
1. What's for dinner? Ask students to go home and make a list of everything that they have for dinner on a particular evening—perhaps with help from a parent, brother, or sister.
2. In the classroom, ask the students to work alone or in groups to analyze where their food comes from. Every food should be traced back to a plant. As each item on a menu is examined, ask the students to create a flow diagram or chain which shows the major sources of each food—from the product they eat all the way back to the plant origin. For example: Me Milk Cow Grass. Some chains will be short; others will be long. Sometimes the students may not be sure what particular animals eat for food, so they will want to ask or do some library research to find out.
3. Have a general discussion with the students: "What are some of the things you have learned from this activity?" After the students have described things they have learned, encourage them to make two generalizations about plants and animals: 1) all animals, including people and wildlife, need food; and 2) all animals, including people and wildlife, depend upon plants for food. (Watch for the insight that ultimately plants need animals, too! The decay of animal life after death into nutrients in the soil provides sustenance to plants as well!)

Age: Grades 3—7 (and older)
Subjects: Science, Language Arts, Health
Skills: analysis, classification, discussion, drawing, listing, media construction, writing
Duration: 20 minutes or longer
Group Size: any
Setting: indoors
Conceptual Framework Reference: I.A., I.A.1., I.A.3.
Key Vocabulary: food chain, plants, animals

Extensions

1. Create posters of the menus showing the food chains involved in each. Add soil, water, sun, and air—since these are necessary to plants, people, and all animals too!

2. Create a master list of all the plants that were identified. Look to see which plants we seem to depend upon more than others. Some students might be interested to know that other groups of people—like people in other parts of the world who live in different environments—could come up with a very different list of plants upon which they depend.

3. Adopt a rock! Did you know that everything you ate for breakfast (lunch, dinner, or a snack!) started somewhere with a rock! Trace plants to soil, and soil to its parent matter—including rocks!

Evaluation

Using the organisms listed below, construct at least three food chains: people, rabbits, grass, lettuce, mountain lions, robins, earthworms, hawks, mice, insects, wheat, cows, corn, pigs, deer, acorns.

Which of these animals do not need food? horse, snake, frog, people, robin.

All of the food eaten by animals must first come from _____ ?
(Although the objective of this activity stressed that animals rely on plants, please accept any reasonable response—like soil, sunlight.)

LITTER WE KNOW

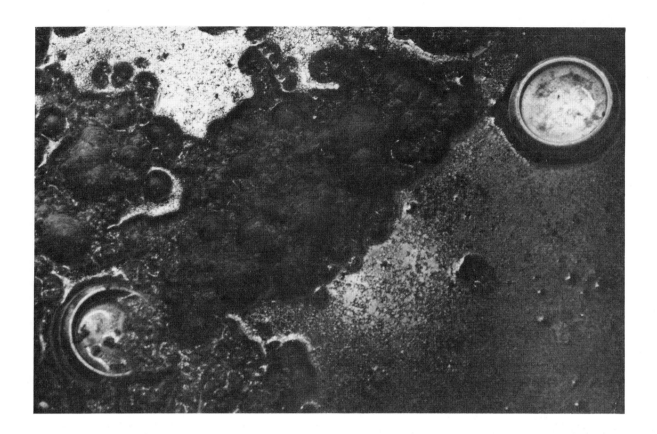

Objectives
Students will be able to: 1) identify and evaluate ways that litter pollution can endanger wildlife; and 2) propose ways they can help eliminate these dangers.

Method
Students collect and evaluate litter, making collages.

Background
Environmental pollution affects all forms of life. Litter is unsightly. It also exposes wildlife and other animals to illness, injury, and death.

Monofilament fish line may get tangled on legs and beaks of water birds like geese and herons. Some of these birds need to run short distances to take off when they fly. The fish line prevents this. It also interferes with their swimming. Birds with long bills often get line wrapped around their bills and cannot open them to eat. They starve to death. The line also gets tangled in their wings, preventing the birds from flying.

Age: Grades 4—6
Subjects: Social Studies, Language Arts, Science, Art, Math
Skills: analysis, classification, computation, discussion, evaluation, media construction, observation, problem solving, small group work, synthesis
Duration: minimum of 45 minutes
Group Size: small teams of three to five students
Conceptual Framework Reference: I.B., I.B.2., I.B.3., I.C., I.C.3., I.C.4., I.D., V.A., V.A.5., V.B.1., VI.A.5., VII.A., VII.A.1., VII.A.2., VII.A.3., VII.A.4., VII.B., VII.B.1., VII.B.2., VII.B.3., VII.B.7
Key Vocabulary: litter, pollution

Sometimes fish or birds get into the loop portions of plastic six-pack can holders. The animal continues to grow, but the loop won't stretch. A slow death results. These loops can also get tangled around the feet of waterfowl.

Half-open cans are a problem. Animals, like deer, can cut their tongues on the cans. Sometimes smaller animals get their heads stuck inside such cans and they can't eat. Starvation is the result. Mice and chipmunks crawl into opened bottles and get trapped inside, unable to get a footing on the slippery glass to push themselves out through the small opening.

Shiny bottle caps or pop-tops may be eaten by wildlife, including fish, injuring or killing them. Cigarette butts, cellophane wrappers, and styrofoam cups, eaten by deer, can cause internal problems.

Broken glass from bottles and other glass objects can injure people, pets, and wildlife.

You can contact your state fish and wildlife agency, or other state agencies, for additional information about problems resulting from litter, including local examples. Such personnel and others, including representatives of private environmental, conservation, and animal welfare organizations may also be available to assist you in considering alternatives for reducing litter problems.

The major purpose of this activity is to alert students to the dangers of litter pollution, and to consideration of responsible actions people can take to minimize consequences of litter pollution.

Materials large sheets of butcher
paper for mounting collages, glue, different types of litter

Procedure

1. Divide the class into three or four teams.
2. Ask each team to bring a collection of litter to class in a paper bag. Suggest they look in parks, camping areas, or school grounds. NOTE: They should not take things out of garbage cans.
3. Have the teams make and display collages of these items.
4. Discuss the effects of litter. Optional: Ask a wildlife expert to join the class for the discussion. If available, show a film or read brochures on the subject.
5. Ask the students to assign a numerical value to each kind of litter. The item potentially most harmful to wildlife has the highest score, least harmful has the lowest score.
6. Have each team figure a total score for their collage based on the numerical values of each piece of litter.
7. Propose and evaluate ways that people can eliminate litter pollution. Can manufacturers make cans with openings other than pop-tops? Could they devise another method of packaging six-packs? How could people fishing have more control over losing their fishing line? How can individuals be instructed about the dangers as well as the unsightliness of littering? What can the students do personally—as individuals, as groups, or as family units—to eliminate or reduce their own litter?

Evaluation

Name four ways that litter can harm wildlife.

List three things you can do to eliminate these dangers.

Propose what you consider to be one of the most effective ways to eliminate or reduce litter.

TRACKS!

Objectives
Students will be able to identify common animal tracks.

Method
Students make plaster casts of animal tracks.

Background
Looking for evidence of wildlife is one method of determining what types of animals are around. Signs such as burrows, nests, droppings, or food litter can be identified—but the easiest signs to interpret are animal tracks.

Animal tracks can be the basis for several types of investigations. Identifying the tracks you find will help fill in a species list of those animals found in your area. Wildlife population estimates can be made from observing the number of tracks found during a specified length of time. Habitat requirements of individuals can be determined by finding their tracks in certain areas and not finding them in others.

Track hunting is really very easy. Just find a spot of level ground with fairly soft, fine, textured soil. Smooth it over, and come back later to see what has been there! Obvious places for your smooth spot would be near water or on well worn trails. Larger animals will use the more open areas, while a small spot the size of your hand cleared under some bushes will reward you with many different little tracks of mice, shrews, and reptiles.

Tracks can be preserved and collected by making plaster casts of them. This simple procedure will allow you to "collect" tracks and add them to other evidence like bones, nests, or scats that you already may have collected.

Once these tracks have been observed or preserved, a lot of information about the animal that made them can be discovered. For example, all mammals have basically the same foot structure. They just use the parts in different ways. If we look at an animal's foot in relation to the human hand, we find that some animals walk on their hands—like raccoons and bears. Others walk or run on their toes, like cats and coyotes, while some walk on their "toenails" or hooves like deer and elk.

By looking at a track, we can make some determinations about how that animal lives. We can notice what part of the foot it walks on, whether claws are present, and how many steps are taken in a measured distance.

The major purpose of this activity is for students to become sufficiently familiar with evidence of wildlife to be able to identify a few animal tracks common to their area.

Materials
plaster of Paris, containers for mixing, spray shellac or plastic, vaseline, cardboard, knives, sandpaper, loops of wire (optional), black ink or paint

Procedure
1. Take your class on a field trip to a nearby lake, stream, or wildlife refuge area—somewhere where there will be lots of tracks!
2. Divide into small groups to find tracks. You may want to divide the students into groups according to areas in which they will look for tracks; e.g., one group under bushes, one group at a meadow's edge, one group near a pond's edge. Prepare the students in advance to assist them in looking carefully and responsibly.
3. Once a track is found, clean it of loose particles of soil, twigs, leaves, and other litter.
4. Spray the track with shellac or plastic from a pressurized can if available.
5. Form a two-inch wide strip of cardboard or tin into a ring surrounding the track. Press firmly into the ground to give support, but allow at least one inch to form the edge of the mold for the plaster. Square forms can be made by cutting milk cartons horizontally—one of the easiest ways to make the forms!

Age: Grades 4—7
Subjects: Science, Art
Skills: analysis, application, comparing similarities and differences, psychomotor development, synthesis
Duration: two 45-minute periods or longer
Group Size: small groups of two to five
Setting: outdoors
Conceptual Framework Reference: I.B., I.B.1., I.B.3., I.B.4.
Key Vocabulary: tracks, evidence

---

6. Mix about two cups of plaster of Paris in a tin can or plastic bowl, adding water slowly until it is about as thick as heavy cream. Pour carefully into the mold until the plaster is about to the top. Allow plaster to harden at least 15 minutes before lifting it out of the track. If the soil is damp, hardening may take longer.

7. When the cast is hardened, lift the cast out, remove the ring, and clean the cast by scraping it with a knife blade and washing.

8. Back in class, apply a thin coating of vaseline to the track and surface of the cast. Place it on a flat surface and surround the casting with a two-inch strip of cardboard or tin as before.

9. Mix plaster of Paris and pour into the mold, making certain that the top surface of the casting is smooth and level with the mold. If you plan to use the casting as a wall plaque, place a loop of wire in back of the casting while the plaster is still soft. Allow two hours for plaster to harden.

10. Carefully remove the mold when the plaster is dry. Separate the two layers and wipe the excess vaseline from the face of the cast and track. Scrape any rough places with a knife blade, or use fine sandpaper to smooth the surface. Wash the completed cast in running water.

11. When the cast is thoroughly dry, paint the inside of the track with India ink or black poster paint. Label each cast with the name of the track, and the student's name. A coat of clear shellac or clear plastic may be applied to protect and preserve the casting.

Evaluation

Draw and label tracks of animals common to your area.

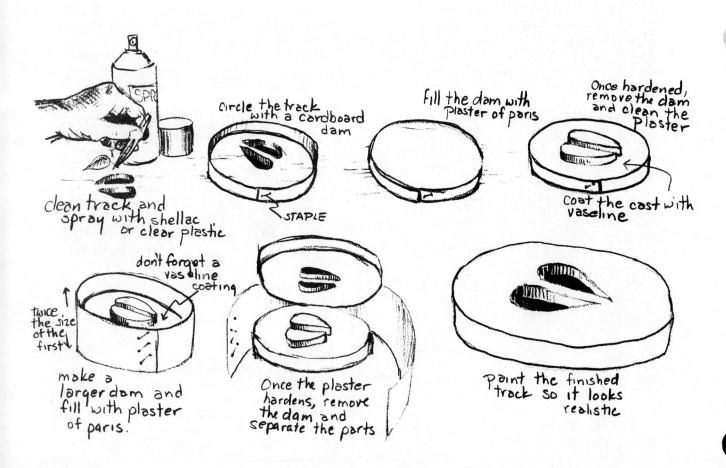

clean track and spray with shellac or clear plastic

circle the track with a cardboard dam

STAPLE

fill the dam with plaster of paris

Once hardened, remove the dam and clean the plaster

coat the cast with vaseline

twice the size of the first

don't forget a vaseline coating

make a larger dam and fill with plaster of paris.

Once the plaster hardens, remove the dam and separate the parts

paint the finished track so it looks realistic

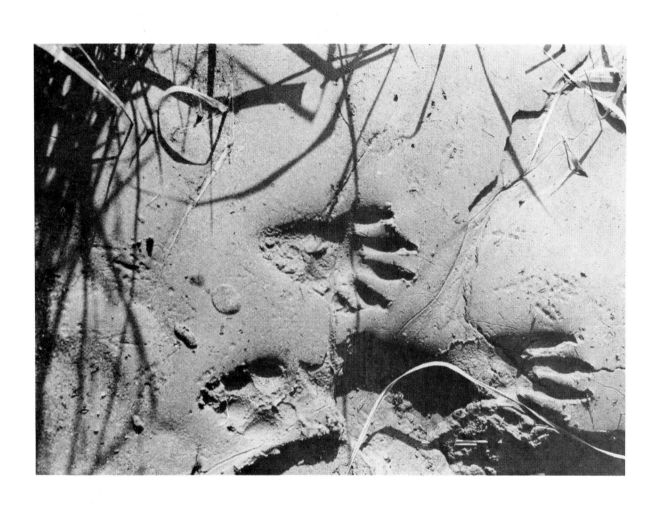

57

DIVERSITY OF
WILDLIFE VALUES

WILD WORDS...
A JOURNAL-MAKING
ACTIVITY

Objectives
Students will be able to: 1) observe and describe their surroundings, particularly in out-of-door settings; and 2) record their observations and descriptions in a written and visual form.

Method
Students go into an outdoor setting to make and write in journals they design.

Background
NOTE: This journal-making activity can be used effectively as a means to record data and personal observations in combination with many Project WILD activities.

A naturalist is a person who studies nature, especially by direct observation of plants, animals, and their environments. Naturalists often spend a lot of time in the out-of-doors, and they often record their observations in some form—from sketches, drawings, paintings, and photos, to poetry and prose. Each person's motivation will be unique, and may include sheer joy in learning more about natural systems, interest in contributing to scientific research, love for the art of writing as literature, and simple satisfaction in being outside.

People benefit today from the insights and observations of people who have delighted in, and been fascinated by, the wonders of the natural environment. Henry David Thoreau, Walt Whitman, Enos Mills, John Muir, and today's Edward Abbey and Annie Dillard are among those who have captured their insights in words and offered them to others.

Most of the naturalists who put their observations in poetry and prose carry with them a small journal as they wander the woods, streams, lakes, oceans, deserts, and other natural environments.

The major purpose of this activity is for students to make their own journals, and to acquire experience in using a journal to record their observations in out-of-door settings.

Age: Grades 4—12
Subjects: Language Arts, Science
Skills: application, description, discussion, drawing, media construction, observation, visualization, writing
Duration: one 20—45-minute period; recommend using the journal produced through this activity as a place for recording data, observations, images, etc., in other activities
Group Size: any
Setting: outdoors
Conceptual Framework Reference: II.A., II.A.2., II.A.3., II.A.4., II.B., II.B.3., II.E., II.E.1., II.E.3., II.F., IV.D.2., IV.E.2., V.A., V.A.4., V.A.5, V.A.6.
Key Vocabulary: journal, observation, naturalist

Materials

construction paper for journal covers, mimeo or other un-lined paper (preferably white), staples and stapler, marking pens, crayons, pencils

Procedure

1. Go outside to some pleasant outdoor setting. It might be an open area on the school grounds with clear sky above, near a large and inviting tree in a park that shades the earth on a hot day, or any outdoor setting from the immediate school grounds to a remote, wilderness setting.

2. Ask the students to sit quietly, listening carefully for any sounds. Ask them to look with "soft eyes"—that is, eyes that do not focus specifically on any one thing, but broadly sense what is in the environment. The students may move their heads at first in a scanning motion until they are accustomed to seeing without focusing on one thing at a time. "Hard eyes" are good for looking closely at a squirrel running up a tree. "Soft eyes" are good for seeing all the trees, the sky, the ground in an area—noticing the squirrel moving out of the corner of one eye, a bird moving skyward out of the corner of the other eye, and feeling the warmth of the sun from above. Encourage the students to try both "hard" and "soft" eyes, trying to notice the differences in how they feel and what they see. Both ways of seeing are useful.

3. Talk with the students about what they see, feel, and notice. A "guided imagery" (where the students close their eyes and you ask them to visualize what you describe) can be useful at this point, with the students sitting quietly—now with eyes closed—while you ask them to imagine different things that will enhance their awareness of the outdoor setting. For example, "You are a tall tree standing in the forest. Feel your roots digging deep into the soil. Feel the water from a recent rainstorm seeping into the earth around you. Feel that large rock tangled in your roots. Feel your branches swaying in the breeze, warmed by the sunlight."

And, or, read an excerpt from the writings of some naturalist.

A children's book for young and old students, **Another Way To Listen,** by Byrd Baylor and Peter Parnall (Charles Scribners Sons, New York, 1978) is an excellent way to set a mood and encourage greater awareness of natural surroundings. It includes:

"I used to know an old man who could walk by any corn field and hear the corn singing...Were you surprised to hear it?,' I always had to ask. He said, Not a bit. It seemed like the most natural thing in the world.'"

For older students, any excerpts from, **The Wilderness World of John Muir,** edited by Edwin Way Teale (Houghton Mifflin Company, Boston, 1954) are good. For example, the chapter, "Windstorm in the Forest," is Muir's accounting of climbing a tall tree during a windstorm:

"It occurred to me that it would be a fine thing to climb one of the trees to obtain a wider outlook...Under the circumstances, the choice of a tree was a serious matter...Being accustomed to climb trees in making botanical studies, I experienced no difficulty in reaching the top of this one, and never before did I enjoy so noble an exhilaration of motion. The slender tops fairly flapped and swished in the passionate torrent, bending and swirling backward and forward, round and round, tracing indescribable combinations of vertical and horizontal curves, while I clung with muscles firm braced, like a bobolink on a reed." (page 186)

4. Get out construction paper and white typing or mimeograph paper for the students to make their own journals. Simply fold the paper in half with the construction paper on the outside and the white paper inside. Staple along the seams so that the booklet stays together. Provide marking pens and crayons so the students can put their name, a title, and a drawing on the cover of their book. Or, make or buy more durable journals before going outside to start using them.

5. Give the students some time—about 15 minutes is fine to begin—to start getting accustomed to using their journal. Structured activities can be inserted at this point, or, each can find a quiet place to make a drawing of something they see. They could begin to write a few words of description, or a poem about their feelings in being outside in that place at that time. The important thing to stress is that the journal is theirs—for them to fill with whatever they choose. It is not the same thing as a diary that might be written in every day. It is a special way to keep memories and ideas about things in the natural environment. Encourage them to take their journals with them sometimes when they are outside, and regularly if possible— perhaps tucked in a backpack or a purse. It is especially good for those times when they are alone outside—perhaps walking to and from school, at a park over a weekend, on a camping trip with family members, etc. One of them may be the next John Muir or Annie Dillard!

6. Discuss the value of journals. In addition to recording impressions, feelings, and observations, a journal can become a log of important data to be referred to later. It can reflect changes in ecosystems, vegetative types, animal populations—as well as attitudes about things. It can hold images as well as words.

Extensions

1. See "Animal Poetry" and "Drawing on Nature."
2. Select an animal habitat. Find a spot within that habitat. (The students should literally experience the habitat as closely as possible to the perspective of the animal they choose to be; e.g., lying down on their backs looking skyward. They should not damage the animal's habitat, and they should still be near enough to you to hear your instructions.) Write one word that describes the animal you have chosen to be. On the next line write two words that describe what you look like. On the next line write three words that describe how you move, or where you live. On the next line write two words about how you contribute to the ecosystem where you live, or how you live. On the last line, write another word that describes who you are. For example:

Bird
Large, Strong
Soaring, Diving, Twisting
Predator, Hunter
Red-Tail

Evaluation

Write a description of some place that you like, but that you have not visited in a long time. Include details about what it looks like, how you feel when you're there, and what you like about it.

Go outside. Find a very small living thing. Look at it as closely as possible, without harming it. Write a short description or poem about this small living thing.

ANIMAL POETRY

Objective
Each student or group of students will be able to recognize and experience the inspirational value of wildlife.

Method
Students go outside to imagine themselves as animals, and then write poems.

Background
Poetry is an art form, accessible to every student in some way. A poem is an organized way of expressing insight through language. Meter and rhyme combine as one kind of poetry. People have others, including song and free verse.

The major purpose of this activity is for students to experience wildlife as the inspiration for a poem—and to successfully write the poem! NOTE: This is an excellent companion to "Wild Words: A Journal-Making Activity."

Materials
writing materials

Procedure

1. Everyone can be a poet, at least to some extent—and yet lots of people think any kind of poetic expression is beyond their capacities. This activity is designed for every student—or group of students—to create a poem.

2. Go outside. Find a pleasant setting on the school grounds, in a park, wooded area, or other natural environment. Ask everyone to pick an animal to think about. Any animal is okay, although some should be wild animals. Ask everyone to close their eyes for a few minutes and imagine they are the animal, living in its natural environment. With their eyes closed, you can guide their imagining process with a few words—or simply leave this process to the students on their own.

3. Give everyone five minutes to go find a spot to "become" that animal. Imagine how long it lives, where it travels, how other plants and animals look from its perspective. When the students return, ask everyone to write a short poem about their animal. Poems can be free verse or rhyming. Cinquain and haiku are in-

teresting forms. Or, do a group poem. Everyone thinks of one animal. Each person contributes one word. One or more students or the instructor can put all the words together to form the poem while the others discuss their experiences in "becoming" an animal.

NOTE: Students can imagine they "are" their animal without giving the animal characteristics of humans which are not applicable.

4. OPTIONAL: Here are a few examples of poetic forms which can be used. These have been excerpted and adapted with permission from **Project Learning Tree** (Washington D.C.: American Forest Institute, 1977.)

Haiku Haiku, originated by the Japanese, consists of three lines of five, seven, and five syllables each. The emphasis is syllabic, not rhyming. For example:

> The hawk soared over
> Spirit bird in my living
> Guide to harmony.

Cinquain Cinquain is derived from the French and Spanish words for five. This form of poetry is also based on syllables—or may be based on number of words—but there are five lines. Each line has a mandatory purpose and number of syllables or words. These are: 1) the title in two syllables (or two words); 2) a description of the title in four syllables (or words); 3) a description of action in six syllables (or words); 4) a description of a feeling in eight syllables (or words); and 5) another word for the title in two syllables (or words). Here are two examples, the first using syllables and the second using words:

Age: Grades 4—7 (and older)
Subjects: Language Arts, Science
Skills: description, invention, synthesis, visualization, writing
Duration: one class period
Group Size: any
Setting: outdoors
Conceptual Framework Reference: II.A., II.A.1., II.A.2., II.A.3., II.A.4., II.B.3., II.F.
Key Vocabulary: poetry, imagine

Panther

Vital, quiet
Moving swiftly to live
Endangered by human patterns
Near lost

Sea Otter

Mammal of living waters
Swimming, sleeping, eating, diving, basking,
playing,
Sensitive indicator of the quality of
continuing life
Still here

Diamante Diamante is a poem shaped in the form of a diamond. It can be used to show that words are related through shades of meaning from one extreme to an opposite extreme, following a pattern of parts of speech like this:

noun
adjective adjective
participle participle participle
noun noun noun noun
participle participle participle
adjective adjective
noun

For example:

egg
light bright
living stretching growing
bird beak wing flight
soaring seeing seeking
feathered fluid
raven

5. The completed poems can be typed or printed neatly—and then displayed with a photograph or black and white pen and ink drawing of the animal. For example:

The Goat, "Mazama"

Rhime ice coats my nostrils
The gale rages from peak to crag
Warm, white wool shaggily hugging my
body. . .
Cautiously I move on rock
Barely noticing the fear
Of the valley below.
The eagle—the feel of snow—
This is my home.

Hal Neace, Teacher
Seldovia, Alaska

Evaluation

If you had to choose between two very comfortable, safe places to live—one with, and one without, wildlife—which one would you choose, and why?

MUSEUM SEARCH
FOR WILDLIFE

Objectives
Students will be able to: 1) identify wildlife portrayed in an art form; and 2) generalize that wildlife has sufficient aesthetic and spiritual value to inspire art.

Method
Students visit a museum or another source of artifacts.

Background
Human relationships to wildlife are often expressed through painting, sculpture, drama, dance, literature, photography, and other means of creative expression. Wildlife has served as an inspiration for art throughout human history.

The major purpose of this activity is for students to recognize one aspect of the value of wildlife—its impact as a source of inspiration for varying art forms.

Materials
none needed, however activity requires trip to local museum or other source of artifacts; recommend combining this activity with a scheduled field trip to such a site, if possible

Procedure

1. This is a field trip! It requires a trip to a local art, natural history, or anthropological museum. NOTE: This activity can be added to a field trip already planned as part of a social studies unit, for example. (If no museum is available, use reference materials.)

2. Check your local community to see which museum, if any, would be appropriate. Make arrangements for your students to visit.

3. Before the trip, discuss different kinds of art that people have created throughout human history—including cave drawings, pottery, baskets, costumes, paintings, sculpture, drawings, dances, photography, literature, and music. Ask the students what might inspire art.

4. At the museum, ask each student to find examples of wildlife represented in art. What kinds of wildlife? What kinds of art? Encourage the students to look closely, since sometimes the image can be so stylized that it is hard to recognize. Ask each student to identify the art form, and the wildlife—and to make a small sketch as a reminder of what they saw. (See "Wild Words." The students can put their sketches in their personal journals.) Or, use a worksheet. For example: Select one animal you saw represented at least three times. How did the artist portray it?

5. As a follow-up, discuss the students' observations with them. Identify which kinds of art seem to include the most images of wildlife (painting, pottery, sculpture, etc.). Compare how one animal—like a deer—might look in different

Age: Grades 3—6
Subjects: Social Studies, Language Arts, Art
Skills: analysis, application, discussion, comparing similarities and differences, drawing generalizations, observation
Duration: 30 minutes if in class using reference materials; 45 minutes or longer if at museum
Group Size: any size, up to 30
Setting: indoors
Conceptual Framework Reference: II.A., II.A.1., II.A.2., II.A.3., II.A.4., II.B.3., II.C.1., II.D.2., II.F
Key Vocabulary: art, artists, inspiration, wildlife

Museum Search For Wildlife Chart

Put a check after the name of the animals you find.

Animal Family	DOMESTIC ANIMALS (TAME)	WILDLIFE (UNTAMED)

art works. Talk about the varying ways artists portrayed wildlife, and some of the students' favorites. Talk about ways wildlife was portrayed during different historical periods. Talk about the relationships between people and wildlife during different periods. What are the clues? What if there were no wildlife?

6. Encourage the students to generalize that wildlife can serve as an inspiration and has aesthetic value.

Variations and Extensions

1. Portray wildlife in an art form of your choice!
2. Make your own wildlife art museum in the classroom. Collect photos or copies of paintings, sculpture, pottery, petroglyphs, weaving, etc. Or, make your own!

Evaluation

A group of people were discussing endangered plants and animals—that is, those that are very close to becoming extinct. Some of the people felt that we should preserve and protect all kinds of plants and animals because we might learn that they could be very useful to us for chemicals, medicine, foods, and clothing, and as intrinsically valuable parts of our environment. Other people said that we do not need all those animals and plants, and we shouldn't worry about them. Suppose you are an artist in the group, and you want to express your opinion about the importance of plants and animals. What will you say? Would your opinion change if you were not an artist? If yes, why? If no, why not?

LET'S GO FLY A KITE

Objective
Students will be able to recognize that wildlife has value as an inspiration for art.

Method
Students design, make, and fly kites.

Background
Wildlife is an inspiration for many forms of art—ranging from music to mime, dance to drama, poetry to painting, gymnastics to gymkhana, and more. Designing kites can be an art form—and one particularly accessible to young people.

The major purpose of this activity is for students to recognize the value of wildlife as an inspiration for art.

Materials
tissue paper of a variety of colors, bamboo strips, small tacking nails and hammers, sturdy kite string (Bamboo is available in window shades as found in import shops; purchase and cut apart.)

Procedure
1. Talk with students about the importance of wildlife as an inspiration for art. Ask the students for examples of different kinds of art where wildlife has been an inspiration.
2. Suggest that there can be more kinds of art than we sometimes think of. At least a small number of people would suggest that the design and successful flying of a kite is a special form of art in itself. This is a kite-making activity!
3. Students can work alone, or with one or two other students. Their task? To design and build a kite, inspired by a wild animal.
4. Give the students some time to begin designing their kites: what animal? what colors? what shape? what size? The kites can be realistic; e.g., employing concepts of "structure," "function," and "adaptations" based on a flying squirrel; or stylized. Let them know that the primary media for their kite construction will be brightly-colored tissue paper and a framing material such as bamboo. After providing some class time for the design work, give the students about two days outside of class to keep talking and thinking about their designs and to work on their plans on their own.
5. About two days later, in class, it's time to build the kites. Get out the tissue paper, bamboo, and other equipment. Give the students that class period to build their kites. Once they are built, it is a matter of waiting till a good day for flying kites. Until the weather is just right, the kites should be stored in a safe place. At least one day, let the kites form a festive display in the classroom. When the weather is right, head out to the best available place for one trial run of each kite! **CAUTION: Be sure to stay away from power lines and cables, and if a thunderstorm is approaching, kites and students stay inside!**

Evaluation
Describe the features of your wild animal that made it seem like a good choice for a kite.

Age: Grades 4—6 (and older)
Subjects: Art, Science, Math (measurement, forms)
Skills: discussion, invention, media construction, psychomotor skills, problem solving
Duration: 20 minutes to start design; 30—45 minutes to build kites
Group Size: one or more students, alone or in small groups
Setting: indoors and outdoors
Conceptual Framework Reference: II., II.A., II.A.3., II.A.4., II.F.
Key Vocabulary: inspiration, art, design, wildlife

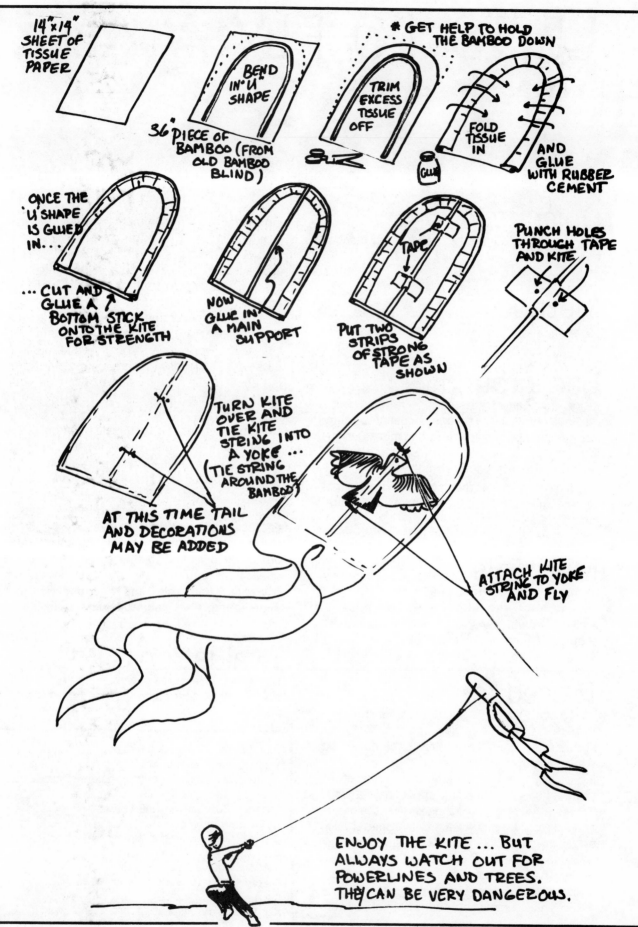

14"×14" SHEET OF TISSUE PAPER

BEND IN "U" SHAPE

36" PIECE OF BAMBOO (FROM OLD BAMBOO BLIND)

GET HELP TO HOLD THE BAMBOO DOWN

TRIM EXCESS TISSUE OFF

FOLD TISSUE IN

AND GLUE WITH RUBBER CEMENT

ONCE THE "U" SHAPE IS GLUED IN...

...CUT AND GLUE A BOTTOM STICK ONTO THE KITE FOR STRENGTH

NOW GLUE IN A MAIN SUPPORT

PUT TWO STRIPS OF STRONG TAPE AS SHOWN

TAPE

PUNCH HOLES THROUGH TAPE AND KITE

TURN KITE OVER AND TIE KITE STRING INTO A YOKE ... (TIE STRING AROUND THE BAMBOO)

AT THIS TIME TAIL AND DECORATIONS MAY BE ADDED

ATTACH KITE STRING TO YOKE AND FLY

ENJOY THE KITE ... BUT ALWAYS WATCH OUT FOR POWERLINES AND TREES. THEY CAN BE VERY DANGEROUS.

ECO-ENRICHERS

Objectives
Students will be able to 1) evaluate the importance of plant and animal matter as contributors to soil; and 2) recognize that wildlife in many forms contributes to the diversity and balance of ecological systems.

Method
Students experiment with soil and earthworms.

Background
Wildlife is an important contributor to healthy ecosystems. The major purpose of this activity is for students to recognize one example of the kinds of significant contributions from wildlife. In this case, earthworms (not always recognized as wildlife) enrich a growing medium, soil.

Materials
enough soil from the same source to fill three 1' × 1' × 1' containers, earthworms, composting material (like kitchen scraps and yard leaves)

Age: Grades 6—12
Subject: Science
Skills: analysis, application, classification, comparing similarities and differences, computation, description, discussion, generalization, kinesthetic concept development, observation, psychomotor development. reporting, research, writing
Duration: minimum of two 50-minute class periods, plus observation of soil boxes for six weeks
Group Size: whole class
Setting: indoors
Conceptual Framework Reference: II.B., II.B.1., II.F., III.B.1.
Key Vocabulary: ecosystem, soil, nutrients, fertility, acidity, alkalinity, porosity, organic, composting

Procedure

1. Select some soil that is not particularly rich—it might be heavily compacted; by a roadside; or in an area where there has been a lot of erosion. Note, however, that soil may look infertile but be rich with inorganic nutrients. Take a large enough sample of the soil to fill three 1' × 1' × 1' containers.

2. With your students, do some simple soil tests to determine the quality of the soil. For example:

a. Look for signs of plant or animal matter in the soil—count the number of species you can identify; examine a sample under a microscope; count the number of organisms in the sample; estimate the number of organisms in the entire quantity of soil in the container based on the number of the sample.

b. Test acidity and alkalinity with pH kits.

c. Check porosity by determining how fast water will run through.

d. Conduct a settling test to see what general proportions of soil components are present; i.e., sand, silt, clay, organic matter.

3. After the soil tests have been completed and recorded, it is time to see what contributions at least one form of wildlife can make to the richness of soil. Divide the soil into the three containers. One container is the "control." The second is for soil and compost only. The third is for soil, compost, and earthworms.

4. Begin adding composting materials (plant and animal matter)—like table scraps, grass clippings, leaves, etc.—to the second and third containers. Add earthworms to the third container. Occasionally water the soil **lightly**—to simulate a rainstorm. You can also lightly water the first box—but **do nothing else to the first box of soil.** NOTE: You can begin with a larger number of earthworms if your soil box is large, and if you want to speed up the process.

5. Since the worms are in a limited environment, you and the students will need to keep adding the food and other composting materials. Compost may be added to the second container, also. Plan on adding materials once a week for three weeks, and watering lightly once a week. Encourage the students to watch for changes in any of the boxes. An observation sheet can be attached to the outside of each box for the students' reporting purposes.

6. At the end of the three-week period, conduct the same set of experiments you originally conducted with the soil. Conduct the tests with all three boxes. In testing the soil in the earthworm box, make sure the students take care not to harm the earthworms; many may die anyway. Be prepared for this possibility, and add additional earthworms as necessary.

7. Discuss the findings. What differences are there in the three soil samples?

8. Now plant some seeds in all three of the soil boxes. Pick a fast-growing seed, like radishes. Seeds from plants native to the area might be available as well. Plant the same number of seeds in each of the soil boxes. Record the date of planting. Record all watering procedures, and changes in the boxes as the plants begin to grow. After three weeks, compare and discuss the results. Describe the importance of plant and animal matter as contributors to soil. Talk about earthworms as one example of the role of wildlife in contributing to healthy environments!

Evaluation

List three ways that earthworms have a positive effect on soil.

Name three other types of wildlife, and describe briefly how each contributes to improving or maintaining soil.

SEED NEED

Objectives
Students will be able to: 1) explain how seeds are carried by animals; and 2) evaluate the importance of wildlife in contributing to ecological systems, based on this example of seed dispersal.

Method
Students gather seeds by going outside and wearing socks over their shoes.

Background
Wildlife contributes to the diversity and balance of ecological systems. One compelling example is in the process of seed dispersal. Many seeds are carried by animals—whether in the coats of fur-bearing animals, or in seeds carried and dropped by some birds.

The major purpose of this activity is for students to understand one example of wildlife as contributors to healthy ecological systems.

Materials
one large fuzzy sock per student, or masking tape segment per student (Optional: one shoe box filled with planting medium per student, cookie sheets or trays in which to place shoe boxes used as planters)

Procedure
1. Ask each student to bring a large, old, fuzzy sock from home—or try to find an inexpensive or free source to obtain a sock for each student. Old socks with holes in them are fine for this activity. Ask each student to put on a sock over one shoe. Wearing the socks over the shoes, go on a walk through a grassy area or field—particularly one that is abundant in seed-bearing plants. (Masking tape over the foot or around the leg sometimes has more sticking power!)
Option for older students: Different students walk in different locations. Contrast seeds found in each location. Create an "environmental map." What ecosystem differences exist in the neighborhood, city, etc.?
2. After walking through the area, look carefully at the socks. What has happened? Discuss briefly

---

Age: Grades 5—6 (and younger)
Subjects: Science, Math (Social Studies for older students with mapping)
Skills: analysis, classification, comparing similarities and differences, description, kinesthetic concept development, listing, observation, writing
Duration: 20—40 minutes or longer for gathering and analyzing data; minimal ongoing time in caring for planted seeds
Group Size: any
Setting: outdoors and indoors
Conceptual Framework Reference: II.B., II.B.1., III.B., III.B.1.
Key Vocabulary: ecosystem, dispersal, seeds, diversity

the seeds and other things that are attached to the socks. If the distance is not too great back to the classroom, the students should keep their socks on their feet until they return. If the distance is too great—they may lose too many of their seeds along the way! NOTE: Wildlife drops seeds too—that's one way they get dispersed!

3. The students should carefully remove their socks. They've gathered their "data"—seeds and other things attached to their socks. Removing the seeds and other particles from the socks—they should examine what they've brought back. Talk with the students about the major kinds of things they seem to have—like seeds, grass, small bits of twigs. Next, discuss the seeds in more detail, talking about the different kinds of seeds they have found: round, skinny, big, small, etc.

4. Each student should record—with words and small drawings—the kinds of things on the sock. Tally the **number** of each kind of thing on a sock as well.

5. Ask the students how different animals' fur might be similar to their socks. Has anyone ever brushed seeds, stickers, and things out of a dog's or cat's fur? Talk with the students about how, so often in nature, seeds are carried by animals almost like the way they carried seeds and things on their socks. Seeds may stick to an animal's fur in one location, and fall off in another. Discuss why such a process is an important one. Evaluate the consequences. How does wildlife contribute to environmental diversity.

6. OPTIONAL: Each student can plant his or her seeds in one of the shoe boxes filled with planting medium (soil or a commercial mix). Be sure the students put their names on their boxes. Water and care for the shoe-box gardens regularly—and see what grows! NOTE: Many wild plant seeds require freezing before they will germinate. If there is a question, put some seeds in ice cube trays and freeze them for several days. **Then** plant them.

Extensions

1. As the seeds in the boxes begin to sprout, measure the plants that grow. Take measurements every fifth day, and plot these measurements on a graph. Primary students can use strips of paper for measurement and use those strips to make an individual bar graph. Intermediate students can measure their plants with a metric ruler and plot their measurements on a line graph.

2. Students can try similar experiments at home, using seeds they find on their own or a neighborhood pet. If they actually get the plants to grow, they can try to match the plants they grow at home from the "pet-carried" seeds to the plants growing outside. Then they can try to figure out how far the seeds might have traveled on the animal!

Evaluation

Draw three different seeds that could be transported on the fur of an animal. Draw an arrow to show the part of the seed that makes this possible.

How are fur-bearing animals important to the types of plants that produce these seeds?

ENVIRONMENTAL BAROMETER

Objective

Students will be able to: 1) observe and count wildlife in an area; 2) discuss why the wildlife is or is not present; and 3) consider ways in which the presence of wildlife can be seen as an indicator of environmental quality.

Method

Students go outside to observe and count or estimate wildlife in an area; do the same in another setting to compare findings; and—optionally—make a school "environmental barometer."

Background

Some species of animals are more adapted to difficult conditions than others. Some, in contrast, are so specialized that it is quite difficult for them to find the food, water, shelter, and other things they need.

Wildlife serves as an important indicator of the overall health of an area of the environment. If there are few wild animals—or little evidence of wildlife—present in an area, it is likely that there is little available food, water, or shelter in the area as well. The kinds of wildlife present are also important indicators. Birds of prey, for example, are high on the food chain. If they are present in an area, that is an indicator that there is some variety of other animals and plants in the area.

The major purpose of this activity is for students to consider the importance of wildlife as an indicator of environmental quality.

Materials

writing materials, poster board or construction paper and marking pens or crayons

Age: Grades 3—5
Subjects: Science, Math, Social Studies
Skills: analysis, classification, comparing similarities and differences, computation, discussion, evaluation, observation, synthesis
Duration: two 30—45-minute periods
Group Size: any
Setting: outdoors and indoors
Conceptual Framework Reference: I.A., I.B., I.C., I.C.1., I.C.2., I.C.3., I.D., II.B., II.B.1., II.B.2., II.B.3., II.B.4., IV.C., IV.D.4., IV.D.5.
Key Vocabulary: evidence, wildlife, environmental quality, habitat, barometer

Procedure

1. Go outside with your students on the school grounds to do a wildlife count. Each student should work alone and have writing materials. Ask each student to find a spot, sit quietly for ten minutes, and observe. (Quiet is very important, to increase the likelihood of seeing wildlife.) The students should record the kinds and numbers of any wildlife they see. They can include **evidence** of wildlife, in addition to actual sightings.

Ask the students to total the number of wildlife in each category, plus make a grand total of the wildlife they observed. If they find evidence rather than sighting wildlife, they should estimate the numbers. Put all the students' information on one master chart.

2. Next, take the students to a setting where wildlife is more abundant. Repeat the process—with each student observing quietly for ten minutes and recording observations.

3. Make a master chart of the information from this second environment.

4. Compare the information from the two charts. Was there any difference in the two settings? Why or why not? Which environment seemed to have the most **different kinds** of wildlife? Where were there the most of any one kind of wildlife, like the most birds? What kinds of food, water, shelter, and space were in each setting to support the survival needs of wildlife? If there were few animals, or many, in either setting—what might this tell us about the quality of the environment? What is environmental quality? Can wildlife be an indicator of environmental quality? Talk about whether it is realistic for every environment to be a good habitat for varieties of wildlife. Discuss the possibility and appropriateness of making efforts to improve environments as habitats for wildlife, and homes for people too.

NOTE TO TEACHER: Several possibilities may arise when doing this activity with your students. Your school may be in an area where there are few, if any, wild animals present—with little access to any other area with much wildlife. If there is no significant difference between your observations in the two settings, you can still talk with the students about what this means. It is also possible that your school is in a wildlife-rich setting—virtually as rich as any other setting in the area. Again, it is all right if there is no significant difference in the number and variety of wildlife observed in each area. **You may also choose to make the observations and create the**

information charts only for one setting, simply analyzing and discussing the quality of the one environment—without using another for comparison.

Extension

Make an environmental barometer to indicate the quality of your school environment as a habitat for wildlife. Share your barometer with other classes. Optional: Show seasonal changes in the barometer's readings.

Evaluation

Each year, thousands of birdwatchers participate in a National Audubon Society bird count all over the United States. The information is kept and compared from year to year to see if changes occur in the total number of birds, or in how many different kinds of birds are sighted. If a steady and long decrease in the bird populations occurred over a period of five years, should **everyone** be concerned—and not just the birdwatchers?

Make a list of things we do in cities and towns that tend to **decrease** the amount and kinds of wildlife that lives there. Make a list of things we sometimes do in cities and towns that tend to **increase** the amounts of some kinds of wildlife.

Identify and describe three things that people could do to increase the numbers and kinds of wildlife living in an area that has little evidence of wildlife.

MAKE A COAT!

Objectives
Students will be able to: 1) identify that some historical and present-day sources of clothing are plants and animals; 2) collect and analyze data to infer the sources of most materials used in clothing today; and 3) distinguish between some examples of renewable and nonrenewable natural resources. (All three objectives are appropriate for upper elementary grades; kindergarteners and 1st grade students may only accomplish the first objective.)

Method
Students make replicas of coats using different materials, and representing varying historical periods.

Background
In all but the most tropical of climates, people need an outside covering to keep warm. When ice flows receded after the last Ice Age about 10,000 years ago on the North American continent, people used fire for part of their warmth. Skins from wild animals were also used; saber tooth tigers, bears, woolly mammoths, and wolves were among the animals hunted for meat and clothing.

American Indian tribes have used animals for food and covering, and some still do as a part of their present lifestyle. Elk, deer, bear, buffalo, seal, and almost all animals killed for food also provided valuable skins for clothing.

When European settlers came to the North American continent, they brought with them a tradition of making clothing out of spun fibers such as linen and wool.

Today we have coats and other clothing made from many materials. We can divide the sources of these materials into two categories: **renewable and nonrenewable natural resources.** Definitions of renewable and nonrenewable natural resources are commonly used within the natural sciences. Use of these terms is intended to describe inherent biological attributes, not to imply value judgements.

Renewable natural resources are living things, with the capacity for regeneration. Trees and wildlife are examples of renewable natural resources. However, even renewable resources have limits. For example, although animals have the capacity for regeneration by mating and bearing offspring, they cannot if their habitat is de-stroyed, pressures are too great to reproduce successfully, etc.

Nonrenewable natural resources are non-living things. Minerals and fossils are examples of nonrenewable natural resources. Although such resources may be replenished over time by natural processes, the time span is enormously long; for example, in the case of accumulations of fossils from which to derive products such as petroleum.

Cotton (from the cotton plant) and linen (from the flax plant) are two major clothing products derived from renewable natural resources--in this case, both from plants. Some clothing products come from animals. Wool, for example, comes from shearing the fleece off sheep, and does not require killing the animal. Other domesticated animals, like cattle, provide clothing products, like leather, and also provide food products. Geese and ducks provide feathers for down jackets.

In scientific terms, animals can be considered a renewable resource. In some cases, however, animal populations are endangered or threatened. In such cases, killing of these animals is forbidden by law. It is also illegal to hunt many animals that are not threatened. Of those anials that are hunted, they are hunted only under laws and regulations. Some people raise ethical questions as to the appropriateness of the use of animals, particularly wild ones, for products such as clothing, food, tools, medicines, cosmetics, jewelry and other ornaments.

Age: Grades K—6 (Grades 2—4 recommended)
Subjects: Social Studies (History, Geography, Anthropology), Science, Art, Language Arts, Home Economics, Math (if measuring is involved)
Skills: analysis, classification, description, discussion, evaluation, invention, media construction, observation, psychomotor skills (cutting, sewing), synthesis
Duration: 45 minutes; 60 minutes possible (two 30-minute periods) for older students
Group Size: small groups; up to total of 20—30 students
Setting: indoors
Conceptual Framework Reference: II.A., II.B., II.C., II.D., II.D.2., II.D.4., II.E., II.F., IV.B., IV.B.1., IV.B.2., IV.D., V.A.1., V.A.2., V.A.3., V.A.5., V.B.1., VI.B., VI.B.1., VI.B.2., VI.C., VI.C.2., VI.C.12., VI.C.16., VI.D., VI.D.2., VI.D.3., VII.A., VII.A.1., VII.A.4., VII.B., VII.B.2., VII.B.3., VII.B.4., VII.B.5., VII.B.7
Key Vocabulary: clothing, renewable resource, nonrenewable resource

---

Most synthetic clothing materials are derived from nonrenewable natural resources, like fossil-based petroleum products. Some people raise ethical questions as to the appropriateness of the use of nonrenewable resources such as fossil fuels, in consideration of questions such as their essentially finite availability as well as costs to humans, wildlife, and the environment often derived from their mining and processing.

There are many aspects, aside from whether or not a resource is renewable, which are considerations in evaluating whether or not to use a particular material for clothing. For example, some materials (e.g., cowhide, petroleum-based synthetics) are derived as byproducts from the development of resources for other, primary purposes (e.g., food, energy). Other sources (e.g., furs) tend to be developed primarily or solely for manufacture of clothing. In addition, nonrenewable resources, such as fossil fuels, are used in obtaining, manufacturing, and distributing clothes made from renewable as well as nonrenewable natural resources.

The pros and cons of appropriate uses of renewable and nonrenewable natural resources are difficult and complex—and may raise social, economic, ethical, and political as well as biological questions. Even the concept that wildlife and other animals is a renewable resource raises ethical objections from some people who feel it encourages the treatment of wildlife as a commodity to be used like food crops such as corn, without regard for the animals themselves.

The major purpose of this activity is simply for students to be able to identify principal sources of clothing. An additional major purpose for elementary age students in the upper grades is for them to be able to distinguish, in scientific terms, between clothing produced from renewable and nonrenewable natural resources.

Materials butcher paper or large shopping bags, scissors, paint, crayons, yarn, wool scraps, heavy thread and needle

Procedure

1. Tell your students they are going to be making coats for themselves, but first, explore what coats are made of and why we need them. Have students answer this question: "On cold days, we wear coats. Where do we get them?" Most students will say, "At a store." Some will say that someone at home made it for them, or it was a gift. If made at home, it will usually be from purchased materials. Children from families who hunt or raise sheep for wool may have coats made from animal materials. "How would you keep warm in a cold climate if you couldn't buy a coat at a store—or if someone in your family or neighborhood couldn't buy the material to make a coat?" NOTE: If your students are from families who make their own clothes directly from plant and animal materials, change the question to: "...if we couldn't make our clothes?"

For Older Students

Discuss the use of renewable and nonrenewable sources of materials. If the students have their coats with them, separate them according to renewable and nonrenewable natural resources.

2. Divide the students into groups of three or four. Assign, or have them choose, different historical periods and places in which to live.
3. Have each group make a coat. Cut a pattern out of butcher paper. Color and paint it to resemble a fur coat, a down parka, or some other kind of coat typical to their historical period. Use a simple pattern for all the coats. For example:

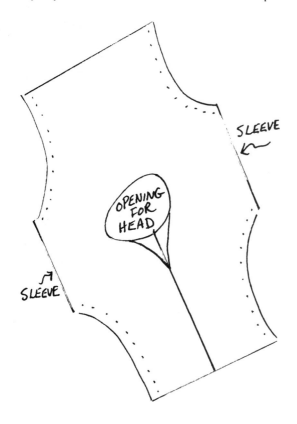

Or, use a shopping bag. Cut neck and sleeve holes. If time and materials permit, each student could make a coat.

Students can sew the seams with carpet or quilting thread and a crewel embroidery needle.
4. Have a fashion show, or display the coats in the classroom. Ask the students to identify their coats, indicating the time period and place represented, and the materials used. Older students should be able to distinguish whether the materials are from renewable or nonrenewable natural resources.

Extensions and Variations For Older Students

1. Divide the renewable resources into plants and animals. Then divide the animal-derived resources into those that require the killing of animals versus those that do not. Talk about under what conditions, if any, **it seems appropriate** to kill animals to get products for human use, like clothing. Talk about under what conditions, if any, **it does not seem appropriate** to kill animals to get products for human use, like clothing.
2. Talk about your reasons for designing your coats as you did, and out of the particular materials you chose. For warmth? Because of the availability of the materials? For convenience? For practicality? Because of the expense of the materials? For fashion? Because you like the looks or feel? For moral or ethical reasons? Because it seemed a wise choice, etc.?
3. Discuss the costs to wildlife of each of the following materials used for clothing: cotton, orlon, vinyl, wool, fur, silk, leather, nylon, rubber, polyester, paper, plastic, acrylic. Under what conditions? Costs to individual animals? Costs to populations of animals? Costs to habitats? Costs to ecosystems? Other costs?
4. Establish your own personal standards for choices in clothing. Identify the basis for your criteria.

Evaluation

Grades K—3 Where did the American Indians and early pioneers get the materials to make their clothing?

Grades 2—6 Which of these materials are from renewable resources, and which are from non-renewable resources: plastic, wool, silk, polyester, paper, linen, cotton, leather, acrylic, rubber, fur, nylon?

Grades 4—6 List four renewable and four non-renewable materials that are used to make clothing today. Describe three ways we make clothing differently today than during pioneer days. What do you think is likely the most important reason American Indians have used furs in the past, and some Alaskan Indians do today? What do you think is the most important reason that most other people do not use furs in their clothing today?

ECOLOGICAL
PRINCIPLES

WHAT BEAR GOES WHERE?

Objectives
Students will be able to: 1) identify three species of bears and their habitats; and 2) generalize that animals are adapted in order to live where they do.

Method
Students construct posters of three different bear habitats.

Background
Polar bears have long necks, slender heads, and white fur. They live along the Arctic coasts, mostly on the polar ice. They feed mainly on fish and seals. Their thick fur keeps them warm, and the webbing between their toes makes them good swimmers. Grizzly bears dig up most of their food, so they have long claws. They also have a distinctive hump between their shoulders. They eat roots, tubers, gophers, marmots, and smaller rodents as well as carrion. They occasionally kill a larger animal for food. Grizzlies tend to live in the edges of forests, but feed mostly in mountain meadows. They have wide heads and a "dished" face. Black bears are quiet, shy animals that live in a variety of habitats from forests to brush or chaparral. They eat mostly nuts, berries, and fruit. They also eat rodents, insects, and occasionally kill larger animals for food. The black bear may be black, auburn, or cinnamon. Black bears are smaller than grizzlies or polar bears and have more pointed heads.

The major purpose of this activity is for students to recognize that animals are adapted to live in different environments, based on the example of three different kinds of bears.

Materials
pictures of the three bear species; three sheets of butcher paper with the outline of one bear species on each, labeled; construction paper; pencils; scissors; glue

---

Age: Grades K—3
Subjects: Science, Art
Skills: analysis, application, classification, comparing similarities and differences, description, discussion, generalization, listing, media construction, observation, psychomotor development, synthesis
Duration: 30 minutes
Group Size: three groups of three to six students each; increase groups as necessary for class size
Setting: indoors
Conceptual Framework Reference: III.A., III.A.1., III.A.3. III.D., III.D.1., III.D.2., I.C.1., I.C.2.
Key Vocabulary: alike, different, adapt, survive, habitat

Procedure

1. Show the students pictures of the three different kinds (species) of bears. Ask them to talk about the things that are alike and are different about the bears.

2. Ask the students to imagine the place where each bear lives. Talk about what is alike and what is different about where the bears live. Think about how each bear looks and whether that helps it to live where it lives. Talk about "adaptation." Animals are "adapted" to survive.

3. Take out three large sheets of paper on which you have drawn the outline of one species of bear in the center of each sheet and labeled it accordingly. (A photo of each bear will serve just as well.)

4. Divide the students into three groups. Give each group one of the sheets of paper with the outline of a bear species and a supply of construction paper, pencils, and scissors.

5. Have each group draw and cut out elements of the habitat of their bear (trees, grassy meadows, and rocks for the grizzly; blocks of ice, snow, fish, and seals for the polar bear; forest

trees, bushes, nuts, fruits, and berries for the black bear) and glue these elements around the picture of their bear. (Make sure that examples of all major habitat needs are included: food, water, shelter, and space in which to live.)

6. Display the finished posters and ask the students what they have learned about bears and where they live. Discuss how each environment has characteristic life forms, adapted to its climate, kinds of available food, etc. Emphasize that all animals adapt to survive.

Evaluation

Describe three kinds of bears, what they need for food, where they live, and how they look.

If someone took polar bears to Yellowstone National Park in Wyoming, and took grizzly bears to the Arctic coast—do you think the bears would be able to live in their new homes if everyone left them alone? Why?

GRAPHANANIMAL

Objective

Students will be able to identify characteristic life forms in two different environments.

Method

Students create picture collections of animals in two different habitats, and then "visit" the habitats by going on a "nature walk" in their classroom, where they tally the number of animals they see and then graph and compare the results.

Background

Different kinds of animals are found in different environments. Each environment is suitable to animals that are adapted to its climate, soils, water, vegetation, and other ecological factors. Just as people need food, water, shelter, and space in which to live, so does wildlife.

The major purpose of this activity is for students to recognize that each environment has characteristic life forms.

Materials

photos or pictures of animals (from magazines), cardboard for mounting photos, notebook paper, graph paper, pencils

Procedure

1. Pick two environments in your state, such as the plains and the forest. Ask students to make a collection of animals for each place. They can draw pictures or cut out magazine photos. Each student should find two animals. Glue the pictures onto heavy paper or cardboard.

2. Ask the students to tell where their animals live. Make a pile for each place and ask the students to put their pictures in the place where their animals live.

3. List the animals in each pile. Some animals will appear on both lists. Ask the students to copy the two lists.

4. When the students are out of the room, place the animal cards in their "environment." Label one part of the classroom as forest, and the other as plains. Put the animals where they live. Some animals may be in both environments. Put the animal pictures in all sorts of places—by a table leg, on a window ledge, etc.—to simulate where they might actually live. If possible, check with fish and wildlife officials in your area to see what the actual proportions of animals are in each of the chosen environments, and use the animal cards accordingly. These people may also have wildlife pictures for various habitats!

5. Bring the students to the "forest" and the "plains" for a "nature walk." Let the students use their lists to tally the animals they see in each place. At the end of the walk, students should total their counts and write that number on their lists. Have the students take turns walking along the "path." A sample list and tally might look like this:

FOREST		TOTAL	PLAINS		TOTAL
RABBIT	₩₩ I	6	COYOTE	₩₩	5
COYOTE	III	3	RATTLESNAKE	III	3
DEER	I	1	PRAIRIE DOG	₩₩ II	7
JAY	III	3	ANTELOPE	II	2

Age: Grades 2—6
Subjects: Science, Math (tally, addition, graph-making and use), Language Arts (word recognition and spelling)
Skills: analysis, classification, computation, kinesthetic concept development, listing, media construction (making and using simple bar graphs), observation, psychomotor development, reading, writing
Duration: two 30-minute periods; one 40-minute period if teacher prepares wildlife pictures
Group Size: 15 to 30 students
Setting: indoors or outdoors
Conceptual Framework Reference: III.A., III.A.1., III.A.3.
Key Vocabulary: environment, habitat, graph (as well as many different animal names)

6. Show the students how to make a bar graph for each of the environments:

FOREST ANIMALS

Give the students graph paper and show them how they can fill in each square for the number of each animal they saw.

7. Using the graphs, compare the two environments: Which animals were seen the most? Which animals were seen the least? How could some animals live in both places? Why can't all the animals live in both places?

Variations

1. Skip having the students collect the animal pictures. If the teacher collects the photos, the activity may begin with the nature walk.

2. Use the strategies for the nature walk when taking any field trip to areas where real animals can be observed.

Evaluation

Name five animals that might be found in each of the following areas: forest, desert, plains, stream, pond, ocean, seashore, park. (Note to Teacher: Please select two areas common to your state.)

Two scientists went to separate parts of the world and studied the animals there. They made these graphs to show the kinds and numbers of animals they found. Do you think they were studying places which were similar or different? Why?

URBAN NATURE SEARCH

Objective

Students will be able to generalize that each environment has characteristic life forms.

Method

Students go outside to observe an environment, using a questionnaire to assist in gathering data.

Background

Every environment has its characteristic life forms—including animals—and the urban setting is no exception. Many of these life forms have adjusted as their habitat has changed from undeveloped to urban. Not only have people altered the environment, the human environment has been shaped by the characteristics of the ecologies within which people live.

The major purpose of this activity is for students to recognize that all environments have characteristic life forms.

See "Wild Words" for a journal-making activity. Students can use their journals for this "Urban Nature Search."

Materials

questionnaires (designed by the teacher), pencils, notebooks or journals (See "Wild Words."), an outdoor setting to conduct this investigation

Procedure

1. Preview and select the route of the nature search. Note stopping places where students can observe and record information.

2. Design a questionnaire to be distributed to the students for use on the "search." The questions and tasks should encourage increased student observation. For example, many of the following phenomena can be designed into this activity:

Tally, describe, and sketch different kinds of plants growing on the north and south sides of buildings. (The differences may be due to temperature variations, sun and shade-loving species of plants, and less evaporation on the north side of building.)

Look for birds. Tally the numbers of different kinds of birds. If they are migratory, sketch the pattern of their flying formation!

Age: Grades 4—9 (and older)
Subjects: Science, Language Arts, Social Studies
Skills: analysis, application, classification, comparing similarities and differences, description, discussion, generalization, kinesthetic concept development, listing, observation, writing
Duration: 45 minutes to one-and-one-half hours
Group Size: any
Setting: outdoors and indoors
Conceptual Framework Reference: I.A.4., I.B., I.B.1., I.B.3., I.C., I.C.1., I.C.2., III.A., III.A.1., III.A.2., III.A.3., III.B., III.B.1., III.B.2., III.D., III.D.1., III.D.2., III.D.3., III.D.4., III.D.5., III.E.2., IV.C., IV.C.1., IV.C.2., IV.C.3., IV.E.5.
Key Vocabulary: investigation, observation, environment

Look for animals establishing "territory." Try to map the animals' territory. (During the mating season, birds can sometimes be seen choosing mates; males fighting, strutting, and dancing around the female species; and nest building.)

Look for evidence of predator/prey relationships. If any mammal, bird, or insect is seen—attempt to determine what animal is its predator or prey.

Record evidence of plant disease and insect damage. It is always interesting to see insect galls or bag worms in their natural setting.

Look for evidence of food chains. For example, if insects are observed, look for partially eaten, damaged or mutilated leaves. Then look for who eats the insects. Draw a food chain and identify the parts.

Try to observe a bee cross-pollinating flowers while gathering nectar for the production of honey. If you're fast, you can observe the specialized organs of the bee, and study them further (from diagrams and photos) back in the classroom.

Sketch trees and list their contributions to the community. (For example, trees can be observed breaking the velocity or speed of the wind. This can reduce wind erosion and might save energy by reducing the winter heat loss from homes in the surrounding area. Trees also serve as part of the wildlife habitat, increase the oxygen content of the air, and have aesthetic value.)

Who likes lichen? Predict what plants and animals have a direct or indirect relationship with lichens. (Lichens will be found growing on rocks, tree trunks, and even on soil. Lichens are really algae and fungi functioning as a partnership in a symbiotic association.)

Trace water's path in an area—like on one street, around one tree, down a hillside. (For example, draw the route of any visible erosion.) Look for results of freezing and thawing on sidewalks and buildings.

Find mulches around trees and shrubs. Record any evidence or observation of life forms. (These mulches allow the soil to absorb and retain large amounts of moisture and reduce evaporation. Mulches also reduce temperature extremes and contain earthworms, as well as microscopic and other life forms.)

Look for evidence of components of habitat. Students can observe first-hand the basic wildlife needs. Match animals with their habitat needs (food, water, shelter, and space in appropriate arrangement). It can be a real challenge for students to determine if all basic needs can be met in the available habitat. Predict what animals should be able to live in the habitats identified.

3. On the field trip, each student should bring a copy of the questionnaire and a pencil and notebook or journal. Remind students not to disturb or destroy any plants or animals they may see.

4. What "characteristic life forms" did the students find that were most surprising? Involve the students in a discussion of their observations, their techniques, and their conclusions. Encourage the generalization, warranted by the results of their investigation, that each environment has characteristic life forms.

Extension

Chart the characteristic life forms found on the search, according to the environments in which they were found. For each animal listed, identify how its basic needs are met. Describe any animal adaptations that seem well-suited to survival in the urban environment. Note any interdependencies between plants and animals, plants and plants, animals and animals. Discuss ways in which people have altered the natural environment and ways in which natural forces have shaped the human environment.

Evaluation

List ten types of plants you might see around the school.

List ten types of animals you might see around the school.

Select any four animals you might see around the school—and describe how these animals find food, shelter, and water in order to survive in the school community. If these animals were not living around people, how might the ways they meet their needs be changed?

Tally, describe, and sketch three plants you find on or near a building:

Indicate whether the plants are on the north, south, east, or west side of the building. Sketch and describe any differences in the kind of vegetation you find on each side of any building.

Tally and sketch any kinds of wildlife you observe. Identify and map the available food, water, shelter, and space for three or more kinds of wildlife you observe in the community. Look for evidence of food chains. Draw three food chains based on your observations of the urban environment and its wildlife and identify the parts.

Trace water's path. Map it. Include illustrations of direct and indirect relationships between wildlife, vegetation, and water in the area of the community you are observing.

GOOD BUDDIES

Objectives
Students will be able to: 1) define symbiosis, commensalism, mutualism, and parasitism; 2) identify animals who live in each type of symbiotic relationship; and 3) explain that symbiotic relationships are examples of the intricate web of interdependence within which all plants and animals live.

Method
Students research pairs of animals, play a card game, and classify the pairs of animals according to three major forms of symbiotic relationship.

Background
Elements of any ecological system live in an intricate web of interdependence. When two species of organisms live in close physical contact with each other, their relationship is called "symbiotic." There are three major forms of symbiotic relationships:

Commensalism A relationship in which one species derives food or shelter from another species without seriously harming that organism or providing any benefits in return.

Mutualism A reciprocal relationship in which two different species live in a symbiotic way where both species benefit and are dependent upon the relationship.

Parasitism A relationship between two species in which one species (the parasite) nourishes itself to the detriment of the other species (the host).

The major purpose of this activity is for students to become familiar with the concept of symbiosis as one example of interdependence in ecological systems.

Age: Grades 4—7
Subjects: Science, Language Arts
Skills: application, matching pairs, reporting, research
Duration: two 30-minute periods; one 45-minute period if background is provided eliminating student research
Group Size: small groups of five or six each
Setting: indoors
Conceptual Framework Reference: III.B., III.B.1.
Key Vocabulary: symbiosis, commensalism, mutualism, parasitism

Materials
cardboard for making cards, marking pens

Procedure

1. Make up several decks of cards (one deck for every five or six students). Each deck should contain 16 card pairs of symbiotic relationships and one "no buddy" card. Examples of pairs:

barnacle/whale
cowbird/buffalo
bee/marabou stork
hermit crab/snail shell
aphid/ant

pilot fish/shark
oxpecker/rhinocerous
damselfish/sea anemone
gull/brown bear
ostrich/warthog
yucca moth/yucca

tick/dog
cattle egret/cow (African Ankole)
ostrich/gazelle
moth/sloth
honey guide bird/badger

2. Pass out a card to each student (do not include the "no buddy" card), and, by means of looking at a posted list on the chalkboard, have each student find his or her "buddy."

3. These pairs of buddies should then research to find out why they are buddies, answering the following questions: Why do we live together? What advantages and disadvantages do we provide one another? What would happen if one of us wasn't here?

4. Pairs of buddies then give short reports to the class, telling about their relationship.

5. Divide the class into groups of five to six students each, and give each group a deck of cards. Instruct the students as to how to play the game.

6. Deal out all the cards. Play starts to the left of the dealer and rotates in a clockwise manner. Each player draws one card from the player to his or her left. After the player has drawn a card, that player may lay down all cards in his or her hand which form symbiotic pairs. When a player does not have any cards left in his or her hand, the game is over. The player with the largest number of pairs at the end of the game is the winner. One player is left holding the "no buddy" card at the end of the game.

7. To culminate the activity, discuss the definitions given in the background information for **commensalism, mutualism,** and **parasitism.** Go through the list of symbiotic pairs and, as a group, decide to which classification each pair belongs. "Good buddy" pair members may be called upon to help decide the classification. Stress that symbiotic relationships are just one example of the interdependence of all elements of ecological systems. In a way, as the Northwest Native American Indian Chief Sealth has said, "We all share the same breath."

Evaluation

Define: symbiosis, commensalism, mutualism, parasitism.

Give two examples of pairs of organisms which have these symbiotic relationships: commensalism, mutualism, parasitism.

WHALE

BARNACLE

GULL

BROWN BEAR

FOREST IN A JAR

Objectives

Students will be able to: 1) observe and describe succession; and 2) summarize what they have learned about how environments can change.

Method

Students conduct an experiment using soil, water, seeds, a plant, and a jar; and then draw a poster to represent their observations and findings.

Background

Succession is a term used to describe the ever-changing environment and the gradual process by which one habitat is replaced by another. Many habitats that appear to be stable are changing before us. In this activity, students will be able to see in miniature how a swampy area can be succeeded by a forested habitat.

The major purpose of this activity is for students to recognize the process of succession.

Materials

pint or quart jars (one per student or small groups of students, or one for the entire class), water, soil, aquatic plants (one per jar), two cups bird seed

Procedure

1. Place two inches of soil and three inches of water in a jar. Place the jar at a window, **without a lid,** and allow it to settle overnight.
2. Plant an aquatic plant in the jar. It should grow well in this environment. If your classroom has no windows, substitute a grow-light.
3. Do **not** replace the water that evaporates from the jar.
4. Once or twice a week, have students add three or four bird seeds to the jar. While there is water in the jar, the seeds should germinate and then rot. Continue adding seeds even after the water evaporates.
5. As the water evaporates down to the soil, the aquatic plant will die. The bird seeds will now find the environment suitable for successful growth. Sunflower seeds, which grow large, can be added to represent forest trees. You will now need to add water, as a substitute for rainfall, to keep the soil damp to keep things growing.
6. Have each student make a poster, drawing, or other visual representation of what they saw happen to their "pond." Ask them to talk about what they have learned about how environments can change. Introduce the term, "succession," to older students.
7. OPTIONAL: Take a field trip to a pond. What plants are growing in the water? What plants are growing on the shore? What parallels are there between this real pond and the "pond" in the jar? Make a second drawing of this real pond. Compare the similarities and differences between the two.

NOTE: See "Pond Succession," and use it as an extension to this activity.

Age: Grades K—6
Subject: Science
Skills: analysis, application, comparing similarities and differences, description, discussion, drawing, generalization, invention, media construction, psychomotor development, research
Duration: five to ten minutes for one or two days a week for several weeks; 20 to 30 minutes for summary activity
Group Size: any
Setting: indoors; outdoors optional
Conceptual Framework Reference: III.A., III.A.1., III.A.3., III.B., III.C., III.C.1., III.C.3., III.C.4.
Key Vocabulary: evaporation, change, succession

Evaluation

Describe three changes you saw happen to what was inside the jar.

Number these drawings to show their order from what would be most likely to be first, to what would be likely to last.

Draw lines from each of these animal names to the places above where they would be most likely to live.

fish   turtle   raccoon   squirrel   deer

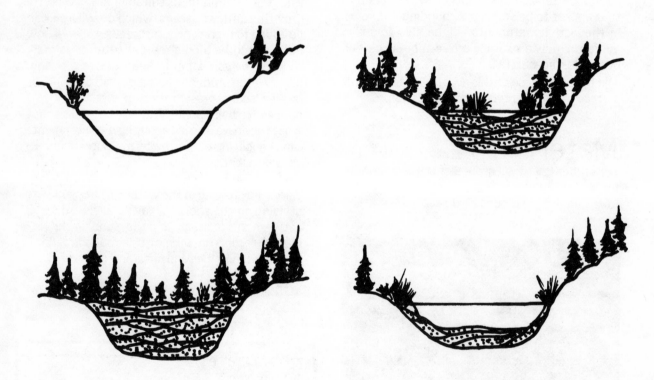

POND SUCCESSION

Objectives

Students will be able to: 1) recognize that natural environments are involved in a process of continual change; 2) discuss the concept of succession; 3) describe succession as an example of the process of change in natural environments; and 4) apply understanding of the concept of succession by drawing a series of pictures showing stages in pond succession.

Method

Students create murals showing three major stages of pond succession.

Background

Succession is a term used to describe the ever-changing environment and the gradual process by which one habitat is replaced by another. Many habitats that appear to be stable are changing before us—perhaps at a slow rate in human eyes, but evolving rather quickly according to the earth's clock.

For example, a shallow pond may be transformed into a marshy, then forested, area in only a thousand years or so. Wind-blown or water-borne spores of algae are the first inhabitants. Eggs of flying insects are deposited. Small fish and amphibians arrive through the inlet. Surrounding sediments begin to fill the pond, some borne on wash-out from rainfall, some entering through the pond's inlet. Marshy plants growing along the shoreline spread inward as sediments fill the pond. Land plants also spread inward and replace the marsh plants as the ground is consolidated. As more plants and animals enter the system, more opportunities for habitat become available to others. Changes from ponds to forest are only one example of succession.

The major purpose of this activity is for students to discover that the environment is not static, but changing, and to see an example of how these changes progress over time, through experience with the concept of succession.

Materials

long pieces of drawing paper for murals; tape for securing paper to walls; crayons

Procedure

1. Review with students the idea of succession—the orderly, gradual, and continual replacement of one community of plants and animals with another.

2. Start by talking about a pond. How many people have seen a pond? What did it look like? After a description of ponds, ask the students to imagine what a pond would look like from a side view if you could see under the water and show the nearby environment. For example:

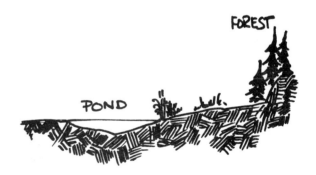

Age: Grades 4—9
Subjects: Science, Social Studies
Skills: analysis, application, comparing similarities and differences, description, discussion, drawing, media construction, observation, small group work, synthesis, visualization
Duration: one or two 30—minute periods or longer
Group Size: any
Setting: indoors (outdoors optional)
Conceptual Framework Reference: III.A., III.A.1., III.A.3., III.B., III.B.1., III.C., III.C.1., III.C.2., III.C.3., III.C.4., III.D., III.D.1., III.D.2., III.D.3., III.D.4., III.D.5.
Key Vocabulary: succession, sediment, change, pond

3. Explain to the students that they will be drawing a series of three views of a pond over a time period of about 800 years. The first (left-hand) section will show the pond as it is today, the middle section how it might look 500 years later, after natural changes, and the third (right-hand) how the pond could look in 800 years. (These time periods are approximate and can vary greatly.)

4. Discuss with them the possibilities of plant and animal life in the first section. What kinds of plants and animals live: in the water; along the shoreline; in the surrounding area?

5. Then give each group their piece of paper which they will divide into three equal sections (by folding or drawing). Instruct them to fill in the first section with their drawing of the pond and the surrounding area. Set a specific time frame for the students to draw (about ten minutes).

6. Bring the class together again for a discussion of the second section—to be labeled "500 Years Later." Consider the following items:

a. What changes in the environment have taken place?

b. How will the pond look now?

c. What lives and grows in the water now that it is much shallower and smaller?

d. What lives and grows around the shoreline—which is now marshier? (marsh animals and plants, perhaps some willow bushes)

e. What lives and grows in the surrounding area? (larger trees, same types of animals) Have each group complete the second section of their mural, labeling it "500 Years Later."

7. Repeat the process for the third section, labeling it "800 Years Later" and discussing the following topics:

a. By this time the pond is almost totally filled with sediment, leaving only a small marshy area with perhaps a stream running through. What changes have taken place?

b. What lives and grows in the environment?

c. What lives and grows where the shoreline used to be? (bushes, small trees)

d. What effects does the pond succession have on the surrounding area? (different animals, trees requiring less water)

8. After the murals are completed, students should sign them. Then they may be displayed in the classroom for all students to see and discuss differences and similarities between the various murals. Ask the students to summarize what they have learned, including how succession is one example of the ongoing process of change in natural environments.

Variation

Use a stream table filled with standard soil to illustrate in three-dimensional, dynamic ways the processes of succession! Fill the table with soil, make an indentation in the center to represent the pond; run water into the table to represent rainfall, streams feeding the pond, etc.; and watch the pond fill as sedimentation takes place. This can show the geologic life cycle of the pond. Add replicas of plants and animals during successional stages for even more interest!

OPTIONAL: Visit the real thing if you can!

Evaluation

Draw a picture, with explanations, to show stages in pond succession.

THE THICKET GAME

Objectives

Students will be able to: 1) define adaptation in animals; and 2) generalize that all animals make some adaptations in order to survive.

Method

Students become "predator" and "prey" in a version of "hide and seek."

Background

Animals are adapted to their environment in order to survive. Animals may be adapted to changes in their habitats. For example, snowshoe rabbits have a white winter coat to blend with a snowy environment and a tan summer coat to blend with summer ground and vegetation colors. Chameleons change color to blend with their surroundings. The walking-stick insect can look like a twig or stick. Fawns have spotted hair that resembles dappled light on the forest floor.

The major purpose of this activity is for students to understand the importance of adaptation to animals.

NOTE: See "Seeing is Believing" and "Surprise Terrarium" for other elementary-age adaptation activities.

Materials

blindfolds; outdoor area like a thicket or other vegetated area where students can safely hide

Procedure

1. Take the class to a "thicket."
2. Blindfold one student who will be the "predator." The predator counts to 15 slowly while the others hide. The students hiding must be able to see the predator all the time.
3. After counting, the predator removes the blindfold and looks for "prey." The predator can turn around, squat, and stand on tip-toes—but not walk or change location. The predator should see how many students he or she can find, identify them out loud and describe where they are. When identified, they come to the predator because they have been "eaten." These prey now become predators.
4. When the original predator cannot see any more students, all the predators now put on blindfolds. The original predator counts aloud to ten. All the remaining prey are to move in closer, but still try to be "safe" and hidden. All the predators remove their blindfolds and take turns naming students they can see.
5. Repeat the process if several students are still hidden. When only one or two are left hidden,

Age: Grades K-6
Subjects: Science, Physical Education, Language Arts
Skills: analysis, application, description, discussion, generalization, kinesthetic concept development, observation, psychomotor development
Duration: 30 minutes
Group Size: minimum of five students
Setting: outdoors
Conceptual Framework Reference: III.D., III.D.1., III.D.2.
Key Vocabulary: adaptation, predator, prey

have them stand up and identify themselves; it may be surprising how close these prey were to the predators—an example of successful adaptation because of how well they blend with their environment in order to survive. Introduce the term "adaptation."

6. Play the game again one or two times.

7. Discuss what would have made it easier to be the last one or get very close to the predators. Some ideas that may come out are: changing color (clothes); wearing clothing that doesn't stick to plants; being of smaller size; climbing a tree.

8. Ask the students to summarize what they have learned. See if the students can think of other examples of adaptation in animals. Generalize that all animals are adapted to survive.

Evaluation

Describe the importance of adaptation to animals. Give at least two examples of animal adaptation.

ADAPTATION ARTISTRY

Objectives
Students will be able to: 1) identify and describe the advantages of bird adaptations; and 2) evaluate the importance of adaptations to birds.

Method
Students design and create imaginary birds, and write reports including descriptions of the birds' adaptations.

Background
NOTE: See "Thicket Game." Use as an introduction to the concept of "adaptation," followed by "Adaptation Artistry."

Birds have a variety of adaptations—including characteristics of beaks, feet, legs, wings, and coloration. These adaptations have evolved so that the bird is better suited to its environment and lifestyle. A variety of major adaptations are listed below:

Adaptation		Bird	Advantage
Beaks	pouch-like	pelican	can hold fish, a food source
	long, thin	avocet	can probe shallow water and mud for insects, a food source
	pointed	wood-pecker	can break and probe bark of trees, for insects, a food source
	curved	hawk	can tear solid tissue, like meat, a food source
	short, stout	finches	can crack seeds and nuts, a food source
	slender, long	humming-bird	can probe flowers for nectar, a food source
Feet	webbed	duck	aids in walking on mud, transportation
	long toes	crane, heron	aids in walking on mud, transportation
	clawed	hawk, eagle	can grasp food when hunting prey
	grasping	chicken	aids in sitting on branches, roosting, protection
Legs	flexor tendons	chicken	aid in perching, grasping
	long, powerful	ostrich	aids running, transportation
	long, slender	heron, crane	aids wading, transportation
	powerful muscles	eagle, hawk	aids lifting, carrying prey, transportation
Wings	large	eagle	aids flying with prey, soaring while hunting
Coloration	bright plumage	male birds	attraction in courtship, mating rituals
		female birds	aids in camouflage while nesting, protection in shelter
	change of plumage with seasons	owl ptarmigan,	provides camouflage protection (brown in summer, white in winter), protection in shelter

The major purpose of this activity is for students to realize that there are advantages for birds in looking how they do, recognizing some of the ways in which birds are physically adapted to their environments.

Materials
drawing, painting, clay sculpture or papier mache' materials; construction paper and glue; pencil and paper

Age: Grades 4—9
Subjects: Science, Art, Language Arts
Skills: analysis, application of concepts, description, discussion, drawing, invention, media construction, observation, problem solving, reporting, synthesis, writing
Duration: one or two 45—minute periods
Group Size: any
Setting: indoors (outdoors optional)
Conceptual Framework Reference: III.D., III.D.1., III.D.2.
Key Vocabulary: adaptation

Procedure

1. Discuss with the students the various adaptations given in the background section of this activity, listing the charts on a chalkboard for reference by the students. Or, brainstorm a list of bird characteristics, name the birds with such characteristics, and describe the advantage of the adaptation represented by the characteristic.
2. Tell the students they will each have a chance to design their own original bird—one well adapted to its habitat. Each student should decide:

• where the bird will live
• what it will eat
• its type of mobility
• its sex

3. Based on these choices, the students will decide the adaptations that are necessary for their bird, and write them down before proceeding further.
4. Using their list of adaptations, each student will create his or her own original bird; for example, by drawing or sculpting it.
5. In conjunction with each drawing or sculpture, each student should write a short report which includes the name of the bird and its food sources, habitat, and lifestyle. Students should also include their lists of adaptations, the reasons for the adaptations, and the advantages provided by the adaptations.

6. Completed projects may either be submitted to the teacher, presented to the class, or displayed in the classroom.
7. Optional: Go outside and identify adaptations on real birds!

Extensions

1. Make mobiles of the completed birds.
2. Prepare a slide presentation on an overhead projector showing different types of bird adaptations.
3. The teacher could give the students examples of bird adaptations on the overhead projector or a ditto sheet and the student could explain the reasons for these adaptations.
4. Collect pictures of birds to develop a bulletin board showing some of the adaptations discussed. Look for pictures showing bird parts compatible with the "invented" birds. Display the invented birds. Use the bulletin board during parent conferences.

Evaluation

Name two bird adaptations for each of the following body parts, listing their advantages: beaks, feet, legs, wings, color.

SEEING IS BELIEVING or THE EYES HAVE IT!

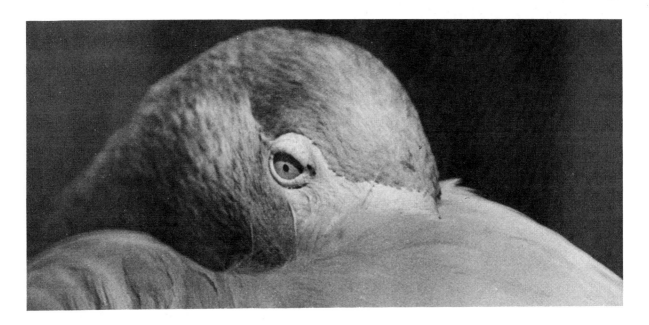

Objective
Students will be able to identify different kinds of vision as an example of adaptation in animals.

Method
Students use kaleidoscopes, binoculars or telescopes, and fish-eye mirrors; imagine what animals might have such vision; and make posters showing animals that do have such vision.

Background
NOTE: See "Thicket Game" for information about animal adaptation. Also "Surprise Terrarium."

Vision is one example of animal adaptation—with different kinds of vision well-suited to the needs of different kinds of animals.

The major purpose of this activity is for students to recognize different kinds of vision as examples of adaptation in animals.

Materials
set up three learning stations: one with a kaleidoscope, one with binoculars or telescope, and one with a fish-eye mirror or photos taken with such a lens; magazines with wildlife photos or wildlife stamps; glue; poster material.

Procedure
1. Set up three stations or learning centers in the classroom: one with kaleidoscopes (the kind you

Age: Grades K—6
Subjects: Science, Language Arts, Art
Skills: analysis, application, classification, comparing similarities and differences, description, discussion, generalization, inference, invention, kinesthetic concept development, media construction, observation, psychomotor development, small group work, synthesis
Duration: five—ten minutes or longer at each learning center; 30 minutes for discussion and posters
Group Size: one or two students at a time at learning centers; any size group in summary activity
Setting: indoors, at learning centers
Conceptual Framework Reference: III.D., III.D.1., III.D.2.
Key Vocabulary: adaptation, vision, kaleidoscope, binocular, fish-eye lens

can see through); the second with either binoculars or telescopes; and the third with a fish-eye mirror (or photos of objects taken with a fish-eye lens on a camera).

2. Have the students visit each station, trying out the different kinds of vision. (Younger students may require assistance in using the equipment.)

3. Ask the students to guess what kinds of animals might have each of these three types of vision, emphasizing that the way an animal sees is a form of adaptation. Adaptation is something animals have in order to survive in an environment. For example:

Binoculars—Predatory birds (eagles, hawks, owls) have acute distant and depth of vision similar to telescopic vision. They do not have tunnel vision, however, as a telescope might suggest; they have exceptional peripheral vision. This allows them to see their prey from great distances.

Kaleidoscopes—Insects have compound eyes. Each facet of their eye functions like a separate eye and allows them extreme peripheral vision. This allows them to detect predators.

Fish-eye mirror or photos—Fish have eyes with wide-angle perception. They can see predators, prey, and other food sources.

4. Divide the class into three groups and have each group cut out magazine pictures and make a poster for one of the three stations, showing the kinds of animals that have that particular kind of vision.

Extensions and Variations

1. Have students write a paragraph with the title, "I'd like to see like a_____", in which they could describe how they would see things and why they would like to be able to see that way. They could also describe what that animal's view of the world would be like.

2. Students could make eyeglasses, and—by drawing or cutting out magazine photos—show the colors, shapes, or patterns of an animal's eye. Or, they could create a small collage showing what that animal's view of the world would be. The art work occupies the space on the eyeglasses where the lens would normally be. Unlined tagboard paper is thin enough to cut out eyeglass shapes without tearing easily.

Evaluation

Each of the following animals has either **kaleidoscope, binocular, or fish-eye mirror eyes:** trout, owl, fly, eagle, cricket. Identify which kind of vision each animal has.

How do the eyes of eagles help them to hunt better?

SURPRISE TERRARIUM

Objectives

Students will be able to: 1) identify camouflage as an example of adaptation in an animal; and 2) describe the importance of adaptation to animals.

Method

Students observe a live animal using camouflage techniques.

Background

NOTE: See "Thicket Game" and "Seeing is Believing."

One of the most important ways that living things survive is by their ability to adapt—to climate, soils, water, vegetation, other life forms, and other ecological factors.

Animals that use camouflage techniques can be particularly interesting and visually compelling to young students as a means of illustrating the concept of adaptation.

The major purpose of this activity is for students to recognize that animals adapt to survive.

Materials

terrarium with vegetation, and one animal suited to the kind of habitat components represented in the terrarium (the animal should be one that uses camouflage as a form of adaptation to survive; e.g., leaf hopper, tree frog, tree lizard, walking stick, grasshopper, earthworm); photos of animals using camouflage or magazines the students can use to find photos

NOTE: See the National Science Teachers Association's "Code of Practice on Animals in Schools" in the Appendices for suggestions concerning proper housing and care for animals in the classroom.

Procedure

1. Make a "surprise terrarium" for your students, and bring it to class. The terrarium should contain an animal that is hard for the students to see at first, because the animal uses camouflage as an adaptation technique.

2. Encourage the students to observe the terrarium, wondering if an animal might live there. Ask them to describe what they see.

3. Ask the students to think of animals that blend with their environments. Talk about their ideas. Show photos, or bring in magazines and ask the students to look for pictures of animals that look so much like where they live they are hard to see. Are the animals camouflaged? Camouflage is one way animals adapt in order to survive.

4. If they haven't found the animal who is living in their terrarium, encourage them to look very closely until they do.

5. Ask the students to summarize some of the things they have learned about "adaptation" and its importance to animals.

6. Optional: If the camouflaged animal was brought into the classroom from the wild, the students may participate in the process of returning the animal to its natural home. This is a good time to talk about human responsibilities for proper care of animals used for instructional purposes, as well as a potential way to see the animal camouflaged in its natural setting.

Evaluation

Name two animals that use camouflage, and talk about how camouflage is important to these animals.

Age: Grades K-3 (and older)
Subjects: Science, Language Arts
Skill: application, discussion, generalization, observation
Duration: 20—30 minutes
Group Size: any
Setting: indoors
Conceptual Framework Reference: III.D., III.D.1., III.D.2.
Key Vocabulary: adaptation, camouflage

POLAR BEARS IN PHOENIX?

Objective
Students will be able to identify problems for an animal moved from its natural environment to captivity.

Method
Students design and draw a zoo enclosure appropriate for the survival of a polar bear in a hot, arid climate.

Background
Polar bears are aquatic animals. They spend 90% of their time in the water, and the remaining 10% on land. They are able to get their food from the sea during both of the arctic seasons; the three month summer of continuous daylight and the nine month long, dark winter. They do, however, range on the tundra in summer, feeding on leaves and fruits of tundra plants and an occasional muskox or caribou, which a polar bear can outrun over short distances. These bears range over broad distances on the ice, travelling southward in winter to stay near open water and shifting ice floes, diving for fishes, catching seals as they come up for air. They eat seaweed in difficult times.

One of the main functions of a zoo is to display animals in their natural habitat. The local environment must be adapted to suit the animal's wants and needs in order for the animal to survive and thrive. In the case of polar bears, that represents quite a challenge!

In captivity, polar bears do not like being enclosed, making it very difficult to gain access for maintenance of their enclosure. On smooth surfaces, they have a habit of twisting around on their hindquarters in such a way that their back paw claws get very little use, growing too long, and becoming imbedded in their skin. Infant bears require heat and the solitude of a den during their first several months of life. Father bears, if not kept separately, have been known to kill even moderately grown cubs.

Age: Grades 2—6
Subjects: Science, Language Arts, Social Studies
Skills: analysis, application, comparing similarities and differences, discussion, drawing, evaluation, invention, observation, problem solving, synthesis, visualization
Duration: 45 minutes
Group Size: any
Setting: indoors
Conceptual Framework Reference: I.C.1., I.C.2., III.A., III.A.1., III.A.2., III.A.3., III.D., III.D.1., III.D.2., III.D.3., III.D.4., III.D.5.
Key Vocabulary: zoo, adaptation, survival

In the heat of summer, the bears spend most of their time in the cool recesses of their dens or in the cool, deep water in their pool. The Smithsonian Zoo in Washington, D.C. has air-conditioned their dens and installed windows in the side walls of their pool for sub-surface viewing of the animals. The keepers also change the bear's diet in summer in order to reduce the thickness of the bear's fat layer, thus keeping the bears cooler.

In designing a zoo enclosure for a polar bear, students should take this information into consideration:

Polar bears weigh 700 to 900 pounds at maturity, with a length of up to ten feet. They can jump ten to twelve feet into the air from a standing position.

The enclosure should contain everything the animal needs to survive: a sleeping place, hiding place or den for solitude, pool, source of drinking water, food, and space for exercise. The enclosure should look as unlike a cage as possible. Also consider:

- temperature (day, night)
- humidity
- floor covering
- slope of floor (for cleaning)
- color
- light intensity (day, night)
- length of day
- water
- food, diet
- plant life
- air pressure
- wind velocity and direction
- maintenance

The major purpose of this activity is for students to recognize that animals are adapted to the environments in which they have lived for a long time. If people move animals to environments different from those for which the animals are adapted, then special attention must be paid to creating conditions in which the animals can live.

Materials paper for drawing; crayons

Procedure

1. Introduce polar bears to the students with a brief description of their habitat and habits. Try to include some pictures of both young and mature animals. (See "What Bear Goes Where.")
2. Tell the students they will each have the opportunity to design their own zoo enclosure for a polar bear that is being moved from its natural habitat in northern Alaska to the desert environment of Phoenix, Arizona. What do they need to consider? Compare and contrast the two environments. Identify and describe the bear's habitat needs. What can be done to meet those needs in Phoenix? Students may want to work individually or in teams.
3. Give each student a large piece of paper and crayons. If possible, have them list some of the major features they would like their enclosure to include on a separate piece of paper before beginning to draw.
4. Display the drawings on a bulletin board. Allow the class time to view the drawings and discuss merits and drawbacks of the various enclosures.
5. As a summary, discuss some of the problems these bears would have in captivity. Talk about the responsibilities people have to meet animals' needs if we put them in captivity.

Extensions

1. Visit a polar bear at a local zoo, if one is available.
2. Visit any animals in captivity. Compare the animals' natural habitat to that provided in the captive conditions.

Evaluation

Describe five problems a polar bear would face in captivity. Suggest possible solutions for each of these problems, explaining your reasoning.

QUICK FROZEN CRITTERS

Objectives
Students will be able to: 1) discuss predator/prey relationships, including adaptations; 2) describe the importance of adaptations in predator/prey relationships; and 3) recognize that limiting factors—including predator/prey relationships—affect wildlife populations.

Method
Students play an active version of "freeze tag."

Background
NOTE:
This activity is best done after one or more that introduces the concepts of "adaptation" and "limiting factors." See the cross references for suggestions.

Predator: An animal that kills and eats other animals for food.

Prey: An animal that is killed and eaten by other animals for food.

Limiting Factors: There are many influences in the life history of any animal. When one of these (e.g., disease, climate, pollution, accidents, shortages of food) exceeds the limits of tolerance of that animal, it becomes a limiting factor. It then drastically affects the well-being of that animal. Predators are limiting factors for prey. Prey are limiting factors for predators.

Animals display a variety of behaviors in predator/prey relationships. These are adaptations to survive.

Some prey behaviors are: signalling to others, flight, posturing in a fighting position, scrambling for cover, and even "freezing" on the spot to escape detection or capture by predators. The kind of behavior exhibited partly depends on how close the predator is when detected by the prey. Each animal has a threshold for threat levels. If a predator is far enough away for the prey to feel some safety, the prey may signal to others that a predator is near. If the predator comes closer, the prey may try to run away. If the predator is too close to make running away feasible, the prey may attempt to scurry to a hiding place. If the predator is so close that none

of these alternatives is available, the prey may freeze in place. The closer the predator comes to the prey animal, the more likely it is that the prey will "freeze" in place. This "freezing" occurs as a kind of physiological shock in the animal. (Shelter or camouflage may also make them invisible to the predator when they freeze.) Too often people who come upon animals quickly and see them immobile infer that the animals are unafraid when, in reality, the animals are "frozen", or, as the adage goes, "frozen stiff."

The major purpose of this activity is for students to recognize the importance of adaptations to both predators and prey and to gain insight into limiting factors affecting wildlife populations.

Age: Grades 4—6 (can be modified for younger and older students; simplify the discussion for younger students.)

Subjects: Science, Physical Education (Language Arts optional: See Variations and Extensions.)

Skills: analysis, description, discussion, evaluation, generalization, kinesthetic concept development, observation, psychomotor development

Duration: 20 to 45 minutes

Group Size: best with at least ten students; one "predator" per every four to six "prey."

Setting: indoors or outdoors

Conceptual Framework Reference: III.D., III.D.1., III.D.2., III.E., III.E.1., III.E.2.

Key Vocabulary: predator, prey, adaptation

Materials
food tokens (pieces of cardboard), enough for three per student; gym vests or other labelling devices to mark predators; four or five hula hoops to serve as "cover" markers; pencil and paper to record number of captures, if desired

Procedure
1. Select any of the following pairs of animals:

Prey	Predators
cottontails	coyotes
ground squirrels	hawks
deer	cougar
quail	foxes

Identify students as either "predators" or "prey" for a version of "freeze tag"—with approximately one predator per every four to six prey.

2. Using a gymnasium or playing field, identify one end of the field as the "food source" and the other end as the "shelter."

3. Four to five hula hoops are placed in the open area between the "shelter" and the "food." These represent additional shelter or "cover" for the prey and can be randomly distributed on the field. (If hula hoops are not available, string might be used—or chalk on asphalt.)

4. Food tokens are placed in the "food source" zone on the ground. Allow three food tokens for each prey animal. For example:

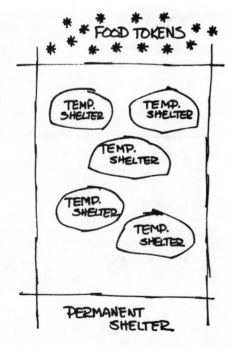

5. Predators should be clearly identified. Gym vests or safety patrol vests might be available.

6. Use a whistle or some other pre-arranged signal to start each round. When a round begins, prey start from their "shelter." The task of the prey animals is to move from the primary shelter to the food source, collecting one food token each trip, and returning to the primary shelter. To survive, prey have to obtain three food tokens. Their travel is hazardous, however. They need to be alert to possible predators. If they spot a predator, they can use various appropriate prey behaviors—including warning other prey that a predator is near. Prey have two ways to prevent themselves from being caught by predators; they may "freeze" any time a predator is within five feet of them; or they may run to cover (with at least one foot within one of the hula hoops.) Frozen prey may blink, but otherwise should be basically still without talking.

7. Predators start the game anywhere in the open area between ends of the field, and thus are randomly distributed between the prey's food and primary shelter. Predators attempt to capture prey to survive, tagging only *moving* (not "frozen") prey. (Optional: Prey can have bandannas in their pockets that the predators have to capture to represent the successful predation.) Predators must each capture two prey in order to survive. Captured prey are taken to the sidelines by the predator who captured them.

8. A time limit of five to seven minutes is suggested for each round of the game. (Captured prey on the sidelines will get restless if rounds are much longer.)

9. Play the game twice, allowing each student to be both prey and predator.

10. Discuss with the students the ways they escaped capture when they were prey. Which ways were easiest? Which were most effective? What means did they use as predators to capture prey? Which ways were best? What did the predators do in response to a prey animal who "froze?" In what ways are adaptations important to both predator and prey? Ask the students to summarize what they have learned about predator/prey relationships. How do predator/prey relationships serve as natural limiting factors affecting wildlife?

NOTE: Establish a ground rule for student behavior: Behave in ways that are not harmful to other students, even when simulating predator behavior; e.g., no full tackles!

Variations and Extensions

1. Play the game for three or four rounds, recording the number of captures each playing period. Have students who are captured become predators, and each predator not getting enough food become a prey animal in the succeeding round. This quickly leads to the concept of dynamic balance as prey and predator populations fluctuate in response to each other.

2. Have the students walk only, or assign different locomotive forms to each animal.

3. Students could select an animal and research its behavior patterns for avoiding detection and capture. Reports or demonstrations of the behavior could be presented to the class.

Evaluation

Pick any predator and prey. Describe each animal's adaptations.

CLASSROOM CARRYING CAPACITY

Objectives

Students will be able to: 1) define carrying capacity; and 2) give examples of factors which can influence the carrying capacity of an area.

Method

Students sit unusually close to each other and describe the results.

Background

NOTE: Also see "How Many Bears Can Live In This Forest?" for another activity about the concept of carrying capacity.

Carrying capacity affects all living things, including humans. Carrying capacity is the number of living things an area of land or water can support at any one time. Different life forms will have a different carrying capacity on the same area. For example, the carrying capacity of an area of land will not be the same for bald eagles as it is for crows.

Carrying capacity is usually limited by some aspect of a species' habitat requirements. These requirements include the quantity and quality of available food, water, shelter, space, and the suitability of their arrangement. Different factors will be important in each case. Natural and human causes both affect carrying capacity. Effects may be short or long term.

Carrying capacity for many species is in a constant state of change, both seasonally and from year to year. For example, it is usually most limited for terrestrial animals in the winter season when food supplies are reduced. Year to year variations may result from factors such as natural disasters, changes in rainfall and temperature patterns, or human interventions. Factors affecting plant growth will affect animals since they are either directly (as herbivores or omnivores) or indirectly (as carnivores) dependent on plants. For example, the damming of a river can affect fish populations which in turn supply a major portion of bald eagle diets. Mining, forestry practices, or land development can eliminate shelter for the eagles' nesting and roosting. A lightning caused forest fire might do the same. A cattle or sheep ranch might seasonally provide the eagles with a bonus of carrion, as might a wintering duck population.

Populations of living things tend to fluctuate naturally around some level. Carrying capacity affects that level. A population may be below carrying capacity such as in the spring following a hard winter, or temporarily above it. The latter situation inevitably results in a decline of the population by a variety of natural limiting factors, e.g., mortality, disease, emigration, and lowered reproductive rate, and usually lasts for a short period.

The carrying capacity of an area can be adjusted by natural factors or by human intervention. As a production or growing seasons ends, available food may decline rapidly as animals use it. A population may naturally fluctuate with carrying capacity. Humans may not always be willing to accept the consequences of such natural events, however. Human intervention can reduce

Age: Grades K—6
Subjects: Science, Social Studies, Language Arts
Skills: analysis, application, comparing similarities and differences, description, discussion, evaluation, inference, kinesthetic concept development, listing, observation
Duration: K—3, 20 minutes; Grades 4—6, 45 minutes
Group Size: any (does require at least a small group)
Setting: indoors or outdoors (designed for classroom)
Conceptual Framework Reference: III.B.6., III.F., III.F.1., III.F.2., III.F.3., III.F.4., III.F.5
Key Vocabulary: carrying capacity, crowded

a population or prevent its expansion to meet an expected natural reduction in carrying capacity. Such an intervention may result in a higher survival rate.

Alteration of habitat quality or quantity may increase or decrease carrying capacity. Environmental degradation may reduce it for affected species. Activities such as development or pollution tend not to be aimed at intentionally reducing carrying capacity but often have this impact. Intentional intervention may be based on a particular management philosophy or practice. Management of an area of land or water in relation to its carrying capacity for certain species can be subject to question and controversy.

The major purpose of this activity is to provide students with a general introduction to the topic of carrying capacity.

The major purpose of this activity is to provide students with a general introduction to the topic of carrying capacity.

Materials
chalkboard; any area with room to sit closely, in crowded conditions, and then move comfortably into a larger area

Procedure

1. Ask your students to sit close together in a group on the floor. They should be fairly tightly packed together. Tell them to pay attention as you give a short lesson in spelling, language, or math. Conduct the lesson for five to ten minutes. Then ask the students to describe what happened during the lesson. Did they feel crowded? How did they act? Is this the way they usually act when they are sitting at their desks, not so close together? Optional: Try this a second time, with the available "habitat" even smaller!

For Grades K—3 Students
2. What if you were animals and you were this crowded? You might be domesticated animals, like cats or dogs or pet rabbits—or you might be wild animals, like deer or elephants. Would you be able to live? Is there enough room for you? What would you need in order to survive? (You would need food, water, shelter, and enough space in which to live, arranged according to your needs.)

The number of plants and animals that an environment can support is called its "carrying capacity." If the classroom were the environment, were there **too many, too few,** or **just the right number** of people for the classroom carrying capacity when everyone sat together and crowded? (If the only area available were the small space with people crowded, there were

probably too many people.) What are examples of things that can happen to affect how many plants and animals an environment can support ("carry")?
3. Ask the students to define carrying capacity, and say why it is important.

For Grades 4—6 Students
2. After students have returned to their seats, work with them in discussion to develop a basic definition of carrying capacity. How was the "carrying capacity" of their classroom instructional area affected when they were sitting so crowded and close together? Ask the students how the behavior of a population of animals might change if the population suddenly exceeded the carrying capacity of a habitat, or if the size of a habitat was suddenly decreased. Why might an animal population exceed the carrying capacity of a habitat? How might a habitat or its carrying capacity be suddenly decreased in size? What are some of the ways that the carrying capacity of a habitat might be increased? (For example, by providing some of the basic survival needs of animals. Some could be from natural causes, like increased rainfall and mild winters. Some can be from human actions like putting out nesting boxes, planting food crops, artificial feeding, and revegetation programs.)
3. Introduce the students to the idea that the earth we live on may have a set carrying capacity. In what ways, if any, are people, domesticated animals, and wildlife affecting the carrying capacity of the planet earth? Are there positive effects? Negative effects?
4. Ask your students to summarize what they have learned by listing, "Some Important Things to Remember About Carrying Capacity." Ask them to share their lists.
NOTE: Especially when discussing the carrying capacity of the planet, avoid frightening or depressing the students; instead, emphasize the importance of learning about some difficult ideas in order to be able to contribute to effective, constructive, and informed actions. We may face even the most difficult problems with optimism—as we do our work to study and learn along the way.

Evaluation
List four things that influence carrying capacity. How could a farmer or rancher increase an area's carrying capacity?
How could a farmer or rancher decrease an area's carrying capacity?

MUSKOX MANEUVERS

Objectives
Students will be able to: 1) evaluate the effectiveness of some adaptations in predator/prey relationships; and 2) describe the importance of predator/prey relationships as limiting factors in wildlife populations.

Method
Students simulate muskoxen and wolves in a highly involving game of physical activity.

Background

The muskox is a large, shaggy herbivore called "omingmak" or "the bearded one" by the Eskimos, or Inuit (ee-new-eet), as they prefer to be called. A male muskox may weigh over 600 pounds at maturity, and mature females about 350 pounds. A young muskox may weigh only about 19 pounds at birth. These animals are inhabitants of the arctic regions of Alaska, Greenland, and Canada.

Muskoxen often are found in herds of 20 to 30. Both sexes will vigorously defend the young, usually forming a line or circle around them, facing the threatening predator. Such a circle renders the animals relatively safe against natural predators, particularly wolves.

In this activity, the roles of bulls and cows are differentiated in ways not typical of actual muskoxen. Again, both sexes vigorously defend the young.

The major purpose of this activity is for students to recognize adaptation and limiting factors in a predator/prey relationship.

NOTE: This activity was inspired by a "New Game," and adapted to teach concepts related to wildlife. Although this activity does not illustrate all the complexities of predator/prey relationships, it does illustrate broad concepts.

Materials
two different colors of rag "flags;" twelve of one color, three of another

Procedure

NOTE: The following procedures will be based on a group size of 33 students.. The activity will work with as few as 15 students, and the group size can be increased to approximately 50. Simply adjust the categories of muskoxen proportionately (approximately four times as many of both calves and cows as wolves; two times as many of both calves and cows as bulls; e.g., four calves, four cows, two bulls, one wolf).

1. This is a highly involving activity! It is best done outdoors, in an open, grassy area; however, it is possible to do the activity indoors—even in a classroom—if tables, chairs, and desks can be moved in order to create a large space in which students can do some moving, including "tag-like" running.

2. Once you have established an appropriate physical area for this activity, divide your group of 33 students into four groups, consisting of three wolves, six bulls, 12 cows, and 12 calves. Each will have a distinctive role. Provide each calf with a long, brightly-colored rag "flag." The flag should be affixed to the calf's body in a way that it could—if it were within reach—be removed by a wolf. Back pockets are ideal! Each wolf should also have a rag "flag"—of a different color than those worn by calves. The wolves should also wear their flags in a secure but accessible manner.

3. This activity provides students with an opportunity to experience adaptation behavior of both muskoxen and wolves. Muskoxen, herbivores, often graze peacefully in meadowed areas. While grazing, they spread out. Calves typically do not stray too far from their mothers, but the animals do not always stay clustered...except when predators appear! Begin the activity with the students grazing peacefully as muskoxen, and the wolves out of sight of the herd.

4. These are the behaviors each animal should exhibit:

Cows: As soon as grazing begins, the cows should choose a lead cow to watch for predators.. The cows should pick a signal the lead cow will use to communicate to the rest of the herd that predators are approaching. When the lead cow

Age: Grades 4—9
Subjects: Science, Physical Education
Skills: analysis, description, discussion, evaluation, generalization, kinesthetic concept development, observation, psychomotor development, small group work
Duration: 20—45 minutes
Group Size: 15—50; procedures above based on 33
Setting: outdoors
Conceptual Framework Reference: III.D., III.D.1., III.D.2., III.E., III.E.1., III.E.2.
Key Vocabulary: adaptation, predator, prey, defense, limiting factors

3. This activity provides students with an opportunity to experience adaptation behavior of both muskoxen and wolves. Muskoxen, herbivores, often graze peacefully in meadowed areas. While grazing, they spread out. Calves typically do not stray too far from their mothers, but the animals do not always stay clustered...except when predators appear! Begin the activity with the students grazing peacefully as muskoxen, and the wolves out of sight of the herd.

4. These are the behaviors each animal should exhibit:

Cows: As soon as grazing begins, the cows should choose a lead cow to watch for predators. The cows should pick a signal the lead cow will use to communicate to the rest of the herd that predators are approaching. When the lead cow signals that predators are near, all the cows move to form a circle around the calves to protect the calves from the wolves. With the calves in the center of a circle, the cows stand with their backs to the calves, facing outward to watch the wolves. The cows can move very little. Mostly, they stay firmly in one place, moving their upper bodies to block the wolves from reaching the calves. The cows cannot touch the wolves with their hands or feet.

Calves: The calves depend totally upon the cows for protection. Each calf is to hold onto a cow with both hands, around the cow's waist, and only follow the cow's lead. Calves cannot influence the cows' movement.

Bulls: The bulls are the active defenders of the cows and the calves. As the predators near, the bulls form a circle around the cows, who in turn are forming a circle around the calves. The bulls form as tight a circle as they can around the cows and calves, never any farther than one step in front of the circle of cows. The bulls can move, however—but only in a clockwise direction around the circle of cows! The bulls do have use of their hands. As the wolves attack the herd, the bulls try to "kill" them by pulling the flag out of their back pocket, or wherever the flag is attached to the wolf. When a bull kills a wolf, the wolf moves off to the side, "dead," but able to watch the remainder of the activity.

Wolves: Wolves begin the activity out of sight of the herd. They try to get as close as possible to the herd without being detected. Wolves typically work as a unit, so they can attempt a strategy for surprising the herd in order to kill the calves for food. The wolves are mobile, able to move at any time in any direction. They can use any maneuver (except pushing and shoving) to break the herd's defenses. Once a wolf kills a calf—by pulling the calf's flag out of its pocket—temporarily stop the game and move the calf's carcass to the side, where it too can watch the remainder of the activity!

A Note About Sound Effects: This is not a quiet game much of the time. Wolves should be howling, communicating with each other in predetermined ways with signals, and as part of their tactics to startle and confuse the muskoxen. The muskoxen moo loudly.

5. **Muskox Maneuvers in Review:**
a. Muskox herd grazes quietly. Wolves are out of sight of herd.
b. Wolves move in to attack herd.
When lead cow spots wolves, the herd begins defense. A circle is formed, with calves in the center, cows facing out in a circle around the calves, and bulls in an outer circle, also facing the wolves. Each should behave appropriately, as described above.

6. The activity can conclude in several ways. For example:
a. All the wolves could be killed.
b. All the calves could be killed.
c. The wolves could give up in frustration after a period of time with no success in killing a calf.
d. The wolves could kill one or more calves, and the activity conclude at this time, based on the notion that the wolves are going to eat the calf (or calves) and the herd move on.

7. Once the excitement and enthusiasm have peaked—sit down with the students to discuss what happened, and what the activity represents in terms of animal adaptation, predator/prey relationships, and limiting factors. Ask the students to describe and evaluate the predatory behavior of the wolves, and the various defense behaviors of the muskoxen...
What would happen if the wolves could not get into the herd? What would happen if the wolves always got into the herd. Ask the students to distinguish between what would be actual, typical behaviors of muskoxen contrasted with their behaviors in this activity.

Extensions

1. A few students can research and report back to the class with more details about the life and times of muskoxen and wolves—acquiring additional information about their survival needs, habitat, and behaviors.

2. Investigate predatory and defense behaviors of different species in different habitats. For example, selected species of plains, forest, desert, and ocean animals can be compared.

3. Plan a class and parent picnic. Let it be a potluck—with an after dinner activity, "Muskox Maneuvers." It could be good exercise, good fun, and a worthwhile sharing of teaching and learning!

Evaluation

Name a prey species and its predator species. Describe how each is adapted to the other. How does the prey protect itself? How does the predator overcome this protection? Describe the overall effectiveness of each animal's adaptations.

HOW MANY BEARS CAN LIVE IN THIS FOREST?

Objectives
Students will be able to: 1) define "carrying capacity;" and 2) describe the importance of carrying capacity for wildlife and people.

Method
Students become "bears" to look for "food" in a "habitat" during this physically-involving activity.

Background
It is recommended that this activity be preceded by one or more activities on "adaptation" and "limiting factors." See the cross references for suggestions. For additional information about black bears, see "Bearly Born."

Carrying capacity may be defined as the number of plants or animals of a given species that an area of land or water can support. It is the largest population a unit of habitat can support on a year-round basis, or during the most critical period. Carrying capacity for many species is in a constant state of change, both seasonally and from year to year. Year to year variations may result from factors such as natural disasters, changes in rainfall and temperature patterns, or human interventions. Populations of living things tend to fluctuate naturally around some level. Carrying capacity affects that level. A population may be below carrying capacity, such as in the spring following a hard winter, or temporarily above it. The latter situation inevitably results in a decline of the population by a variety of natural limiting factors, e.g., mortality, disease, emigration, and lowered reproductive rate, and usually lasts for a short period.

In this activity, black bears will be the focus in order to illustrate carrying capacity. Black bear habitat limits bear populations especially through the influences of shelter, food supply, and the social tolerances or territoriality of the animal. Shelter or cover is a prime factor. Black

bears need thick cover—not to hide from human beings—but to hide from each other. Spatial limitations are met by adult bears killing young bears or running them out of the area. These young bears must keep moving around until they find an area vacated by the death of an adult or until they die. When food supplies are reduced by factors such as climatic fluctuations, competition becomes more intense. Some adult bears might temporarily move to seldom-used portions of their home range, sometimes many miles away, but most must live on what food is available in the area. These individuals may become thin, occasionally starve, or—in the case of young bears—be killed or forced from the area by more

Age: Grades 3—9 (and older)
Subjects: Science, Social Studies, Mathematics, Physical Education
Skills: analysis, computation, discussion, evaluation, generalization, kinesthetic concept development, listing, observation, psychomotor development

Duration: 20—45 minutes or longer
Group Size: any (adjust number of food squares per size group; less than 80 pounds of food per student)
Setting: outdoors and indoors
Conceptual Framework Reference: III.A.1, III.B., III.B.1., III.B.2., III.B.3., III.D., III.D.1., III.D.2., III.D.3., III.D.4., III.E., III.E.1., III.E.2., III.F., III.F.1., III.F.2., III.F.3., III.F.4., III.F.5.
Key Vocabulary: carrying capacity, limiting factors, habitat

aggressive adults. In this way, the total bear population remains within the carrying capacity of the habitat.

In this activity, "food" becomes a "limiting factor" in a limited habitat. All possible conditions are not covered by the design of the activity. A variety of factors would have an influence in determining the actual carrying capacity of an area; however, by this simple illustration it is possible for students to quickly grasp the essential nature of the concept that any area will have a limit or carrying capacity for the numbers of any kind of animal the area can support.

The major purpose of this activity is for students to gain an understanding of the concept of "carrying capacity."

Materials   five colors of construction paper (two to three sheets of each color) or an equal amount of light poster board; one black felt pen; envelopes (one per student); pencils; one blindfold

Procedure

1. Cut the paper or poster board into 2" × 2" or 2" × 3" pieces. For a classroom of 30 students, make 30 cards of each color as follows: orange—nuts (acorns, pecans, walnuts, hickory nuts); mark five pieces N-20; mark 25 pieces N-10.

blue—berries (blackberries, elderberries, raspberries); mark five pieces B-20; mark 25 pieces B-10.

yellow—insects (grub worms, larvae, ants, termites); mark five pieces I-12; mark 25 pieces I-6.

red—meat (mice, rodents, peccaries, beaver, muskrats, young deer); mark five pieces M-8; mark 25 pieces M-4.

green—plants (leaves, grasses, herbs); mark five pieces P-20; mark 25 pieces P-10.

The following estimates of total pounds of food for one bear in ten days are used for this activity:

nuts	— 20 pounds	= 25%
berries	— 20 pounds	= 25%
insects	— 12 pounds	= 15%
meat	— 8 pounds	= 10%
plants	— 20 pounds	= 25%
	80 pounds	= 100% in ten days

NOTE: These figures are based on actual research data from a study in Arizona, indicating a mature black bear could typically eat about eight pounds of food per day in a ten-day period. These percentages would vary in different parts of North America. For example, a bear in the state of Alaska would likely eat more meat (fish) and fewer nuts than an Arizona bear.

Keeping these figures in mind, make and distribute the appropriate number of food cards for your size group of students. There should be less than 80 pounds of food per student so that there is not actually enough food in the area for all the "bears" to survive.

2. In a fairly large open area (e.g., 50' x 50'), scatter the colored pieces of paper.

3. Have each student write his or her name on an envelope. This will represent the student's "den site" and should be left on the ground (perhaps anchored with a rock) at the starting line on the perimeter of the field area.

4. Have the students line up on the starting line, leaving their envelopes between their feet on the ground. Give them the following instructions: "You are now all black bears. All bears are not alike, just as you and I are not exactly alike. Among you is a young male bear who has not yet found his own territory. Last week he met up with a larger male bear in the big bear's territory, and before he could get away, he was hurt. He has a broken leg. (Assign one student as the crippled bear. He must hunt by hopping on one leg.) Another bear is a young female who investigated a porcupine too closely and was blinded by the quills. (Assign one student as the blind bear. She must hunt blindfolded.) The third special bear is a mother bear with two fairly small cubs. She must gather twice as much food as the other bears. (Assign one student as the mother bear.)"

5. Do not tell the students what the colors, initials, and numbers on the pieces of paper represent. Tell them only that the pieces of paper represent various kinds of bear food; since bears are omnivores, they like a wide assortment of foods, so they should gather different colored squares to represent a variety of food.

6. Students must walk into the "forest." Bears do not run down their food; they gather it. When students find a colored square, they should pick it up (one at a time) and return it to their "den" before picking up another colored square. (Bears would not actually return to their den to eat; they would eat food as they find it.) Pushing and shoving—any competitive activity—is acceptable as long as it is under control. Snatching food right out from under the blind bear or the crippled bear is natural—but stealing from each other's dens is not. Remember that if bears fight (which they seldom do) they can become injured and unable to gather sufficient food; then they starve.

7. When all the colored squares have been

gathered, the food gathering and hunting is over. Have students pick up their den envelopes containing the food they gathered and return to class.

8. Explain what the colors and numbers represent. Ask each student to add up the total number of pounds of food he or she gathered—whether it is nuts, meat, insects, berries, or plant materials. Each should write the total weight on the outside of his or her envelope.

9. Using a chalkboard, list "blind," "crippled," and "mother." Ask the blind bear how much food she got. Write the amount after the word "blind." Ask the crippled bear and the mother bear how much they got and record the information. Ask each of the other students to tell how much food they found; record each response on the chalkboard. Tell the students each bear needs 80 pounds to survive. Which bears survived? Is there enough to feed all the bears? If not, how many bears can live in this area? What would happen to the extra bears? Would they all starve? How many pounds did the blind bear collect? Will she survive? What about the mother bear? Did she get twice the amount needed to survive? What will happen to her cubs? Will she feed cubs first, or herself? Why? What would happen to her if she fed the cubs? What if she ate first? If the cubs die, can she have more cubs in the future, and perhaps richer, years? (The mother bear will eat first and the cubs will get whatever, if any, is left. The mother must survive; she is the hope for a continued bear population. She can have more cubs in her life; only one needs to survive in order for the population to remain static.)

10. Discuss the idea that a given unit of black bear habitat can only support a limited number of bears. How many bears survived in this activity? We would call that number of bears the carrying capacity of that area of habitat at the time. Could the carrying capacity change? Under what conditions? Discuss what aspects of establishing the carrying capacity for this area were realistic, and what were not. Continue by discussing the idea that a gallon bucket is only able to contain one gallon of liquid, and no more. That is the bucket's carrying capacity. A can of juice may hold 12 ounces of liquid, and no more. That is its carrying capacity. What about your classroom? Let's say there are 25 students, one teacher, desks, tables, and equipment. At present, there is room enough for all. It is reasonably comfortable and you can work and learn in the space. What if we brought in another group of 25 students—desks, tables, equipment, and all? What if we brought in a third group of students?

What is the carrying capacity of your classroom? Or, what if the size of your classroom were cut in half? What would that reduction in available habitat do to the carrying capacity of the area? Talk about the bucket, the classroom, and the bear habitat. What similarities and differences are there among the three related to the concept of carrying capacity?

11. Wrap up with a discussion of the idea that any piece of land can support only so many plants and/or animals. That is the land's "carrying capacity." Does the earth have a carrying capacity? Could the earth's carrying capacity be decreased as a result of some human activities? Could the earth's carrying capacity be increased as a result of some human activities? To what extent can individual people and societies exert a positive influence on the global environment?

Extensions

1. Ask each student to record how many pounds of each of the five categories of food he or she gathered. Ask each student next to convert these numbers into percentages of the total poundage of food each gathered. Provide the students with the background information about black bears so that they can compare their percentages with what are typical percentages eaten by black bears in Arizona. Ask each student to attempt to guess how healthy their bear would be. How do the bears' requirements for a diet seem to compare with the needs of humans for a balanced and nutritious diet?

2. Ask the students to arrive at a class total for all the pounds of food they gathered as bears. Divide the total by the 80 pounds needed by an individual bear (approximately) in order to survive in a ten day period. How many bears could the habitat support? Why then did only _____ bears survive when your class did this activity. Is that realistic? What percentage of the bears survived? What percentage would have survived had the food been evenly divided? In each case, what percentage would not survive? What limiting factors, cultural and natural, would be likely to actually influence the survival of individual bears and populations of bears in an area?

Evaluation

Define carrying capacity.
Describe some of the factors which determine carrying capacity for a species of animal.
Explain why carrying capacity is important for wildlife. Explain why carrying capacity is important for people.

VISUAL VOCABULARY

Objective
Students will be able to interpret and identify ecological concepts.

Method
Students review vocabulary through use of pantomime.

Background
NOTE: Use Project WILD "Glossary" as a reference for this activity.

The major purpose of this activity is to increase students' familiarity with terms that are important in understanding wildlife and ecological systems.

Materials
"Glossary;" small pieces of paper with words printed on them; container

Procedure
OPTIONAL: Go outside for this activity. The environment is conducive, and noise level less a problem.

1. Give students handouts with words and their definitions on them. The words selected should encompass a broad variety of ecological concepts and also be easily portrayable by a small group of students. Some good selections would be: carnivore, herbivore, omnivore, extinction, preda-

Age: Grades 4—7 (and older)
Subjects: Science, Language Arts, Drama
Skills: application, invention, kinesthetic concept development, observation, problem solving, psychomotor development, reading, small group work, synthesis, visualization
Duration: 30 minutes or longer if students research definitions first
Group Size: requires two students; best with at least two teams of four students each
Setting: indoors or outdoors
Conceptual Framework Reference: III.
Key Vocabulary: wildlife concepts

119

tion, prey, commensalism, mutualism, parasitism, food chain, pollution, habitat, shelter, prescribed burn, and ecosystem.

2. List all the words on small pieces of paper and put them in a container.

3. Divide the class into groups of four. Each group draws one word from the container, looks up the definition using the handout, and decides how to pantomime that word. Allow about five minutes for the groups to prepare their mimes.

4. Groups of students then take turns miming their word to the class. Set a time limit of one minute per group.

5. The rest of the class may use the handouts as a guideline for guessing the word being mimed.

6. Groups gain one point for a successful miming (having their word guessed within the one-minute time limit) and one point for guessing another group's mime correctly.

7. If time permits, repeat the drawing and miming using different words, but keep the groups intact. Or, have "star mimers" assist students who muddled their mimes!

NOTE: This can be a good way to review vocabulary used in a unit of study.

Variation

Define words together in class orally. List words and definitions on a chalkboard. Good review! This encourages students to think and remember. It can save paper, too. Leave the room or erase the board to do pantomiming. This provides a challenge and encourages good memory retention.

Evaluation

Pick any 15 words important to understanding wildlife. Write definitions for each.

RAINFALL AND THE FOREST

Objectives

Students will be able to: 1) correlate rainfall data with vegetative communities; 2) correlate vegetative communities with animal life; 3) recognize interrelationships among living and non-living elements of the environment; and 4) understand that populations and the fluctuations of those populations are influenced by ever-changing climatic conditions.

Method

Students work with state highway and vegetative maps to determine relationships between rainfall, vegetation, and animal habitats.

Background

Many natural systems affect wildlife survival and population fluctuations. An inch or two more rain per year may allow forest instead of grassland, thus creating habitat for forest wildlife; it may encourage or interfere with animal reproduction, depending on species and time and amounts of rainfall.

NOTE: This activity is useful for understanding distributions of plant and animal communities in some but not all states.

Food, water, shelter, and space in the appropriate arrangement are all fundamental to wildlife populations; all of these relate to plants in some way. Among other influences, plants are the product of rainfall amounts and temperatures. Rainfall is controlled by such factors as wind direction, elevation, proximity to bodies of water, etc. Essentially, specific rainfall amounts create specific types of plant communities; e.g., grasslands, chaparral, or tropical rain forest. Each of these plant communities supports specific types of animals.

Twenty-five or more inches of rain in northern Arizona commonly produce a fir forest which is not habitat for antelope or buffalo, but is habitat for squirrels, blue grouse, and perhaps elk.

Age: Grades 6—9
Subjects: Science, Social Studies
Skills: analysis, application, comparing similarities and differences, discussion, generalization, synthesis
Duration: minimum of one hour; preferably two to three hours
Group Size: groups of two or three
Setting: indoors
Conceptual Framework Reference: III.A., III.B., III.C., III.D., III.F.
Key Vocabulary: vegetation, rainfall, rain shadow, elevation, community, habitat

Similar amounts of rain, in other parts of the world, will usually produce communities of similar but different plants and animals.

This activity is designed for students to learn that specific habitats are the key to specific wild-life; populations of those wildlife species will fluctuate within those habitats; conditions within habitats continually change; and specific conditions, e.g., ten inches of rainfall, will create specific vegetative types and those specific plants allow for special animal types. Open grass-lands, for example, created by approximately ten inches of rain, tend to be suited to grazing animals like buffalo, antelope, and prairie dogs. Forests, created by more rainfall, may be more suited to Stellar's jays, fox squirrels, and porcupines.

Materials
highway map of state (one per each group of two or three students), one sheet of tracing paper the same size as the map (usually about 19'' × 24'' or 17'' × 22''), four crayons of different colors per group, information including elevation and rainfall annually for 25 to 30 communities within the state, vegetative map of state (one per each group of two or three students)

Procedure
1. Discuss the concept of interrelatedness with your students—the idea that all things, living and non-living, are connected.

2. Divide your students into teams of two or three. Give each group a highway map of your state, one sheet of tracing paper the same size as the map and four crayons of different colors. Also supply each team with information listing 25 to 30 communities around the state, including their elevation and annual rainfall. (Students could have developed this in the form of a data sheet beforehand.)

3. Ask the student groups to outline the state on the tracing paper. Have students separate the list of communities into four rainfall-level groups, such as: 0''—5'', 5.1''—10'', 10.1''—15'', 15'' plus. (You may need to adjust these categories depending on the typical rainfall amounts within your state.)

4. Assign a color for each level of rainfall. Ask the students to make a large dot of the appropriate color for each community at its location on the tracing paper over the map. Community names are not necessary on the tracing paper.

5. Consolidate each color into rainfall patterns. Lines between areas should run between dots of different colors, not from dot to dot. Color maps.

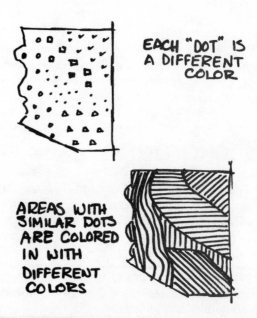

EACH "DOT" IS A DIFFERENT COLOR

AREAS WITH SIMILAR DOTS ARE COLORED IN WITH DIFFERENT COLORS

6. Have students fold the highway maps and put them aside. Issue a vegetative map of your state to each group. These maps usually may be obtained through university agricultural extension services or botany departments. Highway and vegetative maps should be the same size, as nearly as possible.

7. Find similarities in shapes created on student maps and those on vegetative maps. What rainfall level fits what vegetative type? Your correlations will not be exact, but should be graphic. Most of the time, more than one vegetative type will be covered by one rainfall amount. How much rainfall is needed for grassland, chaparral, pine forest, for example? Determine and list rainfall amounts for each vegetative community. Keep in mind that the student map has only 25 to 30 points of reference; there are thousands of data points used to develop the vegetative map, so they will not be identical, but should be visibly similar.

8. Discuss rainfall in your area: Where does your rain come from? What influences rainfall patterns in your state? Does elevation influence rainfall? Why? What is rain shadow? Can you see where the topography influences rainfall in your state? Can you find two cities or towns that are at almost the same elevation, yet receive very different amounts of rain? Why is this? Would these rainfall/vegetative patterns be similar in other parts of the world? Would similar influences function all over the world?

Extension

Obtain habitat maps of several mammals in your state. Translate these data to another transparent overlay. Identify correlations between these data and the vegetative map. (Start with animals which are herbivores, or omnivores. Save carnivores for last.) Habitats for reptiles and birds will also give good correlations. Have students make graphic representations, or write reports, about the interrelationships between rainfall, plant communities and various species of animals.

Evaluation

Write an essay describing the importance of rainfall and vegetative types to wildlife habitat.

NOTE: This activity has been adapted from the *Project Learning Tree Supplementary Activity Guide for Grades K through 6* (Washington D.C.: American Forest Institute, 1977.) Adapted with permission.

OWL PELLETS

Objective
Students will be able to construct a simple food chain.

Method
Students examine owl pellets and reconstruct rodent skeletons.

Background
On the floor of abandoned buildings, beneath a grove of tall trees, or under other structures that offer shelter from daylight, you may find some very interesting outdoor study items. They are uniformly dark gray, from one and one-half to three inches long and three-quarters to one inch in diameter. You might think of them as mouse kits. Complete with bones and fur of one or several small rodents such as field mice, owl pellets offer a unique opportunity for learning about wildlife around us.

Age: Grades 3-7
Subject: Science
Skills: analysis, comparing similarities and differences, generalization
Duration: 20-45 minutes
Group Size: two or three students working in groups
Setting: indoors
Conceptual Framework Reference: III.B., III.B.1., III.B.2.
Key Vocabulary: owl, pellets, food chain

Owls are not picky eaters like certain other raptors. They swallow their prey as nearly whole as possible. Fur and bones however, cannot be digested, nor will they pass through the digestive system. About 12 hours after consuming a meal, the "pellet" is coughed up and dropped to the ground below.

Owl pellets are clean of all flesh and virtually odorless. After a short drying period they can be handled easily by all age groups. Because they are found under the perch they may occasionally be "whitewashed" by the bird. Pellets will keep almost indefinitely if dry and protected in a plastic bag or closed jar. Those collected on a field trip or during the summer can be saved for later examination. Pellets may also be purchased through scientific supply catalogs.

Owl pellets have been used for scientific study of small mammals and their distribution. With owls doing the collecting, the scientist must only locate the owl roost to obtain the skulls and bones of the small prey living in the area. From these parts, the species can be identified. This has helped map the areas occupied by certain small creatures that might otherwise have escaped detection.

Once the bones are separated from the mass of fur in the pellet, a number of anatomy lessons are possible. Hip bones and the upper leg bone with its large ball joint are readily identified. The scapula or shoulder blade, ribs, other leg bones, vertebrae and foot bones along with the skull are all recognizable when sorted out.

The major purpose of this activity is for students to construct a simple food chain, recognizing interdependence in ecological systems through study of owl pellets.

Materials owl pellets, dissecting tools, posterboard, glue

Procedure

1. Locate some owl pellets under trees or in abandoned buildings where owls may roost. Or, pellets may be purchased from a scientific supply distributor.
2. Divide the students into small groups of two to three. Give each group of students an owl pellet and basic dissecting tools.
3. Have groups of students separate the bones from the fur in their pellet.
4. Determine if there are bones from more than one animal in the pellet.
5. Lay out the bones to form as complete a skeleton as possible. Skeletons may be glued onto posterboard for display.
6. See which group can make the most complete skeleton!

Evaluation

Draw a picture of a simple food chain.

127

MANAGEMENT AND CONSERVATION

WILDWORK

Objective
Students will be able to name and describe three wildlife occupations.

Method
Students brainstorm a list of wildlife-related careers, prepare presentations, and dramatize occupations for their classmates.

Background
State and federal government agencies employ many specialists to help preserve and manage the wildlife resource. These employees do field work, conduct laboratory research, and oversee human interactions with wildlife. Universities and colleges, private and non-profit wildlife oriented agencies, zoos and museums, private industry, and others all employ people trained in the wildlife field. Some individuals (artists, photographers, etc.) photograph, paint, draw or write about wildlife for magazines, books, films, and television.

The major purpose of this activity is for students to become familiar with career possibilities available in wildlife-related fields.

Materials
writing materials

Procedure
1. Ask the students if they've thought about what careers they might be interested in pursuing when they grow up. What kinds of jobs sound interesting? What about working with wildlife?
2. In a class discussion, find out what kinds of jobs students imagine exist in animal-related fields. Do any of their parents have animal- or wildlife-related jobs? Make some suggestions about possible careers and compile a list of occupations that students have brainstormed.

Age: Grades K-6
Subjects: Career Education, Language Arts, Social Studies, Science
Skills: description, discussion, listing, synthesis
Duration: ten minute introduction; 20 minutes for presentation or longer depending on size of group
Group Size: any
Setting: indoors
Conceptual Framework Reference: IV.F.10.
Key Vocabulary: occupation, vocation, career

3. From this list, have each student choose one job to portray to the class. Encourage them to bring props from home to help in their portrayal; items such as stuffed animals, toy cameras, research notebooks, outdoor dress, and magazine pictures can be used.

4. Have each student, in turn, name, describe and portray his or her occupation to the class. (Or, portray first, and have the students guess the occupation!)

5. Wrap up with a discussion of the range of careers available in wildlife-related fields.

Extension

Contact someone in a wildlife-oriented job and ask that person if he or she would be willing to contribute a class visit or letter describing the job and other wildlife-related jobs. Have the students prepare questions in advance for the visitor. (Government wildlife agencies usually have a descriptive leaflet about jobs. Write for a copy.) Compile a class letter to that individual, incorporating any questions that students might have. Some good questions to ask could be:
Why did you choose this career?
What education was necessary to prepare you for this job?
How hard is it to get a job after you are trained?
What do you do in a typical day's work?
How much do you actually work with wildlife? How much with people? How much record keeping, reporting, etc.?
Do you work with people who have other wildlife-related careers?
Share the letter of reply with the class or have the professional visit the class to answer questions.

Evaluation

Name and describe three jobs in which someone works with wildlife or other animals.

What kind of training is required for each job?

Are there lots of jobs available in wildlife-related fields? Please explain your response.

OH DEER!

Objectives

Students will be able to: 1) identify and describe food, water, and shelter as three essential components of habitat; 2) describe the importance of good habitat for animals; 3) define "limiting factors" and give examples; and 4) recognize that some fluctuations in wildlife populations are natural as ecological systems undergo a constant change.

Method

Students become "deer" and components of habitat in a highly-involving physical activity.

Background

A variety of factors affects the ability of wildlife to successfully reproduce and to maintain their populations over time. Disease, predator/prey relationships, varying impacts of weather conditions from season to season (e.g., early freezing, heavy snows, flooding, drought), accidents, environmental pollution, and habitat destruction and degradation are among these factors.

Some naturally-caused as well as culturally-induced limiting factors serve to prevent wildlife populations from reproducing in numbers greater than their habitat can support. An excess of such limiting factors, however, leads to threatening, endangering, and eliminating whole species of animals.

The most fundamental of life's necessities for any animal are food, water, shelter, and space in a suitable arrangement. Without these essential components, animal cannot survive.

This activity is designed for students to learn that:

a) good habitat is the key to wildlife survival;

b) a population will continue to increase in size until some limiting factors are imposed;

c) limiting factors contribute to fluctuations in wildlife populations; and

d) nature is never in "balance," but is constantly changing.

Wildlife populations are not static. They continuously fluctuate in response to a variety of stimulating and limiting factors. We tend to speak of limiting factors as applying to a single species, although one factor may affect many species. Natural limiting factors, or those modeled after factors in natural systems, tend to maintain populations of species at levels within predictable ranges. This kind of "balance in nature" is not static, but is more like a teeter-totter than a balance. Some species fluctuate or cycle annually. Quail, for example, may start with a population of 100 pairs in early spring; grow to a population of 1200 birds by late spring; and decline slowly to a winter population of 100 pairs again. This cycle appears to be almost totally controlled by the habitat components of food, water, shelter, and space, which are also limiting factors. Habitat components are the most fundamental and thereby the most critical of limiting factors in most natural settings.

This activity is intended to be a simple but powerful way for students to grasp some basic concepts: that everything in natural systems is interrelated; that populations of organisms are continuously affected by elements of their environment; and that populations of animals do not stay at the same static number year after year in their environment, but rather are continually changing in a process of maintaining dynamic equilibria in natural systems. The major purpose of this activity is for students to understand the importance of suitable habitat as well as factors that may affect wildlife populations in constantly changing ecosystems.

Materials

area—either indoors or outdoors—large enough for students to run; e.g., playing field; chalkboard or flip chart; writing materials

Age: Grades 4—12

Subjects: Science, Math, Social Studies, Physical Education

Skills: application, comparing similarities and differences, description, discussion, generalization, graphing, kinesthetic concept development, observation, psychomotor development

Duration: 30—45 minutes

Group size: 15 and larger recommended

Setting: indoors or outdoors; large area for running needed

Conceptual Framework Reference: I.C.2., III.B., III.B.2., III.B.3., III.B.5., III.C., III.C.1., III.C.2., III.E., III.E.1., III.E.2., III.F., III.F.1., III.F.2., III.F.3., III.F.4., III.F.5., IV.C., IV.C.1., IV.C.2.

Key Vocabulary: habitat, limiting factors, predator, prey, population, balance of nature, ecosystem

Procedure

1. Begin by telling students that they are about to participate in an activity that emphasizes the most essential things that animals need in order to survive. Review the essential components of habitat with the students: food, water, shelter, and space in a suitable arrangement. This activity emphasizes three of those habitat components—food, water, and shelter—but the students should not forget the importance of the animals having sufficient space in which to live, and that all the components have to be in a suitable arrangement or the animals will die.

2. Ask your students to count off in four's. Have all the one's go to one area; all two's, three's, and four's go together to another area. Mark two parallel lines on the ground or floor ten to 20 yards apart. Have the one's line up behind one line; the rest of the students line up behind the other line.

3. The one's become "deer." All deer need good habitat in order to survive. Ask the students what the essential components of habitat are again: **food, water, shelter,** and **space in a suitable arrangement.** For the purposes of this activity, we will assume that the deer have enough space in which to live. We are emphasizing food, water, and shelter. The deer (the one's) need to find food, water, and shelter in order to survive. When a deer is looking for **food,** it should clamp its hands over its stomach. When it is looking for **water,** it puts its hands over its mouth. When it is looking for **shelter,** it holds its hands together over its head. A deer can choose to look for any one of its needs during each round or segment of the activity; **the deer cannot, however, change what it is looking for;** e.g., when it sees what is available, **during that round. It can change again what it is looking for in the next round, if it survives.**

4. The two's, three's, and four's are food, water, and shelter—components of habitat. Each student gets to choose at the beginning of each round which component he or she will be during that round. The students depict which component they are in the same way the deer show what they are looking for; that is, hands on stomach for food, etc.

5. The game starts with all players lined up on their respective lines (deer on one side; habitat components on the other side)—and **with their backs to the students at the other line.**

6. The facilitator or teacher begins the first round by asking all of the students to make their signs—each deer deciding what it is looking for, each habitat component deciding what it is. Give the students a few moments to get their hands in place—over stomachs, mouths, or over their heads. (As you look at the two lines of students, you will normally see a lot of variety—with some students water, some food, some shelter. As the game proceeds, sometimes the students confer with each other and all make the same sign. That's okay, although don't encourage it. For example, all the students in habitat might decide to be shelter. That could represent a drought year with no available food or water.)

7. When you can see that the students are ready, count: "One . . . two . . . three." At the count of three, each deer and each habitat component turn to face the opposite group, continuing to hold their signs clearly.

8. When deer see the habitat component they need, they are to run to it. Each deer must hold the sign of what it is looking for until getting to the habitat component person with the same sign. Each deer that reaches its necessary habitat component takes the "food," "water," or "shelter" back to the deer side of the line. This is to represent the deer's successfully meeting its needs, and successfully reproducing as a result. Any deer that fails to find its food, water, or shelter dies and becomes part of the habitat. That is, in the next round, the deer that died is a habitat component and so is available as food, water, or shelter to the deer who are still alive. NOTE: When more than one deer reaches a habitat component, the student who gets there first survives. Habitat components stay in place on their line until a deer needs them. If no deer needs a particular habitat component during a round, the habitat component just stays where it is in the habitat. The habitat person can, however, change which component it is from round to round.

9. You as the facilitator or teacher keep track of how many deer there are at the beginning of the game, and at the end of each round you record the number of deer also. Continue the game for approximately 15 rounds. Keep the pace brisk, and the students will thoroughly enjoy it.

10. At the end of the 15 rounds, gather the students together to discuss the activity. Encourage them to talk about what they ex-

perienced and saw. For example, they saw a small herd of deer (seven students in a class size of 28) begin by finding more than enough of its habitat needs. The population of deer expanded over two to three rounds of the game, until the habitat was depleted and there was not sufficient food, water, and shelter for all the members of the herd. At that point, deer starved or died of thirst or lack of shelter, and they returned as part of the habitat. Such things happen in nature also.

11. Using a flip chart pad or an available chalkboard, post the data recorded during the game. The number of deer at the beginning of the game and at the end of each round represent the number of deer in a series of years. That is, the beginning of the game is year one; each round is an additional year. Deer can be posted by five's for convenience. For example:

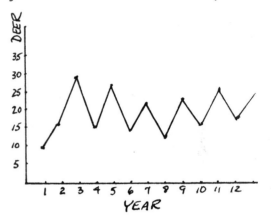

The students will see this visual reminder of what they experienced during the game: the deer population fluctuated over a period of years. This is a natural process, as long as the factors which limit the population do not become excessive, to the point where the animals cannot successfully reproduce. The wildlife populations will tend to peak, decline, and rebuild, peak, decline, and rebuild—as long as there is good habitat and sufficient numbers of animals to successfully reproduce.

12. In discussion, ask the students to summarize some of the things they have learned from this activity. What do animals need to survive? What are some of the "limiting factors" that affect their survival? Are wildlife populations static, or do they tend to fluctuate, as part of an overall "balance of nature?" Is nature ever really in "balance," or are ecological systems involved in a process of constant change?

Extensions

1. When you have finished tabulating the graph data and discussing it, ask the students if they

have ever heard of the Hudson Bay trappers in American history. Tell them, briefly, who they were.

There is a hundred years, or more, of records of the activities of these trappers. In those records are some interesting data. These data refer to pelts shipped from America to Europe, particularly the pelts of snowshoe hares and lynx.

Researchers have found that snowshoe hare populations seem to peak about every seven to nine years and then crash, repeating the process over each comparable time period. So, a snowshoe hare population graph would look like this:

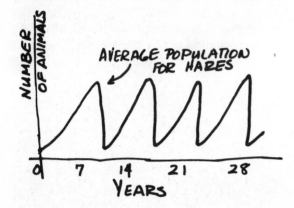

It has also been discovered that lynx populations do the same thing—except that they do it one year behind the hare populations. The combined graph would look like this:

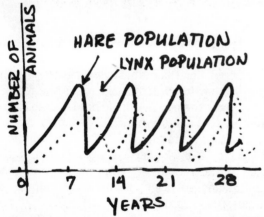

Graph this right over the deer graph that you made, adding first the hares, and then the lynx. Ask the students:

• Which animal is the predator? Which prey?
• Are predators controlling the prey, or are prey controlling the predators? (We have been brought up to "know" that predators control the prey—and are now discovering that this is not so. The number of prey animals available tells us how many predators can live in the area.)
• Is this like the deer habitat game we just played? Who controls? (Sometimes the habitat— when the deer population is not too large; some-

times the habitat—when the deer population "gets on top of it" and destroys the vegetative food and cover.)

2. Some recent research has added a new dimension to the story of the snowshoe hares and the lynx.

It has been found that a major winter food of the hare is a small willow. As hare populations grow, the use of the willow plants grows too. But, when the willow plant has been "hedged" or eaten back so far, the plant generates a toxin (poison) which precludes use by the hare. That is when the hare population crashes, followed by the crash of the lynx population about a year later. Then the willow, relieved of pressure, begins to grow again. The hare population begins to grow in response, and last of all, within a year or so, the lynx population follows. And the cycle has begun again—over and over—every seven to nine years.

Discuss the "balance of nature." Is it ever in "balance?"

Evaluation

Name three essential components of habitat.

Define "limiting factors." Give three examples.

Examine the graph. What factors may have caused the following population changes:

a. between years 1 and 2?
b. between years 3 and 4?
c. between years 5 and 6?
d. between years 7 and 8?

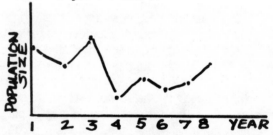

Which of the following graphs represents the more typically balanced population?

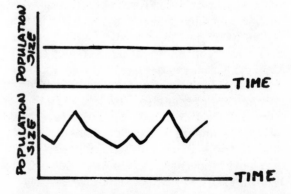

HERE TODAY, GONE TOMORROW

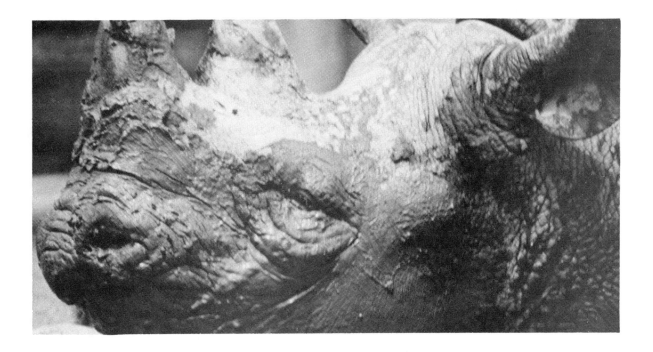

Objectives
Students will be able to: 1) identify and describe some causes for extinction of animal species; 2) define "threatened," "rare," and "endangered" as applied to wildlife; and 3) name threatened and endangered animals living in their area.

Method
Students become familiar with classification of animals, conduct research, and make a master list of threatened and endangered animals locally and/or nationally, including factors affecting the animals' condition.

Background
Some sources report that worldwide, since 1600, about 300 species of wildlife have become extinct, either directly or indirectly as a result of human activities. In 1980, the U. S. Department of Interior listed 276 plants and animals in the United States as being endangered. Some experts predict a loss of identified species (plant and animal) to increase from one species per year worldwide to 100 species per year by the end of this century.

Age: Grades 5-12
Subjects: Science, Language Arts, Social Studies
Skills: analysis, classification, discussion, listing, synthesis
Duration: two 30-45 minute periods
Group Size: any
Setting: indoors
Conceptual Framework Reference: I.D., II.A., II.B., II.C., II.D., II.E., II.F., III.D.3., III.D.4., IV.A., IV.C., IV.C.1., IV.C.2., IV.C.3., IV.C.4., IV.D.5., IV.D.6., IV.D.7., IV.E., IV.E.3., IV.E.4., IV.E.5., IV.E.7., IV.E.10., IV.E.11., IV.F., IV.F.3., IV.F.4., IV.F.5., IV.F.6., IV.F.7., IV.F.8., IV.F.9., IV.F.11., VI.A., VI.A.2., VI.A.3., VI.A.4., VI.A.5., VI.C.13., VI.C.16., VI.D., VI.D.1., VI.D.2., VI.D.3., VI.D.4., VII.A., VII.A.1., VII.A.2., VII.A.3., VII.A.4., VII.B., VII.B.1., VII.B.2., VII.B.3., VII.B.4., VII.B.5., VII.B.6., VII.B.7.
Key Vocabulary: endangered, critically endangered, threatened, rare, extinct, peripheral

---

Although extinction is a natural process, excessive and intensive human activities in the environment have caused a dramatic increase in its rate. Loss of habitat as a result of human activity is considered to be the most pervasive cause of species extermination. Other major causes of species extermination and endangerment include: habitat modification, overexploitation, unregulated commercial harvest, disruption of migration routes and breeding behaviors, contamination by pollutants, human disturbance, "pest" control, competition or predation from introduced species, and natural causes.

Generally accepted definitions of the terms to be used in this activity are:

Endangered—Species in immediate danger of extinction.

Critically Endangered—Species will not survive without direct human intervention.

Threatened—Species present in its range, but threatened because of a decline in numbers.

Rare—Species not presently in danger, but of concern because of low numbers. NOTE: Some species were always rare because of their position in the food chain or due to habitat preference.

Extinct—Complete disappearance of a species.

Peripheral—Scarce in area because it is fringe or marginal habitat.

Listings of animals currently in these categories may be obtained from state or province wildlife agencies.

A list of the U. S. "Endangered Species" is available from:

> Director, Office of Endangered Species
> U. S. Fish and Wildlife Service
> U. S. Department of Interior
> Washington, D. C. 20204

State, province, and federal listings of endangered, threatened and rare species may vary because areas encompass different habitat conditions within their boundaries. An animal or plant may have been lost within one state's boundaries, but may be abundant in another, and therefore not considered threatened. The U. S. Endangered Species Act of 1973 gives the U. S. government power to protect endangered species, under the auspices of the U. S. Fish and Wildlife Service.

The major purpose of this activity is to provide students with a working knowledge of the terminology and factors affecting potential elimination of wildlife species.

NOTE: This activity can be modified to include plant as well as animal species.

Materials
information from state and federal agencies about threatened and endangered animals, poster-making materials, writing materials

Procedure

1. Contact your state or province wildlife agency. Ask for a list of animals in your state or province which are classified endangered, critically endangered, threatened, rare, extinct, and peripheral. Ask, too, for information regarding the reasons for these classifications. For older students and those wanting more depth: Write to the U. S. Department of Interior regarding any comparable information available at the national level. (See Background for address.) Also contact local chapters of conservation organizations (e.g., National Wildlife Federation, National Audubon Society, Defenders of Wildlife) for additional information they might have about species and habitats for which there is concern in your area.

2. Review and discuss with the students the definitions of threatened, endangered, rare, extinct, and peripheral—as used in wildlife conservation, as well as in a dictionary. Understand that words defined in a standard dictionary may have additional legal connotations. Ask each student or group of students to select an animal to learn more about.

3. Ask one or more students to take the information accumulated from the wildlife agencies and private conservation groups and come up with a master list of the animals according to the category in which they can be classified, the classification both locally and nationally, and the principal factors affecting the animals. For example:

Animal Name	State or Province						National						Factors Affecting Animal's Status
	Extinct	Endangered	Critically Endangered	Threatened	Rare	Peripheral	Extinct	Endangered	Critically Endangered	Threatened	Rare	Peripheral	

OR,

Divide the students into teams so they can all participate in constructing this chart; e.g., one team classifying mammals, another reptiles, birds, fish, insects, etc.

4. Make copies of this information for all the students. Discuss the findings. What seem to be the most prevalent factors affecting the animals; e.g., habitat loss, pollution, impact from introduced species?

Extensions (for younger students)

1. Make a poster display showing the principal reasons for endangerment and the animals that are endangered in those ways. Poster displays could be made separately for both state and national endangered species.
2. Have a schoolwide contest in which students create posters honoring endangered species—from plants to wildlife.
3. Write a short essay, poem, or song about plants and animals facing extinction. What are these organisms "worth?" What are we humans losing?

Extensions (for older students)

1. Find out what is being done concerning the endangered plants and animals in your state or province; at the national level; at the international and worldwide levels. What can each of us as individuals do?
2. Each student can pick an endangered animal to find out more about. What will be the consequences of the disappearance of this species? What are the trade-offs involved? What alternatives are available? What contributions does the animal make ecologically? Economically? Medicinally? Aesthetically? Intrinsically? Pool and discuss all the students' findings.
3. Explore the possibility that extinction can apply to human cultural forms; e.g., traditional languages, native peoples.
4. In ten minutes, name as many animals as you can that are not legally endangered or threatened. Find out what species have been taken off the endangered species list, how, and why.
5. Research, analyze, summarize, and interpret findings related to the following question: Why care about endangered species?

Evaluation

Arrange the following terms in a list so that they progress from the least amount of danger to a species to the greatest amount: endangered, rare, threatened, extinct, critically endangered. Describe two reasons for possible concern when animal species become extinct.

Who decides what species are endangered or threatened and how do they decide?

Describe principal causes for extinction.

WHO LIVES HERE?

ple, with their sophisticated transport systems, have changed the wildlife populations of islands and continents. Many plants and animals that we take for granted as native residents of the United States actually were not on this continent when the first European settlers came; other original species have been destroyed.

Changes that once took place gradually have been accelerated by human manipulation of wildlife populations. (For example, pet dogs and cats brought to South Sea islands decimated native wildlife populations that had evolved unthreatened by predators.) Human beings sometimes move animals to their advantage, sometimes to their ultimate disadvantage, with mixed results for people and the environment. Some introduction of animals to new areas is accidental; some is intended, for example, as a management strategy. (See "Planting Animals.")

The major purpose of this activity is to acquaint students with the distinction between native and non-native species, as well as benefits and liabilities involved in introducing non-native species to areas.

NOTE: This activity can be adapted to include native and non-native plants as well.

Objectives
Students will be able to: 1) identify some native and non-native animal inhabitants of their area and of the United States; and 2) give some examples of effects of introducing animal species to an area where they were not originally found.

Method
Students research and write reports about native and introduced animal species, and conduct a class "quiz" and discussion.

Background
Fossil remains indicate that even in prehistoric times animal populations had migrated to different geographical regions in response to climatic and other conditions. These migrations took place over long periods of time. In some cases original inhabitants of an area would die out, having moved away or become extinct.

Natural land and water barriers have prevented some species spreading to certain areas. But peo-

Materials
access to research materials, writing materials

Procedure
1. Explain the background information to your students. Then, go around the room asking each student to guess if the animal you name is a native (indigenous) or non-native (introduced) species to the area of the United States it now

Age: Grades 4—9
Subjects: Language Arts, Science, Social Studies
Skills: classification, description, discussion, evaluation, generalization, public speaking, reading, reporting, research
Duration: two to three 45-minute periods
Group size: whole class, individual research
Setting: indoors
Conceptual Framework Reference: IV.E., IV.E.4., IV.E.5., IV.E.8., IV.E.9., IV.E.10., IV.E.11., VI.C.12., VI.C.13., VI.C.15., VI.C.16.
Key Vocabulary: native, non-native, indigenous, introduced species, migration

inhabits. Optional: get photos of each. For example:

Some introduced species

brown trout; pheasant; carp; Norway rat; nutria; Chukar partridge; starling; English sparrow; Barbary sheep; African onyx; Axis deer; Hungarian partridge

Some native species

Wood rat; elk; bald eagle; mule deer; marmot; woodchuck; wolverine; bluebird; coyote; red fox
*This list will vary greatly from place to place. Check for local and regional accuracy.

2. Ask each student to choose one of these animals to research, including:
• Is it native to the area it inhabits?
• What, if any, are the benefits of its presence?
• What, if any, are the detrimental effects of its presence?
• What is the history of its presence? (If introduced, include how and why it was introduced.)
• What wildlife regulations, if any, exist concerning this animal? (Your state or province wildlife agency will have this information.)

3. Ask students to write short research papers on their animals. Also, have each student write the name of his or her animal on a piece of paper. Collect these and use them for a native/non-native quiz. Have the students vote "native" or "non-native" as each animal name is pulled from a box. Then have the student who did research comment on that animal. Students can direct the voting, presentations, and discussion. Were there some surprises; e.g., animals thought to be native that turned out to be introduced? Based on all the animals studied, do there seem to be more positive or negative effects from introducing non-native species to environments?

Extension
Do the same activity with plants!

Evaluation
Name five species that are native (indigenous) to the United States.
Name five species that are non-native (introduced) to the United States.

When animals are introduced to new areas, they can either become extinct or be successful in their new home. What usually happens to other animals when an introduced species is successful? Why?

List and explain four reasons why animals may be introduced to an area.

PLANTING ANIMALS

Objectives

Students will be able to: 1) describe reasons for "transplanting" animals; and 2) identify one animal that has been transplanted in their own state or province.

Method

Students write a letter to a state or provincial wildlife agency for information and make dioramas of transplanted animals in new habitats.

Background

NOTE: This activity can be used independently or as an excellent extension for both "Who Lives Here?" and "Here Today, Gone Tomorrow."

Wild animals are sometimes introduced or re-introduced to suitable habitat. These animals may be called "transplants." Transplanting takes place for a variety of reasons, including: providing a new home to species which were crowded elsewhere; re-introducing animals to historic habitats; providing people with a new population of animals for consumptive and non-consumptive purposes; providing a natural check and balance in an ecosystem; restoring ecosystem diversity; and aesthetically enriching the local environment.

Introductions can have both positive and negative consequences. For example, re-introduction of predators can contribute to a healthy ecosystem as natural limits are thus placed on prey populations. Negative consequences can occur. For example, some transplanted animals can go into shock and die; an animal population may be introduced for which there is no natural predator, with overpopulation of the introduced species and habitat degradation the result; and a new species can usurp food, water, and shelter with harmful effects on native species.

The major purpose of this activity is to acquaint students with the concept of "transplanting" animals.

Materials

writing materials; magazine photos, scissors, glue, boxes for dioramas (optional)

Age: Grades 4-9
Subjects: Language Arts, Science, Art
Skills: analysis, discussion, media construction, psychomotor development, research, synthesis, visualization, writing
Duration: two 45-minute periods, longer if diorama is constructed
Group Size: any
Setting: indoors
Conceptual Framework Reference: IV.A., IV.A.1., IV.A.2., IV.A.3., IV.A.4., IV.C., IV.C.1., IV.C.2., IV.C.3., IV.C.4., IV.E., IV.E.4., IV.E.5., IV.E.8., IV.E.9., IV.E.10., IV.E.11., VI.A., VI.A.1., VI.A.2., VI.A.3., VI.A.4., VI.A.5., VI.B., VI.C., VI.C.12., VI.C. 13., VI.C.15., VI.C.16.
Key Vocabulary: habitat, transplant, introduced, niche (for grades 7 or older), diorama, wildlife agency, management

Procedure

1. In a class discussion, review what wildlife species are found in your local area, state, or province; and what wildlife species may once have been found there, although they are no longer present. (See "Who Lives Here?" and "Here Today, Gone Tomorrow.") Would the class like to know if there was a new wild animal living in the area? How would it have gotten there? On its own? Put there by people? Why?

2. Help the class to write a letter to the state or provincial wildlife agency inquiring about newly introduced or re-introduced wildlife species in your region or local area. The following kinds of questions could be included:

• What species of animal was transplanted?

• Why was it introduced into that area? Did it once live there naturally?

• Was another species displaced? (For grades 7 and older: Which niche did it fill? See "Which Niche.")

• If the species was re-introduced, what previously had happened to the animals or habitat to cause their disappearance from the area?

• If habitat changes influenced this disappearance, how have these changes been corrected?

• When were the animals plentiful in the area and when did they disappear?

• When did this transplanting project take place? How did it take place?

• What indications, if any, are there that the transplant has been successful?

• What positive and/or negative effects, if any, have taken place for the transplanted animals, for other animals in the area, for the habitat?

3. Based on the information from the wildlife agency and any other research, ask the students to summarize what they have learned.

Extensions

1. When you receive an answer, have the class make a diorama of the animal in its new, "transplanted" habitat. These dioramas can be made by the class as a group in a large cardboard box, or by small groups of students working as a team, or by individual students using shoe boxes. Cut out magazine pictures of the animal and its habitat elements, back them with cardboard, and prop them up to create a diorama. Natural materials may also be used to create the background landscape.

2. Write a poem from the perspective of the animal. See "Animal Poetry."

Evaluation

List and explain four reasons for transplanting animals. Explain any major reasons for not transplanting animals.

SMOKEY THE BEAR SAID WHAT?

Objectives
Students will be able to: 1) identify positive and negative consequences of forest and grassland fires; and 2) describe some of the changes fire can make in ecosystems.

Method
Students brainstorm positive and negative effects of forest and grassland fires; conduct research; and create murals showing changes from fire in forest and grassland ecosystems.

Background
In managing public lands, government agencies for many years have been making a slow movement to change their attitudes toward forest and grassland fires. Whereas once all fires were suppressed or vigorously fought, some now are allowed to burn as part of a natural cycle within the forest and grassland ecosystems. In fact, there has been a movement to "prescribe" fires under some conditions and in some places in an effort to replicate natural cycles that contribute to maintaining healthy ecosystems.

Such "prescribed burns" are planned and tended by qualified resource managers. Prescribed burning is only employed after several agencies and their qualified personnel agree on the type, size, and location of burn needed. Such fires usually are designed to reduce the fuel load in a given area. Reducing the fuel load in a forested area, for example, can prevent fires from getting so hot that they eliminate virtually all life forms and even scorch the soil. That is, fires every five to ten years in some forest types can clear the heavy underbrush without harming the larger trees in the forest. A major fire after a 50-year accumulation of brush and maturing timber, however, can cause intensely hot and destructive fires.

Students may ask why—if some fires are helpful—the U.S. Forest Service symbol of "Smokey the Bear" says, "Only **you** can prevent forest fires."

Age: Grades 4-6
Subjects: Science, Social Studies, Art, Language Arts (research)
Skills: analysis, classification, comparing similarities and differences, description, discussion, evaluation, listing, media construction, research, small group work, synthesis, visualization
Duration: one class period, 45 minutes
Group Size: two groups, from two to 15 students each
Setting: indoors
Conceptual Framework Reference: I.B., I.C., I.C.1., I.C.2., I.C.3., I.C.4., I.D., III.A., III.A.1., III.A.3., III.B., III.B.1., III.B.3., III.B.4., III.C., III.C.1., III.C.2., III.C.3., III.C.4., III.D., III.D.1., III.D.2., III.D.4., III.E., III.E.1., III.E.2., III.F., IV.A., IV.A.1., IV.A.2., IV.A.3., IV.A.4., IV.B.2., IV.C., IV.C.1., IV.D., IV.D.2., IV.D.4., IV.D.5., IV.E., IV.E.4., IV.E.5., IV.E.10., IV.E.11., V.A., V.B., VI.B., VI.B.4., VI.B.5., VII.A., VII.B.
Key Vocabulary: prescribed burn, management

This message is aimed at humans causing fires by error and accidents, like from carelessness in camping situations. The message also warns us about the terrible destructiveness of intentional fires set by people for malicious and mischievous purposes. Again, the only people who may be authorized to set prescribed forest and grassland fires are those who are fully qualified professionals, trained in the study of ecological systems to reinstate fire as a natural management tool. It is still correct, of course, that fires can have negative as well as positive effects. Forest products companies, for example, in most cases would rather harvest trees than see them burn. If a fire is too large, too fast, and too hot—wildlife can't easily move to safety. Individual animals may die. Short-term and long-term loss of vegetation can have a variety of effects, including impact on wildlife, and increase in silting and sedimentation in the waters.

There are, however, possible benefits as well—particularly in the case of those smaller burns that do not get exceedingly hot. For example, forest and grassland fires can:

- maintain and enhance fire-dependent habitats such as prairies, savannas, chaparral and jack-pine forests.
- increase soil productivity by releasing and recycling nutrients tied up in litter and undergrowth.
- prepare soil for germination of some seeds.
- activate heat-dependent seed varieties, e.g., lodgepole pines.
- contribute to an "edge effect," providing a greater variety of food and shelter sources for wildlife.
- open up the habitat, generating new growth, diversity, and abundance of food plants, e.g., for large herbivores.

The major purpose of this activity is for students to become familiar with positive and negative effects of fire (forest and grasslands) on wildlife species and their habitat.

Materials art supplies, butcher paper or other paper for mural display

Procedure

1. Begin this activity with a discussion about forest and grassland fires. Students' reactions probably will be negative at first; point out that while one harmful effect of forest fires is the destruction of habitat for wild animals, in some cases fire can improve habitat.

2. Brainstorm possible positive and negative effects of forest and grassland fires. Keep the list of brainstormed ideas posted for the students' reference.

3. Divide the class into two groups—one to find out more about forest fires and one to find out more about grassland fires. Using the brainstormed list as a beginning point, students in each group can volunteer to find out more about some of the topics. (A few students might do this research, or all the students can be involved. In addition to topics the students have identified as possible positive and negative effects of such fires, other useful topics might include: definitions of "prescribed," "crown," "ground," fires, etc.; U.S. Forest Service, National Park Service, and other federal and state agency policies toward forest and grassland fires; information about number of different kinds of fires typical in specified areas during a year, e.g., accidentally caused by people, arson, lightning, and prescribed; examples of historical and present-day cultural groups who use fire to improve wildlife habitat; and plant species dependent upon fire to open seeds.)

4. Once any necessary research has been done, ask the students to divide into groups to make two murals—one of a forested area and one of grasslands. Each mural should portray changes from before to during and after a fire. Analyze and discuss positive and negative consequences of forest and grassland fires. Compare similarities and differences in the two areas.

Variation

Do the murals first. Then have the students research to find out if their murals are accurate. Correct and make additions to the murals after the research is completed.

Extension

1. Design and make Smokey the Bear Coloring Books for primary-age students in the school. Have a local forester or wildlife manager check it for accuracy before it is distributed. Show how fires can be both positive and negative. Also show that only trained foresters can set fires for forest management; the rest of us—when camping, hiking, wood gathering, etc. need to remember what Smokey still says, "Only you can prevent forest fires!"

2. Visit and study a forested or grassland area that has burned.

Evaluation

Describe two differences between grassland that is burned frequently and grassland that is never burned.

Describe two differences between forested land that is burned frequently and forested land that is never burned.

Name ten species of plants and animals that are helped by fire under some conditions, and ten species that usually do better when fire is absent in forest or grasslands.

Summarize conditions in which fire can be helpful, and conditions when it is usually not helpful.

CHECKS AND BALANCES

Objectives

Students will be able to: 1) evaluate hypothetical wildlife management decisions; and 2) identify at least four factors which can affect the size of a wildlife population.

Method

Students become managers of a herd of animals in a paper-and-pencil and discussion-based activity.

Background

Wildlife managers attempt to maintain healthy populations of wild animals, while factors—both avoidable and unavoidable—affect the populations. Some of these factors are loss of habitat, weather conditions, pollution of food and water sources, development of other natural resources, poaching, and recreation pressures. Many people are unaware of how such pressures can affect wildlife.

In the United States, it is the legal responsibility of state wildlife agencies to manage the wildlife populations within their respective states. It is the legal responsibility of the U.S. Fish and Wildlife Service, under the U.S. Department of the Interior, to govern some policies and programs affecting migratory species of animals (principally birds) and threatened or endangered species, as well as illegal importation and expor-

Age: Grades 6-12
Subjects: Mathematics, Science, Vocational Agriculture
Skills: analysis, computation (calculating percentages), evaluation
Duration: one to two 45-minute periods
Group Size: any
Setting: classroom
Conceptual Framework Reference: I.C.3., I.C.4., I.D., III.A.1., III.C., III.C.1., III.C.2., III.E., III.E.1., III.E.2., III.F., IV.A., IV.A.1., IV.A.2., IV.A.3., IV.C., IV.C.1., IV.C.2., IV.C.3., IV.D., IV.D.1., IV.D.2., IV.D.3., IV.D.5., IV.E., IV.E.1., IV.E.4., IV.E.5., IV.E.6., IV.E.7., IV.E.10., IV.E.11., VI.A., VI.A.2., VI.A.3., VI.A.4., VI.B., VI.C., VI.C.12., VI.C.15., VI.C.16., VII.A., VII.B., VII.B.2., VII.B.4., VII.B.7.
Key Vocabulary: management, population, herd

tation of animals and animal products, illegal interstate transportation of all species, with additional responsibilities related to the overall well-being of U.S. wildlife.

Wildlife management is based on the best scientific and technical knowledge available. Such knowledge is growing; however, it is still limited, and is continually affected by changes in the complex relationships between wildlife, human beings, and their shared environments.

In a sense, everyone shares responsibility for wildlife management. Although there are legally responsible agencies, their work requires the thoughtful and informed cooperation of citizens. There are frequently differences of opinion about the most appropriate policies and programs affecting wildlife. Individual citizens, private conservation groups, private industry, community groups, and others all make important contributions to the overall conservation and protection of wildlife and its habitat.

The major purpose of this activity is for students hypothetically to assume the role of wildlife managers, and thus gain insight into some of the complex variables that influence stewardship of wildlife. This activity is not designed to provide a comprehensive understanding of all possible factors which can affect wildlife.

Materials
paper and pencils; paper to make condition cards; dice, one per student

Procedure
1. Each student is asked to be the manager of a moose (or other animal) population. The carrying capacity of the habitat is 100 animals. The point of the activity is to end up with a viable population after nine rounds, simulating nine years. If at any time the student's population reaches less than 10 or more than 200 individual animals, that student no longer has a viable "herd" and watches the other students until the conclusion of the activity.

2. Each student has a beginning population of 100 animals. The cards are separated into three decks of a total of 36 cards: a condition deck (18 cards), a reproduction deck (9 cards), and a management deck (9 cards). Shuffle the cards within each deck. Explain that cards will be drawn in the following sequence: condition card, reproduction card, condition card, management card. This sequence of draw will be repeated, each repetition representing an annual cycle (the students may think of each draw as representing a different season, e.g., autumn, winter, spring, summer). As each card is drawn, it is read aloud to the entire class. Each student then rolls his or her die and follows the instructions on the card to determine his or her herd population's new size. Some computations will result in fractions; numbers may be rounded to the nearest whole. NOTE: Students may object to the use of dice to determine the impact of decisions made for wildlife management purposes. Their concerns are appropriate; wildlife management is based on more than the chance elements reflected in the use of dice. However, chance has its impacts as well, as in the case of weather conditions in a given year. Encourage the students to discuss and consider what is realistic, and what is unrealistic, about the impact of dice in this activity—encouraging the recognition that wildlife management is far more complex than can be represented through this activity.

3. Wrap up the activity with a class discussion. Include topics such as:

- Identify and describe what appeared to be the impacts of the condition, reproduction, and management cards.
- Given one of the objectives of this activity—to evaluate hypothetical management decisions—what seemed to be the benefits and/or liabilities, if any, of management decisions made?
- Did populations "managed" under different strategies by different students show different trends? How do these compare? Would students "manage" differently if given a second chance?
- What aspects of this activity seemed realistic? Which didn't?
- What are examples of ways that habitat can be improved? Short term? Long term?
- Is human management of wildlife populations necessary? Beneficial? Why or why not? For people? For the animals?

Variation

Add a monetary aspect to the activity. Students allowing hunting might have more available revenue for projects like habitat enhancement based on income from sale of hunting licenses. Other expenses might include salaries of wildlife managers, funds for research, feeding animals in severe conditions, relocation, etc.

Evaluation

Name four factors that can affect the size of a wildlife population.

Some wildlife managers have said that wildlife management involves more management of people than of wildlife. Explain what they might mean by the comment.

INSTRUCTIONS FOR MAKING CARDS

Make the following cards, according to three categories: **Reproduction Cards, Condition Cards, Management Cards.** There are 36 cards in total. The number in parentheses indicates how many of each card are to be made. NOTE: The numbers of cards and the suggestions for numerical manipulations, e.g., three times the roll, are relatively arbitrary. They are designed for students to recognize that a number of diverse factors can affect wildlife; the numerical weights should not be interpreted literally.

(After using these cards once, students may want to experiment with making additional cards, or changing these cards. Students may also want to make additional complete sets of cards for use by small groups or individual students.)

NOTE: As the cards are read aloud, be certain to note differences in decreasing or increasing herd size by percentage or by number.

Reproduction Cards

Reproduction Card—Excellent Year (3)
This has been an excellent reproduction year. Increase your herd by (100/your current population size) times five times your roll, if your current population is over 50 individuals. If your population is between 50 and 10, increase your population by the number equal to five times your roll. If your population is under ten, you may not reproduce.

Reproduction Card—Average Year (6)
This has been an average reproduction year. Increase your herd by (100/your current population size) times three times your roll, if your current population is over 50 individuals. If your population is between 50 and 10, increase your population by three times your roll. If your population is under 10, don't reproduce.

Condition Cards

Weather Card (2)

_____(Students need to specify what) has had a serious negative impact on the survival of the herd. Decrease your herd by the percentage equal to five times your roll.

Weather Card (2)

_____(Students need to specify what) has had a dramatic positive impact on the survival of the herd. Increase your herd by the percentage equal to five times your roll.

Habitat Destruction Card (2)

_____(Students needs to specify what) has occurred, destroying critical habitat. Decrease herd size by the number five times your roll.

Predator Card (1)

Predation has occurred, affecting the herd size. Decrease herd size by the percentage equal to your roll.

Habitat Degradation Card (4)

_____(Students need to specify what) has occurred, damaging critical habitat. Decrease herd by the number equal to three times your roll.

Disease Card (1)

Disease has struck the herd. Decrease herd by the percentage equal to your roll.

Habitat Loss Card (5)

_____(Students need to specify what) has resulted in a loss of critical habitat for the herd. Decrease herd by the number equal to five times your roll.

Poaching Card (1)

Poaching—illegal killing of animals—has reduced the size of the herd. Decrease herd by the number equal to two times your roll.

Management Cards

Habitat Restoration Card (1)

_____(Students need to specify what) has occurred, restoring critical habitat. Increase herd by the percentage equal to five times your roll.

Habitat Alteration Card (2)

_____(Students need to specify what) has occurred, altering critical habitat. Increase or decrease (students choose which before rolling the die) herd by the percentage equal to three times your roll.

Habitat Improvement Card (1)

_____(Students need to specify what) has occurred, improving critical habitat. Increase herd by five times your roll.

Research Card (1)

_____(Students need to specify what) research has been successfully accomplished. Increase or decrease (students choose which before rolling the die) herd by two times your roll.

Law Enforcement Card (1)

_____ (Students need to specify what) law enforcement activities have protected the herd against illegal actions like poaching. Increase herd by the percentage equal to two times your roll.

Education Card (1)

_____(Students need to specify what) education activities have led to increased understanding of wildlife and habitat. Increase or decrease (students choose which before rolling the die) herd by the percentage equal to two times your roll, or by two times your roll.

Habitat Acquisition Card (1)

Habitat acquisition has increased the area of available and suitable habitat. Increase herd by five times your roll.

Hunting Card (1)

A request for a hunting season has been made. Do you wish to allow hunting in your area? If yes, decrease your herd by the percentage equal to five times your roll. If no, record no change in the size of your herd.

NO WATER OFF A DUCK'S BACK

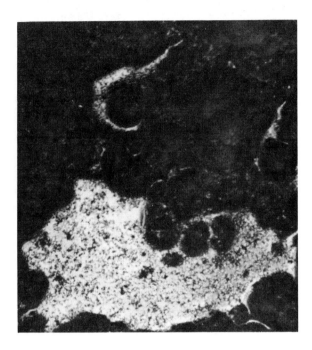

Objectives
Students will be able to: 1) identify ways oil spills can affect birds adversely; and 2) describe possible negative consequences to wildlife, people, and the environment from human-caused pollutants.

Method
Students conduct experiments using water, oil, hard-boiled eggs, detergent, and feathers.

Background
The impacts of environmental pollution often are difficult to see. A major oil spill, however, provides dramatic evidence of potential impact to wildlife. Examples include damage to feathers, killing of embryos when oil seeps into eggs, suffocation of fish when gills are clogged, and death to marine and terrestrial animals by ingesting food and water contaminated by the oil.

People are involved in efforts to prevent oil spills and their consequences. They also are involved in efforts to "clean up" after such spills take place. Such actions are not always successful, and sometimes they have unfortunate consequences as well. For example, detergents frequently used to clean oil from the feathers of birds caught in spills may also remove natural oils. Birds released before these natural oils are replaced may drown because the feathers no longer repel water. Birds also may be more susceptible to disease during this time of stress, and may be weakened to the extent that it is more difficult for them to secure their necessary food and water. Obviously, the food and water sources may also be affected in quality.

Oil spills are just one example of the kinds of pollutants that can have adverse short- and long-term effects on wildlife, people, and the environment. The impact of DDT on the food chain is well-known, as another of many possible examples. DDT's influence on thinner egg shells in bald eagles and other birds is well documented, one more in a combination of factors which contribute to threatening, endangering, and eliminating species.

The major purpose of this activity is for students to examine some of the possible consequences of human-caused pollution for wildlife, people, and the environment.

Age: Grades 6—12
Subjects: Science, Mathematics, Social Studies, Language Arts, Home Economics
Skills: analysis, computation, discussion, drawing, estimation, generalization, graphing, observation
Duration: one to two 45-minute periods or longer
Group Size: small groups of three to four recommended
Setting: indoors
Conceptual Framework Reference: I.C., I.C.1., I.C.3., I.C.4., I.D., IV.C., IV.C.1., IV.C.3., IV.E., IV.E.4., IV.E.7., IV.E.10., V.A., V.B., VI.A., VI.A.2., VI.A.3., VI.A.4., VI.A.5., VI.B., VI.B.2., VI.B.3., VI.C.1., VII.A., VII.A.1., VII.A.2., VII.A.3., VII.A.4., VII.B., VII.B.1., VII.B.3., VII.B.4., VII.B.5., VII.B.6., VII.B.7.
Key Vocabulary: pollution, oil spill, trade-off

Materials
used motor oil, shallow containers, eye dropper, hand lens, feathers (natural); liquid detergent (dishwashing liquid); hard-boiled eggs

Procedure

1. Divide the class into groups of three or four. Each group needs a shallow pan partially filled with water. Add a known amount of oil, one drop to one dropper full, depending on the size of the container. Observe the interaction of oil and water. Measure the area covered by the oil. Using this information, estimate the area that might be affected by an oil spill involving:

1. A tanker truck holding 8,000 gallons.
2. A ship holding 300,000 gallons.
3. A supertanker holding 83,000,000 gallons.

Discuss and compare estimates with other groups. Graph estimates and compute average figures.

2. Put enough oil in a small container to submerge three hard-boiled eggs. Add the eggs. Put the eggs under a good light and watch closely. Remove one egg after five minutes and examine it—before, during, and after peeling off the shell. Try to remove the excess oil from the outside before attempting to peel the egg. Remove the second egg after 15 minutes and the third egg after 30 minutes, repeating the procedure, examining each carefully. Discuss observations. What effect could oil have on the eggs of birds nesting near the water?

3. Examine a feather with a hand lens. Sketch what you see. Dip the feather in water for one or two minutes, and examine again with a hand lens. Sketch and compare to the original observations. Place the feather in oil for one or two minutes, and then examine with a hand lens, sketch, and compare with other sketches. Clean the feather in detergent, rinse in water, and dry it. Examine with a hand lens, sketch, and compare with previous sketches. Discuss changes in the feather after exposure to oil and then to detergents. What effect could these changes have on normal bird activity?

4. Discuss other possible effects on birds from an oil spill. Discuss possible impacts on other wildlife species, on humans, and on the environment. What trade-offs are involved? Do we have to choose between oil and birds, as well as other wildlife? What are some alternatives? What are other examples of human-caused pollutants that can have negative consequences for wildlife, people, and the environment? What is being done or can be done about these as well?

5. Optional: Ask each student to write a report, summarizing the findings of the experiment as well as making recommendations.

Optional Extensions to Classroom Experiment

1. A variety of oils—cooking oil, motor oil, crude oil—could be used, with effects compared. Food coloring can be added to clear oils to facilitate observation of effects.

2. Other pollutants can be used to see what, if any, effects they have on eggs and feathers. Exercise caution, however; do not use any unusually dangerous substances.

Evaluation

How could an oil spill affect the success of birds nesting near the water?

Describe some possible effects of oil on a feather. Explain why the effects of oil are different from those of water.

Describe some possible negative effects of three other human-caused pollutants on people, wildlife, and the environment.

THE HUNTER

Objectives
Students will be able to: 1) describe their feelings about hunting; 2) compare their attitudes to those of other people; and 3) make personal judgements about the appropriateness of hunting.

Method
Students read and discuss a story.

Background
People have hunted animals since earliest time. Products of the hunt have been used for a wide variety of purposes including for food, clothing, tools, bedding, medicines, and religious objects.

Centuries of time and modern technologies have tended to urbanize human populations, removing many from the necessity of as much daily contact with natural systems.

By percent of population, fewer people hunt today. For many, the opportunity, interest, and necessity is not available. Many people have lost the knowledge and skills, as well as the need, to hunt. The slaughterhouse and butcher shop serve many instead.

There are still those who hunt. Some seek wild meats for nutrition and purity. Some utilize horns, antlers, and hides for tools, clothing, and decoration. Today in the United States, hunters pay fees to hunt, and hunt under stringent and restrictive conditions, their harvest controlled by management practices and concern for perpetuation of species and habitat.

Hunting has become recognized as a tool of management. For example, it is used to control populations of large ungulates like deer, which tend to overpopulate and destroy their own habitats. A reduced population—whether by hunting, starvation, or other limiting factors—typically recovers quickly where there is quality habitat for the species. Habitat once damaged, however, tends to recover slowly.

Wildlife managers refer to hunting as a means of "harvesting" a wildlife population, based on the characteristics of wildlife as a renewable resource. Wildlife managers use regulated hunting seasons to maintain a population of animals in an area so that the population can reproduce successfully over time, living in a habitat that can be continuously renewed by natural processes.

Hunters pay fees in order to hunt, and simultaneously must follow all regulations of the agency responsible for wildlife management in their state or province. The hunters' fees as well as a portion of taxes on certain hunting-related equipment go directly to continuing management of wildlife resources, purchase and restoration of wildlife habitat, and enforcement of wildlife-related laws.

Why do some people hunt? Most hunters in the United States today find it difficult to express their feelings about why they hunt and kill wildlife. Most hunters say they hunt because they like to get outside. Most would call their hunting recreation and some would call it sport. Most hunters feel they are making a significant contribution to the perpetuation of wildlife species and habitat since the proceeds from the license fees they pay as well as taxes on some hunting- and fishing-relating equipment are used for wildlife management, including major revenue support for most state fish and wildlife programs. Most hunters use some of the products of the hunt for food. Almost no one today uses nearly all products of the hunt as our ancestors typically did from necessity.

Some people are opposed to hunting. They may believe it to be unethical, or that it is biologically unnecessary and even detrimental to the long-range health and genetic vitality of wildlife populations. Another concern is for the suffering of individual animals. The ethical right of humans to take the life of other animals is also

---

Age: Grades 5-9
Subjects: Social Studies, Language Arts, Science, Math
Skills: analysis, comparing similarities and differences, description, discussion, evaluation
Duration: 45 minutes or longer class periods
Group Size: any
Setting: indoors or outdoors
Conceptual Framework Reference: II.A., II.B., II.C., II.D., II.D.2., II.E., II.E.1., II.E.2., II.E.3., II.F., III.C., III.C.1., III.C.2., III.E., III.E.1., III.E.2., III.F., III.F.1., III.F.2., III.F.3., III.F.4., III.F.5., IV.A., IV.B., IV.C., IV.C.1., IV.C.2., IV.D., IV.D.1., IV.D.2., IV.D.3., IV.D.4., IV.D.7., IV.E., IV.E.1., IV.E.2., IV.E.4., IV.E.5., IV.E.6., IV.E.7., IV.E.9., IV.E.11., IV.F., IV.F.1., IV.F.2., IV.F.3., IV.F.4., IV.F.5., IV.F.6., IV.F.7., IV.F.8., IV.F.9., V.A., V.A.3., V.A.5., V.A.6., V.B., V.B.1., V.B.2., V.B.3., VI.B., VI.B.1., VI.B.2., VI.B.3., VI.B.4., VI.B.5., VI.B.6., VI.C., VI.C.1., VI.C.2., VI.C.3., VI.C.4., VI.C.7., VI.C.9., VI.C.12., VI.C.15., VI.C.16, VII.A., VII.B., VII.B.2.
Key Vocabulary: browse, habitat, edge-effect, carrying capacity, adaptation, predator, prey, range, ecological niche, consumer, hunter, hunting, management, responsibility

questioned. Some object to management practices they perceive to be aimed solely at producing wildlife for the benefit of hunters.

Some who do not believe it appropriate to kill for sport or recreation may accept hunting as a tool in managing certain kinds of wildlife and under certain conditions. For example, they may accept hunting when the meat is utilized for food; or hunting to control a species which is harming important habitat.

Others choose not to hunt, but may not take an active stand either for or against hunting.

Within any community, there will be a range of views on the subject.

The major purpose of this activity is for students to examine their own attitudes about hunting.

Materials student copies of story

Procedure

1. Ask each student to think about his or her personal feelings about hunting animals. The students may or may not choose to share their feelings in discussion. Optional: Ask each student to write a brief description of his or her personal feelings about hunting before proceeding with this activity.

2. Provide each of the students with a copy of the following story to read, or read it aloud to the students.

3. After having read or heard the story, ask each student to write their own ending to it. What does Jamie do? Why? How does he feel?

4. Next ask the students to discuss the story and their endings to it. How do they think Jamie feels about hunting? How do they think Jamie feels about the animal he is hunting? How do each of them feel about animals and about hunting? Additional questions for discussion could include: Why is legal hunting allowed? What is the difference between hunting and poaching? Do you think hunting should be allowed? What reasons do people have for hunting? What reasons do people have who believe that hunting should not be allowed? In your judgement, what, if any, are appropriate reasons for hunting to be allowed? In your judgement what, if any, are appropriate reasons hunting should not be allowed? What responsibilities do you think people have if they choose to hunt? What responsibilities do you think people have if they choose not to hunt? NOTE: Set a tone for discussion where each student's personal judgements are acknowledged and respected.

Extensions

1. Find out the following: Who sets the rules and enforces the legal regulations for hunting? (Regulations for legal hunting are established by the state agency responsible for wildlife. All wildlife in the United States, even on private property, is considered to belong to the public. It is managed on the public's behalf by state and federal wildlife agencies. Private organizations and individuals influence management, but legal responsibility belongs to state agencies, with some species and practices involving the federal government through the U.S. Fish and Wildlife Service and other federal agencies.)

2. Check with your state wildlife agency to find out what kinds of hunting, if any, are allowed in your area—as well as when, why, by what methods, with what equipment, at what age, and under what regulations. Also find out what kind of hunter preparation or education is required, if any, for people who want to be allowed to hunt.

3. Check with a diverse and representative range of interested groups for their positions concerning hunting. Some groups may be for hunting, some against, and some may not take an official position. Investigate their reasons for their positions. Check each point of view for accuracy of information provided. For example, groups which could be contacted include: American Humane Association, Defenders of Wildlife, Humane Society of the United States, International Association of Fish and Wildlife Agencies, National Audubon Society, National Rifle Association, National Wildlife Federation, The Wildlife Society, and Wildlife Management Institute, as well as state and federal wildlife agencies.

4. Hold a series of debates. Argue and support positions for and against hunting.

Evaluation

Write an essay describing reasons for and against hunting. Include your personal feelings and recommendations about the appropriateness of hunting.

THE TWINS

By Dr. Clifford Knapp
and Suzanne Iudicello

The twin fawns were born on a May day when the sun dappled the edge of the forest through the newly budding leaves, and apple blossom petals fell in the abandoned orchard like fragrant snow. They were not the only twins that year; food had been plentiful in the valley, and white-tailed deer were sleek and round-bellied.

Even as the doe licked her offspring clean, strength flowed into the young bodies. It hadn't hurt that she had been able, through the fall and winter, to slip into a nearby farm at night for corn, alfalfa, and clover to add to the leaves, twigs, juicy weeds, acorns, and mushrooms the forests and fields offered to the white-tails.

The valley was a generous place for the herd of 60 animals. Where the hillsides dipped down to meet the farm fields, the shady forest ended. This edge meant that food was varied and abundant. It hadn't always been that way.

In the early 1700s, when the valley was first settled, the forests were widespread. Since white-tailed deer require a mixture of forest, openings, and edge, they were present but not plentiful then. By 1900, however, the deer population had been almost eliminated by a human appetite for venison. Too much hunting had reduced the size of the herds. Much of the once abundant forest had been cleared for wood products and use as agricultural lands. This limited suitable habitat for the deer. Later, laws controlled hunting, and changes in land use practices led to a return of some of the forest. The mixture of agriculture and young forests provided the deer herds an excellent environment and, with the regulated hunting, the deer thrived. The young plants that grew in the open areas of the cut-over forest yielded an abundance of food, and by the 1930s there were more deer in the valley than when the settlers first came.

That soft, May afternoon saw another birthday celebrated in the valley. The boy ran out to greet his father who was climbing down off the tractor after a day of making furrows for the spring planting. He looked up into the lined face of his father and barely contained his impatience while the farmer removed his hat and wiped the sweat from his forehead with a big, blue kerchief.

"Is it time?" the boy asked breathlessly.

The man smiled down at his son—a strong, wiry boy, made tough by summers of throwing hay bales and winters of chopping wood.

"Yes, Jamie," he grinned, "It's time." He put his arm across the boy's shoulders and they walked up onto the wide porch, where a table stood decked with early daisies and tiger lilies in a Mason jar, bright orange and yellow paper napkins, and a three-decker chocolate cake with 12 yellow candles. The boy's mother was already sitting at the table, pouring tall glasses of foamy, fresh milk.

"Do you want us to sing first?" she laughed, as Jamie scraped the chair legs across the porch floor in his haste to get to the table.

"Nope. Where's my present?"

"Now, Jamie," his father scolded good-naturedly, "birthdays aren't just for presents. This is a special year for you, and it brings with it not just a gift but some responsibility. You're no longer a little boy. You're a young man. This is not a birthday for toys."

Jamie looked down at his hands on his lap. "I know, Dad; I'm sorry."

But when he looked up again at his father, the excitement and expectation shining in his eyes were not those of a serious young man, but of a boy about to burst with anticipation.

As his mother cut the cake, Jamie's father took from behind the door a long, narrow box, tied with a gold ribbon. "Okay, son, this is what you've been waiting for, and we won't keep you from it."

Jamie tore the ribbon from the box and lifted the cover. There, gleaming from the soft yellow cloth, lay the rifle. It wasn't new, but the gloss on the stock showed a new coat of oil and betrayed hours of careful rubbing, and the barrel shone with new blueing. The scratches he remembered on the dull grey were gone, but the initials his grandfather had carved on the stock were still there.

He drew the rifle from the box, taking care to point it away from anyone as his grandfather and father had taught him. It was much heavier than the .22 he'd lugged through the woods to stalk squirrels.

"It's yours now, Jamie, just as we promised," his father said. "You're 12 now, and old enough to go deer hunting this fall."

Although Jamie thought the fall would never arrive, the summer passed quickly, filled with days of helping his father in the fields, fishing and swimming, and lots of practice with the rifle.

In the hills above the farm valley, the twin fawns gained strength quickly. By June, they followed the doe along the well-worn trails. As summer ripened, they roamed with the herd over the length of the valley and high on the hillsides. They were just two of 50 fawns that had been born that spring, swelling the herd from 60 to more than 100.

They fed on leaves, twigs, fruits, and nuts of the trees and shrubs in the forest, and on the grasses and weeds along its edges. The summer habitat provided abundant food. The doe and her fawns grew strong and healthy on the bounty. This was fortunate, for the stark winter ahead would not offer such abundance.

November blew in rainy and cold, and Jamie was restless after the crisp, bright days of October. The harvest was complete, the fields lay in a stubble under the grey sky, and the few brown apples remaining on the trees were torn down by the wind. He sat in the warm kitchen and looked out at the glistening black branches scratching at the sky.

"Can I go out, Mom?" he asked. She looked up from the lunch dishes at her son, his dungaree cuffs well above the tops of the worn boots, and the elbows frayed out of his plaid flannel shirt. The restlessness was about to burst his skin as his growing body had burst the seams of most of his clothes that summer.

"All right, but wear your father's poncho," she called as he was already halfway out the door, the rifle over his shoulder.

Jamie knew, from his summer forays and from past autumns when he'd been too young to hunt, that the deer often came down to the abandoned orchard to nip at the withered apples that grew on the overhanging trees. That part of the farm wasn't used now, and the orchard had long since overgrown, producing only tiny, bitter fruits, but the deer seemed to like them. He had watched, enthralled, many an evening, as the slender, tawny forms moved delicately and then froze like shadows in the dusk.

As he trotted away from the yellow light in the kitchen window, dusk gathered and the rain turned to sleet. The grey afternoon was threatening to turn bleaker yet. He scrambled over the crumbling remains of a stone wall, and entered the orchard in a blast of wind that nearly took his breath away. "At least it's blowing toward me," he thought, settling in under a tree to wait. Just before nightfall, his patience was wearing thin, his foot was tingling where he had been sitting on it, the rain was trickling under his collar, and the sleet was stinging his face. He was about to stomp his foot to bring it back to life so he could walk home, when the doe entered the orchard; Jamie caught his breath.

The words of the fish and wildlife license agent echoed in his ears as he raised the rifle to his shoulder. "We're going to open the season this year—bucks, does, fawns." The man had punched Jamie's slip of yellow paper for fishing and hunting—the first time he'd been the age to have a license for deer. "This is your first hunting season, son?" he'd asked. "Good luck."

Jamie watched the doe down the barrel of the rifle. She was stretching up, her front feet off the ground, trying to reach a last, wrinkled apple clinging stubbornly to a high branch. The slender neck glistened from drops of rain caught in the soft fur. His heart was pounding and he wasn't sure if he was still breathing. He reached around with his thumb and gently pushed the safety off the rifle.

Just then the twin fawns stepped delicately into the orchard, melting from the darkened tree trunks like slightly smaller shadows of the doe. Jamie lifted his eyes from the barrel to the fawns. They, too, were stretching to try to reach the last brown leaves and few apples high in the branches, but they were too short. They moved close to the doe, where her efforts at pulling on the branches had jostled a few apples to the ground.

Jamie refocused on the doe, sighted down the barrel, and let out a deep breath to steady his hand. A blast of wind ripped through the orchard, carrying sleet and snow before it, ripping a tree branch in its fury. The branch tumbled down and the three deer bolted back into the thicket.

The boy reset the safety on the rifle, and gingerly got to his feet. He looked into the darkening sky and the tossing branches and thought, "I'm glad. Maybe those three will make it through the winter."

Winter hit that night, lashing the valley with wind and snow that drifted into 20-foot mountains, froze into hard crusts, and remained. The herd, trapped on the hillside, didn't move more than a quarter of a mile the whole winter. They competed for the dwindling food supply that remained poking above the snow, and many fawns and does died.

Jamie thought often about the trio, as he looked out over the white landscape.

The grip of the season finally loosened one moist, February day. Rain pelted the snow, turning it to slush and pitted mounds where the mud showed through. Spring and summer returned to the valley, and with them the activity that kept life for a farm boy busy and full.

For the herd, the winter had taken its toll. Most of the fawns had died of starvation and cold, as did many older bucks and does, weakened by age. The herd was reduced from the summer high of more than 100, to fewer than 50. Those remaining ventured down out of the hills to the greening valley where their favored plants sprouted anew. Throughout the spring and summer, they found plenty of food to go around among their reduced numbers, particularly since few fawns has been born after the harsh winter.

Summer's hazy, golden days burned into fall, and as harvest time ended, Jamie's thoughts drifted again to the abandoned orchard and his rifle. One evening he took it out of its wrappings, and cleaned and polished it, wondering if the twin fawns were among this autumn's yearlings.

The frosty straw stubble crunched under his feet as he made his way across the fields to the orchard. The passing of a year had seen more stones fall from the top of the wall, and Jamie noted that the tree that had been his resting place last season was uprooted and lying broken. He concealed himself among the twisted branches, and settled to wait.

The evening was still, the sky a pale salmon color where the sun had just slipped below the hills. Jamie hoped the slight varying breeze would not carry his scent. He slid a round into the chamber of the rifle, wondering how many times his grandfather had sat like this, in this very orchard, with this very rifle. He checked to make sure the safety was on, and settled in.

Dusk fell with the twittering of a few last thrushes, and Jamie started at the sound of a snapping twig. A yearling doe stepped into the orchard, the brush rustling back to fill the space where she had emerged from the forest. Jamie exhaled quietly, trying to relax again, because this year was bucks only, the season restricted because the herd had so dwindled over the harsh winter. He watched the doe nosing among the brown weeds for fallen apples, wondering if she were the fawn of last autumn.

He watched, still, admiring the sleek brown sides and the graceful curve of the neck. The doe raised her head and listened, so close he could see her nostrils flickering to catch a scent. The deer glanced at the forest edge, tensed, then bent her head to browse again as a yearling buck emerged from the same trail, disguised by the thick brush.

Jamie lifted the rifle to his shoulder, nestling it close against the rough wool of his jacket. He looked down the barrel at the young white-tail, wondering if these were the twins of that blustery evening a year ago. He questioned whether this time he would pull the trigger. "He made it through the winter—who am I to kill him now?" he asked himself.

The buck stepped away from the doe, and began pulling apples from the drooping branches. It would be a clean shot, Jamie knew, well away from the doe, certain to be a quick kill. He exhaled, steadied his arm, and concentrated on a patch of rusty brown hair on the animal's shoulder. "I can't look at his head," he thought. "I just have to keep thinking of him as meat for my family." As he thumbed off the safety, he allowed himself one last, stolen glance at the sculptured head, arching up to grasp an apple. Jamie swallowed and . . .

NOTE: "The Twins" is adapted, with permission, from a story which originally appeared in **Open Lands and Wildlife** (Union, New Jersey: Pollution Control Education Center, 1975), a multimedia instructional unit including both teacher and student materials. Thanks to Dr. Clifford Knapp for his cooperation and encouragement in providing the original material for use in Project WILD. Write the Pollution Control Education Center, Township of Union Public Schools, Union, New Jersey, for additional information about **Open Lands and Wildlife.**

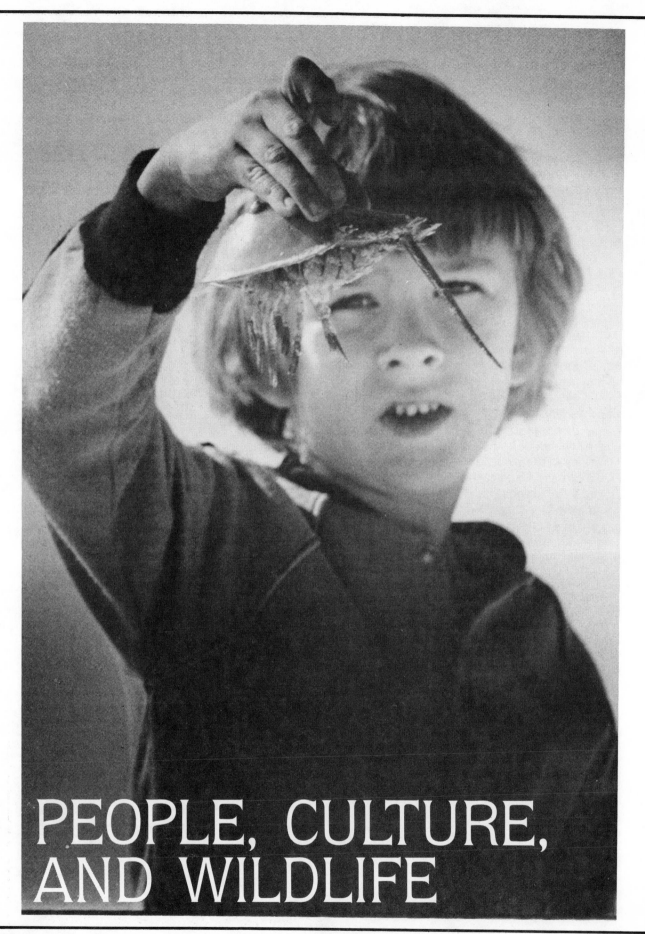

PEOPLE, CULTURE, AND WILDLIFE

LOBSTER IN YOUR LUNCH BOX

Objectives
Students will be able to: 1) identify which foods are derived from plants and which from animals; and 2) recognize that all food sources derived originally from wild plants and animals.

Method
Students plan and calculate the costs of a family's meals for one day; create a classroom chart; and analyze, discuss, and summarize findings.

Background
We all have to eat! All of our food comes directly or indirectly from the wild. Plants, wild and domestic, support animal life. Animal food sources, when not wild, were derived from wild animals. For example, the chicken is derivative from an African wild bird. The major purpose of this activity is for students to recognize that all domesticated plants and animals have been derived from wild sources.

Materials
supermarket advertising in newspapers, scissors, pencil and paper, cookbooks optional

Procedure
1. The following directions may be given to the students:
a. You have been given the responsibility of planning meals for one day for a family of four people.
b. Plan three meals for the day. Make a grocery list of all ingredients that you will need for those meals. Use newspaper advertisements to establish prices of the ingredients, cutting or clipping the ads and attaching them to a piece of paper with the parts of the meal listed alongside the ads. Calculate the cost of each meal. Add up the total cost of all three meals. What is the cost for all four people? What is the cost per person? Use a chart to record your data. For example:

MEAL COST FOR FOUR PEOPLE

	PRODUCT	COST	
MEAL 1	eggs	.80	.20 each
	toast	.24	.06 each
	butter	.12	.03 each
	milk	.60	.15 each
	juice	.60	.15 each
		2.36	.59 each

Age: Grades 4—7
Subjects: Mathematics, Science, Language Arts, Health (nutrition)
Skills: analysis, classification, computation, discussion, listing, media construction, writing
Duration: three class sessions of approximately 30 minutes each: 1) plan menu (at home find ads for costs); 2) calculate costs; and 3) identify plants and animals, discussion
Group Size: two or three students working in groups
Setting: indoors
Conceptual Framework Reference: V.A.1., I.A.3., II.D.2.
Key Vocabulary: domesticated, nondomesticated

2. Using the preceding chart, discuss the following questions:

• What plants or plant products are on your menu? Place a P by these on your chart.

• What animals or animal products are on your menu? Place an A by these on your chart.

• Which prices are higher—plants or animals?

• Older students: What percentage of food on the menu derives directly from plants? What percentage derives from wild animals? From domesticated animals?

3. Create a classroom chart, listing all the plants and animals. Discuss questions such as the following, noting results of the discussion on the class chart.

• Identify what these plants and animals need in order to survive.

• Trace each animal back to dependence on plants.

• Identify which of these plants and animals were once wild, and are now domesticated as a food source. If possible, identify what the original wild plants and animals were from which the foods were developed. Place a D by any domesticated plants and animals.

• Why have plants and animals been domesticated as food sources? (e.g., efficiency, convenience, cultural preference) What are some of the consequences of domestication (e.g., on prices, energy, plants, animals, environment)?

• Summarize the discussion.

NOTE: Students may notice differences in eating habits and preferences; for example, some students may choose no meat or dairy products.

Extensions

1. Trace the life cycle of foods in the grocery store. Find out where the foods come from. Are they locally grown and raised? Imported from foreign countries?

2. Have an International Foods Day. Compare food preferences of different cultures. Look especially at whether food sources are primarily wild or domesticated.

3. Explore the systems under which plants and animals are raised for food. Compare the various systems using a variety of criteria, including consequences to the plants and animals involved; impact on other plants, animals, and people; impact to the environment; efficiency; ethics; economic, social, environmental, ecological costs, etc. Consider short- and long-term costs, as well as primary and secondary consequences.

Evaluation

Mark "p" for plant, or "a" for animal, to indicate whether the following foods come from plants or animals: rice, liver, oysters, carrots, milk, mushrooms, apples, sugar, tunafish, bread, kidney beans, cheese.

Make a list of nondomesticated animals that are used regularly for food by people living in the United States or Canada.

For each of these animals—commonly domesticated and used as a food source for people—name a wild animal in North America which is similar: cow, chicken, pig, sheep, goat.

FIRST IMPRESSIONS

Objectives
Students will be able to: 1) distinguish between reactions to an animal based on myth or stereotype, and those based on accurate information; and 2) recognize the value of animals' contributions to ecosystems—even those that people sometimes respond to with fear.

Method
Students react to a variety of photos, as a beginning to study of contributions of a range of animals.

Background
Many people don't like spiders. Their first reaction may be to recoil if they see a spider; their second may be to kill the animal as quickly as possible. And yet most spiders are harmless to people. In fact, spiders are important contributors to healthy ecosystems.

Spiders are not the only wildlife that frequently raises a response of fright in people. Wolves, snakes, and bats elicit fear among many people in a number of cultures. Bats, however, are viewed as signs of good luck among some people in China. Reactions may vary from species to species in different cultures.

This activity is designed for students to examine their spontaneous reactions to different animals—separating reactions based on information and experience from those based on misinformation and myth—and to recognize the contributions of animals to ecosystems.

Materials
large photos or drawings of a variety of animals, including some the students might think are "cute" and some they might think are "scary."

Procedure
1. Prepare a series of large photos or drawings of a variety of different kinds of animals. As you show a photo to the entire group of students, ask them to take turns saying the first word that comes to their minds as they look at the picture.

Age: Grades K—6
Subjects: Science, Language Arts
Skills: analysis, comparing similarities and differences, generalization, listing; additional skills for older students: description, research, reporting, small group work, writing
Duration: two 20-minute periods; older students: three 30-minute periods
Group Size: any
Setting: indoors
Conceptual Framework Reference: II.A.1., II.A.2., II.B., III.B.1., V.A., V.A.5., V.A.6., V.B.1.
Key Vocabulary: fear, environment, feelings, information

2. With younger students, take the time yourself to write the name of the animal and the words the students suggest on the chalkboard. With older students, have at least two students serve as recorders, writing the words on the chalkboard for the whole group. Let the recorders share the words they think of too, if they like.

3. Ask the students to identify the animals on the list that seemed to generate a response of dislike or fear and those that seemed to generate a popular and generally favorable response.

For Older Students

4. Divide the students into teams, with each team asked to find out more about one of the animals. In their research, they should find out whether the reactions of the students to the animals were based on accurate information and experiences, or were based on misinformation and inadequate information. Each team should prepare a report to present, including a description of the importance of the animal's contribution to the ecosystem.

5. Ask the students to present their reports. Talk about the values and contributions animals make—from ecological to aesthetic. (See Section II of these materials.) Identify animals, if any, where the students change their feelings based on having additional and more accurate information. Identify animals, if any, where the students don't change their views. Talk about "first impressions," contrasted with the importance of basing perceptions of animals, plants, people, ideas, etc., on the best information available.

For Younger Students

4. Ask everyone to help choose an animal that seems especially scary. Tell the students that this animal makes a contribution to the environment in which it lives—and you'll find out what! On your own, or with the help of a local resource person, find out more about the contributions this animal makes—and report back to the students! If possible, and safe, bring in the animal for the students to get to know. See Extensions below. Talk about "first impressions" contrasted with reactions based on knowing more about the animal.

Extensions

1. Bring in one or more live animals—harmless, but ones that students might not want to get close to. For example, a large non-poisonous snake, large non-poisonous spider, toad, or caterpillars. (Make sure the students do not hurt the animal, and that the animal cannot hurt the

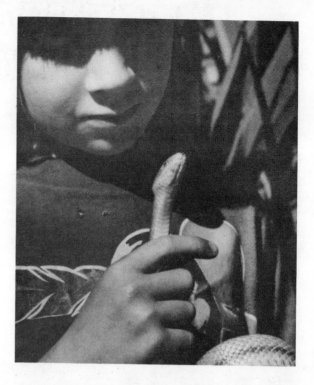

students. Care should be taken in advance of removing any animal from the wild to make sure that it can legally be moved. If the animal was taken from the wild for this activity, see that it is returned safely—exactly to the place where it was originally found if at all possible—at the conclusion of the activity. See the National Science Teachers' Association's "Code of Practice on Animals in Schools" in the Appendices for additional guidance concerning care of the animal.)

2. Draw a picture of a "favorite" animal and one of a "scary" animal. Write a short story about each—including the value of each.

3. Classify animal groups; e.g., mammals, spiders, insects. Which groups seem to be most "loved," "feared," etc.

Evaluation

What might someone say about a snake, a spider, a wolf, and a deer if they liked the animal? What might someone say about each of these animals if they did not like the animal?

Invent a story—that you tell or write—about someone's reactions to one of these animals: brown bat, bullfrog, spider, garter snake, marsh hawk. If the person is afraid of the animal, describe the importance of the animal to the environment. Try to persuade the person to change his or her "first impressions."

AND THE WOLF WORE SHOES

Objectives

Students will be able to: 1) distinguish between animals based on "real life" and those based on "make believe;" and 2) give examples of real and make-believe animals and their characteristics.

Method

Students divide books into those about "real" and those about "make-believe" animals, and then distinguish between real and fictitious animal characteristics.

Background

Portrayal of animals in books, fairy tales, comics, cartoons, movies, and other media may have an influence on the perceptions young people have of those animals.

The major purpose of this activity is to give students experience in actively distinguishing between realistic and fictionalized portrayal of animals in literature.

Materials

children's books and comics about or including animals, both real and "make-believe"

Procedure

1. Put out a small stack of books for every group of two to four students. Each stack should have some books that portray animals realistically, and some that give the animals unrealistic qualities, like human attributes.
2. Let the students look through the books in their stack, and try to divide them into **books about real animals,** or animals that act in real ways; and **books that are about imaginary or make-believe animals,** or even real animals that act in make-believe ways. If necessary, help the students to make their distinctions.
3. Work quietly with each of the groups to check their classifications into "real" and "make-believe."
4. Ask any volunteer from any of the groups to give an example of a "make-believe" animal. Talk about what makes that animal "make-believe."

5. Ask any volunteer from any of the groups to give an example of a "real animal." Talk about what makes that animal real.
6. Using a chart like the one below, ask the students for examples from the books in their stack to fill in the blanks in the chart:

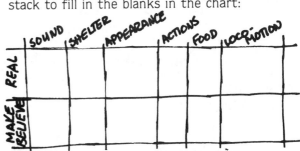

7. Talk with the students about their ideas concerning the importance of being able to tell when something is real and something is make-believe. Talk about why that is important to remember when learning about animals and how they live.

Extensions

1. Pick animals in your favorite stories, like *Stuart Little*, *Charlotte's Web*, *Wind in the Willows*, and *Winnie the Pooh*. Are these "real" or "make-believe?" In what ways?
2. Tally the animals in familiar stories. For example, how many mammals, birds, reptiles, amphibians, fish, insects, etc.?

Evaluation

Name three things a make-believe animal does that a real-life animal cannot do.

Age: Grades 2-5
Subjects: Language Arts, Reading, Science
Skills: analysis, application, classification, comparing similarities and differences, discussion, listing, observation, reading, small group work
Duration: two to three 20-minute periods
Group Size: small groups of two to four students
Setting: indoors (or outdoors)
Conceptual Framework Reference: V.A., V.A.4., V.A.5., V.A.6., V.B., V.B.1.
Key Vocabulary: real, imaginary

SATURDAY MORNING WILDLIFE WATCHING

Cartoons regularly portray animals in anthropomorphic fashion; that is, giving them human qualities or attributes. These may include walking upright, talking, thinking, and building things in a human manner. Many children and even adults come to see animals as being partly human as a result. This misimpression carries strong implications for inappropriate future actions toward wildlife and other animals.

The major purpose of this activity is for students to discriminate between realistic and unrealistic portrayals of animals in cartoons, and to make judgements about what they consider to be positive and negative influences of such portrayals in cartoons.

Objectives
Students will be able to: 1) discriminate between realistic and unrealistic portrayals of wildlife and other animals in cartoons; 2) identify possible influences on people from watching cartoons; and 3) make judgements about appropriate and inappropriate behaviors they think can result from cartoon watching.

Method
Students watch, report, discuss, and evaluate cartoons on television or in comics.

Background
NOTE: This activity can be used as an extension for "First Impressions" and "And the Wolf Wore Shoes."

Donald Duck and Mickey Mouse are two prime examples of universally recognized cartoon characters who have come to us from the animal world. Many other animated wildlife and domesticated animal characters can be found in television and movie cartoons. Saturday morning television watching in the United States offers a wide range of "wildlife watching."

Television animals—including mammals, birds, insects, reptiles, spiders, one-celled organisms, and fish—animated and not, both represent and misrepresent the real world. Sometimes the treatment of these animals models informed and responsible behaviors, and other times it exaggerates the worst of ways to treat wildlife and other animals.

Materials
access to television at home for cartoon watching, or comic books at school or at home

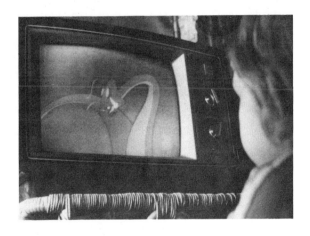

Age: Grades K—6
Subjects: Language Arts, Social Studies, Science
Skills: analysis, classification, comparing similarities and differences, discussion, evaluation, observation (older students: reporting, small group work, synthesis)
Duration: one or two 20—30-minute periods
Group size: any
Setting: indoors
Conceptual Framework Reference: V.A., V.A.4., V.A.5., V.A.6., V.B., V.B.1.
Key Vocabulary: wild, tame, influence, real, make-believe

Procedure

1. The required homework assignment is to watch Saturday morning cartoons! If that's not possible, weekday afternoon cartoons will serve. In homes where there is no television, students—with parent permission—might make arrangements to watch cartoons at a friend's house, or comic books may be substituted for cartoon watching on television. (The teacher might arrange to have a supply of comic books with animal characters available in the classroom. Daily newspapers, particularly the Sunday comics, have a range of animal characters as well.)

2. Ask older students to take notes as they watch the cartoons, preparing themselves to respond to questions such as the following: (Younger students should be given these questions to think about while they are watching. They could draw a few pictures to help themselves remember things they want to be able to talk about back in class.)

• Give the names of three animal characters in cartoons.

• Identify whether the real animals upon which these characters are based are wild or tame, or could be either (e.g., duck).

• Describe each of the three cartoon animals: what it looks like, where it lives, what it eats, how it behaves, how others treat it.

3. Back in class, ask the students to report on what they noticed about the ways animals are portrayed in cartoons. Identify whether the animal characters they watched were based on real live animals. If so, were the animals wild, or tame, or could be either? (See Section I, "What's Wild?") Pick one animal and chart information like the following (Older students can each pick one or more animals and construct such a chart). For example:

CARTOON ANIMAL	REAL ANIMAL	TAME	WILD	EITHER	CHARACTER-ISTICS SHOWN IN CARTOON
DONALD DUCK	DUCK			✓	TALKS, THINKS WEARS CLOTHES DRIVES, CRIES
YOGI BEAR	BEAR		✓		TALKS, THINKS ACTS LIKE HUMAN ....

Optional: Describe what an animal would look like, where it would live, what it would eat, how it would behave, and how others would treat it if it were real—contrasted with how it was portrayed in the cartoon.

4. Ask students to discuss the ways they think cartoons might influence people. What kinds of information do they provide? Is the information accurate and real, not real, or sometimes both? In what ways might cartoons encourage people to treat animals? Ask the students to think of one appropriate way to treat an animal, and one inappropriate way to treat an animal, that they have seen in cartoons. (Older students: conduct this discussion in small groups of two to four students. Ask each group to report.) After each of the groups has reported, make a master list for all the students to see and discuss that includes:

• real ways to treat real animals

• ways animals are treated in cartoons that they shouldn't be treated in real life

After looking at the completed lists, make any additions the students think are too important to leave off.

Extension or Variation

Watch a cartoon at school—like Donald Duck, Bugs Bunny, Scooby Doo, Sylvester the Cat, or Mickey Mouse. Bring in a tame real-life counterpart for the students to see, observe, and handle if possible, without harming the animal or the children. Discuss the similarities and differences between the "make-believe" and "real" animal.

Evaluation

Describe five things that cartoon animals can do or that can happen to cartoon animals that are not true for wild animals or for pets.

Describe three ways that cartoon-watching might affect how people act toward animals.

Make a suggestion for how to help people distinguish between real and "make-believe" in cartoons and comics. Explain your reasoning.

CARTOONS AND BUMPER STICKERS

Objectives
Students will be able to: 1) identify cartoons and bumper stickers that are designed to make a statement about some issue affecting natural resources and the environment; and 2) describe the influence of humor as a means for conveying information about such issues.

Method
Students find, analyze, and discuss cartoons and/or bumper stickers.

Background
Humor may be one of the most profound and subtle tools used in influencing people's attitudes. A good laugh can be worth a lot. The process can be an efficient and pleasant means by which to communicate information. It can diffuse differences of opinion, although—if the joke isn't appreciated—it can make the differences seem even greater.

Humorous media are diverse, including monologues by stand-up comics, movies, plays, books, articles, photographs, dance, paintings, commercials, and more. Two of the most popular forms used in contemporary culture to make a political statement quickly are bumperstickers and cartoons.

Stereotypes are a rich resource for the humorist. Stereotypes of animals are frequently used to get a laugh. These may be accurately founded, or sufficiently off-base to perpetuate misunderstanding. "The Big Bad Wolf" may be a classic case of the latter. Fine humor probably exploits realistic characteristics—based in the familiar—by comparison with what could be ridiculous or absurd.

Not all humor is actually meant to be funny. It may be poignant, angry, bitter, or sad. Political cartoonists, for example, frequently pull in a range of such emotions where, after the initial laugh, the response may be, "That's not so funny—it's true!"

The major purpose of this activity is to examine two forms of humorous media in contemporary culture—the bumper sticker and the cartoon. Both may be seen to have some influence on people's attitudes. Some of this influence affects people's perceptions of issues affecting natural resources and the environment.

Age: Grades 6—12
Subjects: Language Arts (Communication, Composition), Social Studies
Skills: analysis, discussion, evaluation, observation, reading
Duration: one 45—minute-period; time outside of class looking for cartoons or bumper stickers
Group size: any
Setting: indoors (may be done outdoors)
Conceptual Framework Reference: II.A.2., II.A.4., II.C., II.C.3., IV.E.11., V.A.4., V.A.5., V.A.6., V.B., V.B.1., VI.B., VI.B.1., VI.B.6.
Key Vocabulary: stereotypes, media, attitudes

Materials

marking pens and strips of construction paper for "bumper stickers," drawing materials for cartoons

Procedure

1. Ask the students to spend some time in the library or at home looking for examples of cartoons or bumper stickers dealing with an environment-related issue in some way. Each student should find and bring in at least one cartoon or bumper sticker. NOTE: Newspapers can be accumulated in the classroom for one month preceding this activity, providing an opportunity to track the conditions leading to some of the cartoons.

2. Ask the students to put their cartoons or bumper stickers up in the classroom where everyone can look at them and read them. Given time for everyone to examine them, questions such as these could be addressed:

- What major topics are the focus?
- What people, if any, are involved?
- What elements of the environment?
- What natural resources, if any?
- What purpose does the cartoonist or author of the bumper sticker seem to have in mind?
- What kinds of emotions seem to be elicited?
- What feelings?
- What actions, if any, do the cartoons or bumper stickers seem to be designed to promote?
- What influence, if any, do you think these will have?
- Who will they influence? In what ways?
- Do the cartoons or bumper stickers seem designed to mislead? Distort? Perpetuate negative stereotypes? If yes, in what ways?
- Do the cartoons or bumper stickers seem designed to inform? Serve accuracy? Encourage constructive, responsible attitudes? If yes, in what ways?

3. Ask the students to summarize their views of the effectiveness and appropriateness of use of media such as bumper stickers and cartoons to attempt to influence people's attitudes.

Extensions

1. Make your own cartoons and/or bumper stickers, inspired by some natural resource or environment-related issues. In fact, you can start this activity this way! (Put the cartoons in a mimeographed or book format—and/or print the bumper stickers—and use them as a source of income for some class project.)

2. Take existing magazine or newspaper photos, and write captions for them.

3. Include analysis of elements of propaganda; e.g., band wagon, in order to demonstrate components of persuasion.

4. Look for humor in other communications media involving natural resources, the environment or other issues; e.g., editorials (newspaper, radio, television, magazines), situation comedies, music, etc.

Evaluation

Describe the significance and usefulness of humor as a way to convey information about environmental topics. Describe its effectiveness as a way to influence opinion about environmental topics.

DOES WILDLIFE SELL CIGARETTES?

Objectives
Students will be able to: 1) identify use of wildlife and other natural images in advertising; 2) critically analyze and evaluate the purposes and impacts of use of such images in advertising; and 3) recommend appropriate uses of such nature-derived images in advertising.

Method
Students evaluate and categorize advertisements.

Background
A cowboy boot manufacturer ran a series of advertisements for its boots showing boot and wearers in conflict with wildlife. In this particular case, the wearer of the boot is about to kill a rattlesnake and a scorpion. There is a sense of drama in the ads—with the boot raised in the air, ready to flatten the offenders. The advertisement portrays a person in battle with forces of nature, and plays on the stereotype that some sort of virtuous strengths might accompany such actions. It also plays on the stereotype that some animals are worthless and should be killed.

In contrast with the images chosen by this advertiser, the rattlesnake and the scorpion could be portrayed as integral components of natural ecosystems in the western United States. The lustre and patterning of the snake's scales, and the grace in motion of both of the animals could be portrayed. Fewer boots would likely be sold—since the marketplace may still be steeped in too many stereotypes of such animals for the fears the first ad plays upon to be quieted. One could imagine, however, the kind of advertising campaign that an Edward Abbey, Annie Dillard, or Ansel Adams might design.

A substantial amount of contemporary advertising exploits people's biases and emotional responses to elements of nature. Advertising, by design, is intended to evoke a response—usually one that will lead to some action, as in buying the advertised product.

The major purpose of this activity is for students to evaluate the uses and impacts of nature-derived images in advertising.

Age: Grades 6-12
Subjects: Language Arts (Communication, Media, Semantics), Social Studies, Business Education
Skills: analysis, classification, discussion, evaluation, observation, reading
Duration: two 45-minute periods
Group size: any
Setting: indoors
Conceptual Framework Reference: V.A., V.A.1., V.A.2., V.A.3., V.A.4., V.A.5., V.A.6., V.B., V.B.1., V.B.2., VI.B., VI.B.3., VII.A., VII.A.1., VII.A.2., VII.A.3., VII.A.4., VII.B., VII.B.3., VII.B.6., VII.B.7.
Key Vocabulary: stereotype, metaphor, advertising

Materials

magazines or newspapers as a source of advertisements

Procedure

1. Ask each student to find at least one advertisement that makes use of some aspect of the natural environment in order to sell its product. The advertisement might show crystal waters, an eagle soaring the skies, an elk standing majestically, a forested hillside, snow-capped peaks, etc. Bring the advertisement to class. If the advertisement is on a billboard, perhaps the student can bring in a photo; if it is from a television commercial, a sketch and/or description will work. NOTE: The teacher may want to establish a file of such advertisements, laminating and keeping them for future use.

2. Working in small groups of two to four, ask the students to examine their advertisements according to questions such as the following:
• What is the advertiser's purpose?
• What image from nature is used to sell the product?
• Does the image have any direct relationship to the product?
• If yes, what is that relationship?
• If no, what purpose does the image serve for the advertiser in attempting to sell the product?
• What feelings, if any, does the ad elicit?
• What stereotypes, if any, does the ad encourage or build upon?
• If not a stereotype based on people's reactions to the image portrayed, does the ad portray a metaphor as a means to sell its product? If yes, describe its purpose. For example, a porcupine might be pictured alongside an electric shaver with, "Get rid of the bristles." The porcupine's quills serve as a metaphor for a stubbly beard.
• Does the advertisement seem to portray the natural image in a realistic way? Describe what seems realistic and what doesn't.
• Identify and describe any ways in which the ad might contribute to practices that could be wasteful, destructive, inappropriate, etc., in terms of wise use of natural resources and the environment.

3. According to criteria the students establish and explain, ask them to categorize the advertisements as appropriate or inappropriate means by which to attempt to sell products.

Extensions

1. For advertisements considered inappropriate; e.g., harmful or misleading, the students could:
a) redesign the advertisement to make it more appropriate in their judgement;
b) write a letter to the advertising company explaining their concerns;
c) write a letter to the managing editor of the magazine or newspaper in which the ad appeared;
d) write an editorial about the ad for a city or school paper; and
e) call other people's attention to the ad and the students' reasons for concern.

2. For advertisements considered appropriate; e.g., constructive or accurate, the students could:
a) write a letter to the advertising company in praise of the ad, explaining the bases for the students' opinions, etc.; and b) call other people's attention to the ad and the students' reasons for praise.

3. Design advertisements to encourage wise use of natural resources, and responsible actions toward people, wildlife and the environment. Send these ideas to the advertising departments of companies that would seem most able to benefit from them with courteous letters of concern and explanation.

Evaluation

Describe two examples of advertisements which portray animals in informative, accurate, or positive ways. Describe two examples of advertisements which portray animals in inaccurate, misleading, or negative ways.

How, if at all, does the use of wildlife help the image advertisers wish to portray?

How, if at all, do the ways wildlife are used in advertising help wildlife? Harm wildlife?

Describe a way that advertisers could use wildlife to the best advantage of both wildlife and the advertisers.

Describe what you believe would be the most responsible and appropriate ways to include wildlife in advertising, if at all.

THE POWER OF A SONG

Objectives
Students will be able to: 1) analyze popular music for environmental messages; and 2) interpret some influences of popular music and other art forms on people's environmental attitudes.

Method
Students listen to songs, analyzing lyrics.

Background
Art reflects the artist. It may also influence one who sees, hears, or feels the art. Social attitudes toward environmental issues are affected by the communications media, including the classical and popular arts.

Historical and contemporary artists have expressed their views about issues, including environmental issues, and have influenced others in the process. The Transcendentalists of the 19th century United States—including Bronson Alcott, Ralph Waldo Emerson, and Henry David Thoreau—influenced some of their generation through their teachings and writings. Their influence continues.

Artists may influence different people in different ways. For example, Joan Baez and Jane Fonda are recognized as talented artists both by people who strongly agree and those who strongly disagree with their political views on specific issues.

John Denver is a popular songwriter and performer who has consistently included what may be described as an environmental theme in much of his music, and has made a statement with his music to public officials as well as private citizens. For example, "Rocky Mountain High" has been identified by some as having had a role in the decision not to bring the Winter Olympics to Colorado in the early 1970s. These words in that popular song spoke to the issue:

*"Now his life is full of wonder
But his heart still knows some fear
Of a simple thing we cannot comprehend
Why they try to tear the mountains down
To bring in a couple more,
More people, more scars upon the land . . ."*

From "Rocky Mountain High." Words by John Denver. Music by John Denver and Mike Taylor. Copyright 1972, 1974 by Cherry Lane Music Company. All rights reserved.

Age: Grades 6—12
Subjects: Language Arts, Music, Social Studies
Skills: analysis, discussion, evaluation, listening
Duration: one 30 to 45-minute period
Group size: any
Setting: indoors or outdoors
Conceptual Framework Reference: I.D., II.A., II.A.1., II.A.2., II.A.3., II.A.4., V.A.4., V.A.5., V.A.6., V.B., V.B.1., V.B.2.
Key Vocabulary: music, song, lyrics, influence, attitudes

John Denver spoke and sang to the U. S. Congress in Washington, D. C., on the Alaska Land Bill issue. Mr. Denver was in favor of protection of Alaska lands as wilderness areas. He sang from a series of songs he has written about Alaska, including "To the Wild Country."

Mr. Denver has also spoken and sung before a meeting of the International Whaling Commission (IWC), in support of a cessation of world-wide commercial whaling. Mr. Denver sang, "I Want to Live."

His album, *Autograph*, features "The Mountain Song" by Tracey Wickland, written in criticism of the possible molybdenum mining of Mt. Emmons near Crested Butte, Colorado, by the AMAX Corporation.

These are a few examples of the strong environmental statements in one songwriter's lyrics and performances. Look also at the musical writings of: Dan Fogelberg, Jackson Browne, Joni Mitchell, Jimmy Buffett, Judy Collins, Stevie Wonder *(The Secret Life of Plants)*, and Paul Winter.

The major purpose of this activity is for students to examine the role of the arts and other communications media in influencing the attitudes of people. In this case, the influence is narrowed to people's attitudes about the environment and issues affecting it.

Materials radio, records, tapes, or song books as sources of popular songs

Procedure

1. Ask the students to listen to the lyrics of popular songwriters in contemporary music. Look for any artists who include lyrics with an environmental message.

2. Bring examples of music with an environmental message to class.

3. Listen to the lyrics. If possible, obtain written versions of the lyrics to at least one song. Identify the particular issues being written about in these songs. If necessary, find out more about the issues in order to attempt to better understand the perspective of the artist as conveyed in the lyrics.

4. The students may find that few contemporary artists include lyrics about environmental issues. Discuss why or why not. Talk about why some might and others don't. Discuss whether people are influenced by the work of popular artists, as in this case—by the lyrics of songwriters' songs.

Extensions

1. Invent your own environmental song! Songs could be about a specific issue, a favorite animal, or general feelings about the environment. Share your song with family, friends, other students at school, your local politician, or anyone else who might enjoy your musical expression!

2. Look for songs and lyrics with harmful environmental messages—from personal to planetary well-being. Look for songs and lyrics with upbeat, hopeful messages. Look for those that seem to be calling for action.

Evaluation

Describe the ways, if any, in which you believe music and other art forms influence people's attitudes. In what specific ways, if any, do such art forms affect people's attitudes toward the environment?

To be WILD

by Dale and Linda Crider

By DALE and LINDA CRIDER

WILDLIFE IN NATIONAL SYMBOLS

Background

The lion is a good example of how wildlife has value as a symbol in many different cultures. It might be a national symbol, serve as a logo for an organization or cause, represent a youth or civic group, or be included in the symbols of a religious group. The lion, for example, is associated with regal qualities—courage, nobility, strength, and power. According to *The Cousteau Almanac* by Jacques-Yves Cousteau and the Staff of the Cousteau Society (Doubleday and Company, New York, 1980, 1981), "Lions appear on the United Nations coats of arms of more countries than any other animal—on those of India, Kenya, Malawi, Singapore, Burma, Burundi, Senegal, Sri Lanka, Swaziland, and several European nations." *The Almanac* continues to point out that lions no longer exist in the wild in most of these countries. (page 365)

Many other species of fauna that have been honored by being made the national symbol of a country are on endangered species lists. Some examples are:

Chile	Andean condor
Dominican Republic	imperial Amazon parrot
Guatemala	quetzal bird
United States	bald eagle

The major purpose of this activity is for students to become acquainted with the diversity of countries and cultures that include wildlife in their symbols.

Objectives

Students will be able to: 1) identify wildlife used in national symbols; and 2) hypothesize reasons wildlife are used in national symbols.

Method

Students research national symbols and make posters to depict their findings.

Age: Grades 4—9
Subjects: Social Studies, World Geography, World History, Anthropology, Government, Art, Science
Skills: analysis, comparing similarities and differences, evaluation (formulating and testing hypotheses), media construction, research, synthesis
Duration: two 45-minute periods
Group Size: any
Setting: indoors
Conceptual Framework Reference: II.A., II.A.1., II.A.2., II.A.3., II.A.4., II.C., II.F., V.A., V.A.2., V.A.4., V.A.6., V.B., V.B.1., V.B.2., V.B.3.
Key Vocabulary: symbol

Materials
access to library reference materials, poster-making materials

Procedure
1. Generate hypotheses about national symbols. Where do they come from? What do they represent? Strength? Natural resources? Cultural heritage?
2. Ask each student or group of students to select one country to research—finding out its national symbol or symbols. The more countries, the more interesting the results will be. Sometimes the symbols will be stylized; sometimes they will be literal and based on actual plants and animals; and sometimes several symbols will be combined. Ask the students to include in their findings information about: the plants or animals the symbols are based upon; characteristics about those plants and/or animals; whether the plants or animals are in abundance, threatened, or endangered; what values they might represent that led to their use in the national symbol; etc.
3. Ask each student or group of students to make a poster depicting their findings.

4. Given hypotheses the students generate about why wildlife are used in national symbols, ask the students whether the findings of their research supported these hypotheses.

Extensions and Variations
1. Examine state, province, or community symbols (e.g., state birds, animals, plants, seal) instead of national symbols.
2. Look at trademarks, logos, and product advertising campaigns.
3. Try coats-of-arms!
4. Many schools use wildlife or other animal symbols as mascots or in school emblems, team names, etc. Survey the local community to compile a list of plants and animals used as school symbols. Contact the schools to find out how the names were chosen.

Evaluation
Identify five animals or wildlife signs that are used as national symbols. What might each species have been chosen to symbolize?

CHANGING ATTITUDES

Background
Attitudes toward wildlife, the environment, and appropriate uses of natural resources have changed and continue to change over time. They also vary greatly from culture to culture, within subgroups of a culture, within communities, and among individuals.

For example, 50 years ago in the United States, predator control was more or less taken for granted, especially in the western United States. There were efforts to control grizzly bears, cougars, coyotes, wolves, hawks, and even eagles. There was even a bounty on many of these animals, as they were considered a threat to domesticated animals and human safety.

Today, there is still much controversy around predator control. However, it is now more generally recognized that these animals have a role in the overall health of ecosystems. Most predators are now protected by law. In some circumstances, predator control is still being carried out, but the trend is toward limiting control to the individual predators causing damage.

The major purpose of this activity is for students to interview members of their community to gain information concerning changes in attitudes about wildlife and the environment.

Objectives
Student will be able to: 1) give an example of a change in attitudes related to a wild animal and/or the environment; and 2) describe factors which may influence change in attitude.

Method
Students design and conduct community interviews, compiling and summarizing findings.

Age: Grades 5—12
Subjects: Social Studies, Language Arts
Skills: analysis, comparing similarities and differences, evaluation, interviewing, public speaking, research, reporting, writing (questionnaire construction, compiling results)
Duration: minimum of three 45-minute periods; out-of-school time for interview
Group Size: any
Setting: indoors and outdoors
Conceptual Framework Reference: V.A., V.A.1., V A.2., V.A.3., V.A.4., V.A.5., V.A.6., V.B., V.B.1., V.B.2., VI.B., VI.B.1., VI.B.2., VI.B.3., VI.B.4., VI.B.5., VI.B.6., VI.C., VI.C.1., VI.C.2., VI.C.3., VI.C.4., VI.C.5., VI.C.6., VI.C.7., VI.C.8., VI.C.9., VI.C.10., VI.C.11., VI.C.12., VI.C.13., VI.C.14., VI.C.15., VI.C.16., VIII.A.1., VII.A.2., VII.A.3., VII.A.4., VII.A.5.
Key Vocabulary: attitude, interview, community

Materials

paper for taking notes and/or tape recorders and tape; information about local laws and regulations affecting wildlife

Procedure

1. Initiate a discussion with students about whether or not they think people's attitudes about some subjects might change, for example, over a generation. Fashion in clothing, furnishings, and food might serve as examples to begin. If not raised by the students, ask them if they can think of any examples of changes in attitudes about wildlife, the environment, uses of natural resources, lifestyles involving natural resources and the environment, etc. Discuss their suggestions, and list the topics they suggest.

2. Ask the students, working in groups of two to four students, to generate a list of questions relating to wildlife and the environment that they might ask of adults in their community. For example:

• How do you feel about wildlife?

• Does wildlife live in your neighborhood? Did wildlife live in your neighborhood when you were a child growing up? What kind?

• What animals, if any, are no longer seen that once were? What animals, if any, are more common now than they once were? What happened?

• What were some attitudes you remember having about wildlife when you were a youngster? Which of these attitudes, if any, have you changed during the past 20 years? What has caused these changes, if any?

• What laws, if any, did you know about when you were young that affect wildlife and the environment? What laws do you know about now which affect wildlife and the environment?

• What are the reasons for such laws? Do you think we need laws protecting wildlife, natural resources, and the environment? Why or why not?

• What general changes, if any, do you think there are in our society's attitudes toward wildlife and the environment—perhaps some changes you think are good and some you do not?

• What problems, if any, involving wildlife are you concerned about?

• What recommendations, if any, do you have about solving those problems?

3. Review the questions generated by each student or group of students before they conduct their interviews. Younger students' questions may be shorter and fewer.

4. Ask the students—working alone or in groups—to interview at least one long-living person in their community. The students should be prepared to take notes, or tape the interviews. You might instruct the students to be sure to take time to listen to any of the stories the people might tell that are slightly off the subject— out of courtesy, and also in recognition that the slightly divergent topics will also be interesting and pertinent in some ways.

5. Next, ask the students to "interview" each other or themselves. That is, record their own responses to these questions as a point of contrast for looking at some changes in attitudes. Optional: Add other people to interview, e.g., family members, wildlife managers, members of city council, farmers, ranchers, animal welfare group members, hunting club members, agricultural agents, private conservation group members, members of preservationist organizations, office workers, people at community gatherings, neighbors, or other community representatives. In choosing people to interview, encourage students to seek diversity and a range of perspectives.

6. Compile the results of the interviews. This might be done in a time-consuming way, where the interviews are transcribed, analyzed, summarized, and discussed. Shorter approaches may also be taken where each group of students is responsible for summarizing the results of their interviews in a one-page format, and then a small group of students volunteers to prepare a summary representing the findings of all of the students.

7. Discuss with the students their findings, including what changes in attitudes have taken place, if any, and what are some factors which might contribute to any changes in attitudes that they have identified.

Extensions and Variations

1. Expand the questions to include any changes in the local community and its natural resources. Include vegetation (e.g., what plants are here that were not here previously; what plants are no longer here); water (e.g., more less, or the same in available quantity, quality); human population; etc.

2. Identify a local controversial issue involving or affecting wildlife or other natural resources. Fact find. What is the issue? How did it develop? What attitudes and information are involved? What possible solutions are available?

3. Start this activity by pretending you were settlers living 100 or 200 years ago. What animals, if any, did you see? How did you live? Day to day, week to week, season to season? After imagining yourself at that time, discuss what your attitudes might have been toward natural resources and the environment. Might they be different today? In what ways?

4. Look in literature for information about historic wildlife populations in your area, the U.S., Canada, or other parts of the world. Compare to present-day populations.

5. Explore Native American Indian attitudes toward wildlife and other natural resources—in historic times, and today.

Evaluation

Describe how you think most people form their attitudes—what they know and how they feel—about animals.

Give two examples of attitudes about animals that you have reason to believe are based on wrong information or not enough information.

Give an example of a change in attitude about an animal that has occurred in this country during the past 100 years. How did this change come about?

If you were going to try to change someone's attitude about snakes from negative (they do not like snakes) to positive (snakes are okay and contribute to ecosystems), how would you do it?

TRENDS, ISSUES
AND
CONSEQUENCES

LEARNING TO LOOK, LOOKING TO SEE

Objectives
Students will be able to: 1) describe differences seen in an environment as the result of casual and detailed observation; and 2) give reasons for the importance of looking closely at any environment.

Method
Students list what they remember seeing in a familiar environment, check their accuracy, and discuss the results; and then apply their experiences and new skills to an unfamiliar outdoor setting.

Background
NOTE: Use this as an introductory activity, especially for activities requiring observation skills.

Looking and seeing can be entirely different things depending on who we are, where we are, what we are concerned about, and our purposes for looking. We look at our classrooms every school day, but if questioned about simple details, we may find that we are totally unaware of the existence of certain objects, colors, sounds, and textures. As we walk through our neighborhoods, we have probably learned to notice only those things which are necessary to aid us in getting to our destination. We may not see a soaring hawk although we may be looking

Age: Grades K—8
Subjects: Language Arts, Science, Social Studies, Art
Skills: description, discussion, listing, observation
Duration: 20—45 minutes
Group Size: any
Setting: outdoors and indoors
Conceptual Framework Reference: I., IV.D.2., IV.E.5., VI.B., VI.B.2.
Key Vocabulary: observe, see, appreciate, sense

at the sky. We may not see a community of ants even though we are looking at the sidewalk. During a walk in the woods, we may leave the trail to see a tree better—and then not see the wildflower we trample even though we are looking at the forest floor as we walk to the tree.

Each of us can train ourselves to see. It takes at least three elements: 1) to learn to be a careful observer, even if we do not have sight through our eyes; 2) to be aware of our surroundings; and 3) to recognize any part of our environment as being part of a larger whole. As we enter a forest community, for example, we are a part of that community as much as we are part of our school community or neighborhood community. At a level, we are members of any community we enter. As a result, we have an opportunity and an obligation to see our neighbors and to be responsible members of each community we enter.

The major purpose of this activity is for students to be given an opportunity to enhance their powers of "seeing."

Materials note pads

Procedure

1. Let's practice seeing things. Cover a desk, bulletin board, other wall display, or table with a large sheet before students come to class. Ask the students to write down all the things they thought they saw there before the area was covered. When their lists are completed, ask them to turn over their papers. Remove the sheet. On the backside of their first lists, have the students make a new list of what they see. What kinds of things did they remember? What kinds of things were most often missed? Let them come up with reasons why they think this happened.

2. Have the students go outdoors and pick one spot near a tree, a fence, a brook, a field, etc. Each student should find a spot alone, at least 50 feet from the closest human neighbor. Allow 15 minutes for this solo, or approximately five minutes for younger students. **The students should look in a broad sense of the word—seeing, touching, listening, and smelling.** They should record everything they "see." (See "Wild Words" for a journal-making activity to use in recording their observations.) Fifteen minutes will provide time for an initial spurt of observations, a plateau, and then another spurt as they begin to realize how much they missed the first time around. (Younger children need only record in their minds; no need to write.)

3. Bring the students together for a discussion, centering on the process they went through as well as their list of sightings. Did they focus on any one area for a long time? Did they continue to shift their gaze? How did they focus their hearing and smelling? Cupping hands around their ears to simulate animal hearing has a dramatic effect on abilities to hear. Blindfolding seems to cause a compensation toward better hearing as well. Moistening the undersurface of the nose and the entire upper lip area increases smelling ability. Note: Our role as teachers is a difficult one in that we are most effective when we teach our students **how** to look and see without telling them **what** to see.

4. Talk with the students about the joy and importance of seeing as fully as we can—as a way of appreciating, respecting, and learning more about the world in which we live. Older students: Discuss the importance of careful observation of our environments beginning with the basis for our fundamental life support systems—air, water, soil, plants, animals.

5. Optional, with older students: Talk about the process of continuing to develop our senses as being a life-long process for each of us. We are always learning, and can learn even more. Sensing more in our surroundings can help us detect changes in our environment, cause us to become curious and ask questions, and help us to become better, more aware and informed decision-makers.

Extensions

1. Blur your eyes. What patterns and shapes do you see?
2. What else did you see? Any living things? What were they? Were they plant or animal?
3. Categorize what was observed as living/non-living—and/or as animal, plant, mineral.
4. Play the game "Animal, Vegetable, Mineral" or "What Am I?"

Evaluation

Think of three of your friends. Without looking at them, write down the color of their eyes, and a description of what they were wearing last time you were together. Check to see if you were right.

TOO CLOSE FOR COMFORT

Objectives

Students will be able to: 1) describe possible negative consequences for people and wildlife under conditions of crowding; and 2) identify ways people can behave in order to reduce negative consequences of crowding for wildlife.

Method

Students experiment with physical distance and levels of comfort in humans, estimate appropriate distances between humans and wildlife under various conditons, hypothesize about indicators of animal discomfort, and summarize reasons to avoid animal discomfort through crowding.

Background

Sometimes wildlife seems to want to say, "Don't get too close!" From a tree branch a bird watches a person approaching; when he or she gets too close, the bird takes flight.

Animals are often threatened when crowded by humans, even though the humans may mean no harm and merely want to observe the animal. Animals may display their discomfort by fleeing, grinding teeth, coiling, hissing, stomping feet, snarling, coughing, or woofing. Flight is the usual way of showing stress. Noises may come when an animal is ready or threatening to attack.

Wildlife photographers have learned that when the wildlife they are photographing begins to act strangely, they have probably gotten too close. Animals may run away if you are outside a certain distance. At a closer distance, they may charge or in other ways respond to the threat of human presence by aggressive behavior.

One way of understanding the way wildlife acts is to recognize that many animals have certain distances that they keep from their own kind. Wolves may demand large areas of range which no other wolf outside of their own pack (family) may enter. Studies show that certain kinds of finches will always leave a certain distance between themselves when they perch on a telephone wire or fence line.

When crowding occurs, many animals react with bizarre, aggressive, disordered behavior, and may develop skin diseases like mange. They may adjust to the crowded conditions, over time, by ceasing reproduction.

In the United States, great blue heron rookeries have been disturbed by the mere presence of people. Rookeries are the birds' breeding grounds. Herons live most of the year as lone individuals; when they come together to breed— to go through courtship and nesting—they experience stress, if disturbed by humans. Under circumstances of stress, they may not breed, may lay few eggs, or may abandon the rookery, leaving eggs or young birds to perish. At a heron rookery in Colorado, wildlife managers have established a 1000 foot limit; no human disturbance is allowed close to the rookery. They are not sure this limit will save the rookery from development pressures, but they know any closer range would certainly disrupt the rookery. The major purpose of this activity is for students to recognize the possible negative consequences for people and wildlife as a result of conditions of crowding.

Materials

none needed

Age: Grades K—7
Subjects: Science, Social Studies, Language Arts
Skills: hypothesis-formation, inference
Duration: ten to 30-minute class period, depending on age of students
Group Size: any
Setting: indoors or outdoors
Conceptual Framework Reference: I.D., VI.A., VI.A.2., VI.A.3., VI.A.4., VI.A.5., VI.B., VI.B.1., VI.B.2., VI.B.3., VI.B.4., VI.B.5., VI.C., VI.C.1., VI.C.2., VI.C.5., VI.C.16., VI.D., VI.D.1., VII.A., VII.A.1., VII.A.2., VII.A.3., VII.A.4., VII.B., VII.B.1., VII.B.2., VII.B.3., VII.B.7.
Key Vocabulary: crowding, disturbance, safety, behavior

Procedure

1. Introduce the concept of discomfort from crowding by asking one student to stand in front of the class. Approach the student slowly, asking the student to tell you when your closeness makes him or her begin to feel uncomfortable. Ask the class whether they allow strangers to approach them as close as they do their friends or family. How do they feel in the middle of strangers on a crowded bus or elevator? Discuss what physical reactions they have in some kinds of crowded conditions, like avoidance of eye contact, nervousness, sweaty palms, etc.

2. Introduce the idea that animals in the wild might also be uncomfortable when approached by strangers.. Talk about why they might be uncomfortable; e.g., fear of predation, need to protect young. Discuss what other conditions might increase or decrease wariness—such as ability to fly away, climb quickly, run fast, swim fast; animal size; whether the animal is alone or with a group, is on a nest, or has young.

3. Have the students make a list of animals they are likely to encounter in the environment, and have them estimate what distance should be maintained from each animal species—both for reasons of personal safety, and for the comfort and safety of the animal. Emphasize that these are just estimates. As a rule, it is better to stay farther away than you think might be necessary than to get too close.

4. Have the students hypothesize about animal behaviors which might indicate discomfort, such as foot stomping, teeth grinding, raising up on hind feet, nervous looking around and eventually flight. Optional: Students can mime or role play such situations, and have their classmates guess what animal they are, in what situation.

5. Discuss ways in which wildlife harassment might occur unintentionally, such as flying too close in small airplanes, getting too close to photograph, calling or heckling for animals to react (especially at zoos), hiking near a nesting site, and using loud vehicles near baby animals, or in places where animals are unaccustomed to seeing them. Explain the possibility that there are certain times of the year when some animals are more sensitive to intrusion, such as at mating season, and during severe climatic conditions, such as heavy winters or drought. What ways can communities minimize disturbances? What can individual people do? Summarize reasons it is important to minimize such disturbance from people for wildlife.

Extensions

1. Draw life-sized outlines of some of the animals and mount them on an outside wall of the school building. Break into small groups; have each group establish a distance from each species which the group feels would be far enough for the animal not to be threatened by the pressure of a person. Using measuring tapes, each group should measure the established "comfort zone" for each species, under different conditions— and then present their suggested distances for the animal comfort zones. Verify the accuracy of these distances under these general conditions by contacting a wildlife resource person. Discuss whether a general rule is apparent about the relationship of the size of the comfort zone to conditions such as size of the animal, presence of young, ability to flee, single or group animal species, etc.

2. What are reasons it is important to minimize such disturbances for domesticated animals, like pets, dairy cows, etc.?

3. What are reasons it is important to minimize such disturbances for people? What actions can we take to do so? With what consequences?

Evaluation

What behaviors might indicate a person speaking in front of a group is nervous?

How might a mother dog let you know that you are getting too close to her and her pups?

Rank order the following, from animals you could get closest to without harming to those you should stay the furthest away from: a heron rookery during breeding season, young raccoons seen in a forest, a large garter snake in the grass of your yard, honey bees around their hives, frogs in a freshwater pond in the summer.

Describe negative results of crowding for humans. Describe negative results of crowding for animals.

SHRINKING HABITAT

Objectives
Students will be able to: 1) describe some effects of human development of land areas on plants and animals previously living in the area; 2) evaluate the importance of suitable habitat for wildlife; and 3) recognize that loss of habitat is generally considered to be the most critical problem facing wildlife today.

Method
Students simulate a process of land development in a physically-involving activity.

Age: Grades 4-7
Subjects: Social Studies, Science
Skills: application, comparing similarities and differences, description, discussion, evaluation, generalization, kinesthetic concept development, observation, synthesis
Duration: one 45-minute period or longer
Group Size: minimum of six students, with one developer, one carnivore, three herbivores, and one tree
Setting: indoors or outdoors, large area with room for people and props
Conceptual Framework Reference: I.A., I.B., I.C., I.C.1., I.C.2., I.C.3., I.C.4. I.D., II.B.2., III.C.1., III.D.2., III.D.3., III.D.4., IV.C., IV.C.1., IV.C.2., IV.C.3., IV.E.10., V.A., VI.A., VI.A.2., VI.A.3., VI.A.4., VI.A.5., VI.B., VI.B.1., VI.B.2., VI.B.3., VI.B.4., VI.B.5., VI.C., VI.C.2., VI.C.12, VI.C.16., VI.D., VI.D.1., VII.A., VII.A.1., VII.A.2., VII.A.3., VII.A.4., VII.B., VII.B.1., VII.B.2., VII.B.3., VII.B.4., VII.B.5., VII.B.6., VII.B.7.
Key Vocabulary: habitat, food chain, development, herbivores, carnivores, vegetation, consequences

Background

All around us, and all over the planet, wildlife habitat is being lost. Whenever an area of land is paved for a shopping center, divided and excavated for homes for people, and sometimes when it is plowed to grow a crop—small animals lose their homes, and frequently their sources of food and water. As these small animals disappear, so too do the larger animals that previously depended upon the smaller animals in the food chain as a source of food. Animals that cannot tolerate human intervention may also disappear without any direct relationship to the food chain. (For example, see "Too Close For Comfort.")

Students can observe this phenomenon near their homes and schools, or at least in their region. This process is happening in large ecosystems and small, all over the earth.

For example, many wetlands on the planet have been filled in and drained to make land for farming and homes. When they are filled in, many kinds of water birds, reptiles, amphibians, crustaceans, and other life forms—including a wide variety of vegetation—are lost. Sometimes the animal forms can move on; most often they cannot.

Some of the tropical forests of the planet have become extremely vulnerable in recent years. Scientists estimate that huge numbers of plant and animal forms exist in these forests that have not even been identified as yet. They are tremendously important sources of the earth's biological diversity. In fact, some scientists warn that as these genetic pools are reduced, the flexibility and thus capacity to survive of the remaining plants and animals on earth will ultimately be reduced.

The major purpose of this activity is for students to simulate some of the potential impacts of land development on wildlife and its habitat, to recognize that this process is one that is taking place in areas all over the planet, and to understand that loss of habitat is generally considered to be the most critical problem facing wildlife today.

Materials

green and blue construction paper; classroom desks, tables or chairs; five or six large bedsheets or blankets for a student group of about 25

Procedure

1. Review with the students the elements necessary for a habitat (food, water, shelter, and space arranged suitably for the particular animal). (See Components of Habitat in the "Cross References.") After some discussion to make sure that the elements of habitat are clearly in mind, tell the students that in this activity they will be simulating wildlife in its habitat.

2. Divide the students into four groups: **herbivores, carnivores, vegetation** (trees, shrubs, grasses, etc.), and people who will be **land developers.** If the students are not familiar with the terms "herbivore" and "carnivore," provide them with working definitions of those terms (herbivore—a plant-eating animal; carnivore—a meat-eating animal; and although not needed for this activity, omnivore—an animal that eats both plants and animals). Plan for three times as many herbivores as carnivores with a small number of developers in proportion to the other two groups. The numbers (amount) of vegetation may vary. For example, two developers, three carnivores, nine herbivores, and six trees or bushes (vegetation).

3. Establish a large area—either in the classroom, with tables, chairs, and desks moved to the sides of the room, or outside—that can be used to simulate the wildlife habitat area before development. The "land developers" are to stay on the sidelines at this time, simply observing the undeveloped land and its wildlife inhabitants— or meeting on their own, nearby, to make plans for development. In fact, they can make their entrance rather suddenly once the wildlife habitat has been established—simulating the arrival of heavy construction equipment.

4. Provide each "herbivore" with:

• two desks or chairs to use as "shelter" (or string or hula hoops);

• three pieces of green construction paper to represent food;

• one piece of blue construction paper to represent water; and

• some of the vegetation portrayed by students.

Provide each "carnivore" with:

• one desk or chair to use as a "lair" (or string or hula hoop);

• space equivalent to that used by three herbivores;

• three herbivores as a potential food source;

• one piece of blue construction paper to represent water; and

• some of the vegetation portrayed by students.

5. Ask the "herbivores" to arrange the food, water, and shelter—including the students who are "vegetation"—in a space to represent their habitat. Once the herbivores have arranged their habitat, ask the "carnivores" to move into the area to establish their lairs and water sources, keeping an eye on the herbivores as possible food sources. For added interest, suggest that the students identify what particular kind of animal they are, and role-play its characteristics. (This phase takes about ten minutes, with the developers planning while the herbivores and carnivores arrange their habitat.)

6. Once all the animals are established in their habitats, it is time for the developers to enter the picture. These developers have been given the opportunity to create a housing and shopping area. (They may use three to seven minutes to construct their development, explaining their actions as they take them.) They are restricted in how much space they can use. They may use the space equivalent to that used by three herbivores. The developers may use the sheets and blankets to build their development. They may remove trees, represented by students (without physically hurting the students), shelter, (represented by desks), food and water.

7. Once they have constructed their development, engage all of the students in a discussion of what happened. What action took place? With what consequences? Would or did any animals die? From what causes? Could the developers have done anything differently to change the consequences? Could they have developed several scattered small areas instead of one large area, or vice versa, with what effects? Would it have reduced negative consequences for wildlife if they put the development in a different area of the habitat? Rather than negative consequences,

were there positive consequences? If so, what were they? How were they achieved? Ask the students to consider and discuss what seemed realistic about the activity, and what did not. For example, sometimes development can take place that enhances the area for some kinds of wildlife. Often, however, it will not be the same kinds of wildlife that were in the area before development. Planners and developers can sometimes add to the vegetation in an area, creating additional shelter and food for some kinds of wildlife, and make water sources available under some conditions, if there is insufficient water in the area.

8. Ask the students to summarize some of the possible impacts on wildlife from human activities like development of land areas. Are there places in your community where wildlife habitat has been lost by human development? Are there places where wildlife habitat has been enhanced by human activity? What choices, if any, are there to development of previously undeveloped areas? What trade-offs are involved; for example, in developing vacant areas within communities rather than undeveloped areas outside of communities? If development does take place, what kinds of actions can people take to minimize the negative consequences for wildlife, vegetation, and other elements of the environment? What about possible economic costs? Social costs? Ecological costs? Aesthetic costs? etc. Discuss loss of habitat as something that is affecting wildlife all over the planet. Ask the students to summarize the importance of suitable habitat for wildlife. Discuss the students' concerns and recommendations.

Extensions

1. Conduct this activity twice, with the students trading roles the second time. When the former wildlife become land developers, they could see if they could produce a development plan that could benefit the area for people and wildlife in some ways. The activity can also be conducted to show differences between developing the entire area—with likely loss of all wildlife in the area—to developing only part of the area, with some wildlife likely to survive.

2. Ask students to complete the following sentence, and discuss their response: "If I were going to build a house for my family in a previously undeveloped area, I would . . ."

Evaluation

Name and describe three animals or plants which used to live in your area, but no longer do.

Describe the changes that seem most responsible for eliminating each of these plants or animals.

Suggest and evaluate the advantages and disadvantages, if any, of possible actions that could have been taken to prevent the elimination of these plants or animals from the area.

Name one kind of wildlife that would do better, and one kind of wildlife that would do worse, in areas in which humans cut down a forest and planted grass; dammed a creek to flood a valley; put in a housing development with large lawns and many shrubs; built a city on a lakeshore with crowded skyscrapers.

MIGRATION BARRIERS

Objectives
Students will be able to: 1) define migration as it relates to wildlife; 2) describe possible impacts on wildlife migration patterns as a result of human activities; and 3) give an example of the importance of land-use planning as it affects people, wildlife, and the environment.

Method
Students draw murals showing deer migration routes and the consequences of development of a highway through the area.

Background
The major purpose of this activity is for students to recognize some of the probems that can arise as a result of human actions affecting aspects of the environment. In this case, road-building through a deer migration route is used as an example.

Materials
drawing materials; large butcher or poster paper; background information about deer or other animals in your region that migrate seasonally on land; information about the animals' habitat needs. Check with local wildlife specialists for assistance.

Age: Grades 4—6
Subjects: Social Studies, Science
Skills: analysis, application, comparing similarities and differences, description, drawing, evaluation, generalization, media construction, observation, problem-solving, reporting, small group work, synthesis, visualization
Duration: one or two 30—45 minute periods
Group Size: any; small groups for mural-making
Setting: indoors or outdoors
Conceptual Framework Reference: VI.A., VI.A.2., VI.A.3., VI.A.4., VI.A.5., VI.B., VI.B.1., VI.B.2., VI.B.3., VI.B.4., VI.B.5., VI.B.6., VI.C., VI.D., VI.D.4., VII.A.1., VII.A.2., VII.A.3., VII.B., VII.B.1.
Key Vocabulary: migration, land-use planning, consequences

Procedure

1. Divide the students into small working groups, with each group provided with drawing materials and a large piece of butcher or poster paper. Ask each group to draw a mural of a deer habitat (or habitat for another migrating land animal in your area) that includes a variety of environments from mountains to valleys. The deer herd in this habitat lives in the mountains in the summer and moves or migrates to the valleys in the winter. Ask the students to put in appropriate vegetation, water sources, and pictures of other animals in addition to the deer that might live in this environment. The students may choose the time of the year to be represented in their mural. Ask them to put their herd of deer in the area they think the deer would most likely be living at that time of year. Also ask them to draw a set of arrows to show the path they think the deer would likely take each year during the time they move from one feeding area to another; for example, from the mountains to the valleys as winter nears, and from the valleys to the mountains in the summer. (Note: Get background on the animal habitat characteristics and migration patterns in your area or region, if possible.)

2. Once the murals are complete, either ask the students to describe what they have included in their murals, pointing out the deer travelway... OR...simply move on to the next step in this activity. The next step is to tell the students that a major highway has been proposed for the area they have drawn. The highway is to be built somewhere in between the mountains and the valleys that the deer travel to and from in their annual migration. An Environmental Impact Statement has been done which indicates that it is possible to build the highway in ways that can minimize the negative consequences for wildlife and other elements of the natural environment. The Environmental Impact Statement is being contested in court, therefore it is not clear whether the highway will actually be built. Introduce the concept of land-use planning to the students. Each group is attempting to plan for the land use in their area, represented by their mural. Ask each group to discuss how they could draw a highway on their mural in a way that they think would have the least possible negative consequences. How could the highway be built in a way that would do the least harm to the environment and its wildlife? They could consider impact to the environment during the actual road construction, ways to minimize run-off and erosion, replanting any areas where vegetation is destroyed in the building, and replanting with what kinds of plants. Ask them to pay particular attention to the herd of deer and its migration pattern, trying to figure out a way for the deer to move from their summer to their winter ranges and back again. NOTE: Sometimes this can be done by buildng underpasses or overpasses for the deer to use so that they don't actually have to try to cross the highway. Sometimes the highway can be built in such a way that the migration route is avoided entirely. Groups that achieve a consensus—making a land-use planning decision—can draw the highway on their murals.

3. Ask each group to report. What land-use decisions did they make? With what consequences? To the deer? Other wildlife? Vegetation? Soil? People? Ask them to identify solutions they think would be acceptable, those that would be unacceptable, and for what reasons. What about convenience to people in transportation? Other possible questions include: What about costs to the builder of the highway? Who pays the builder? Is it actually taxpayer dollars? What are some of the factors to be considered in land-use decisions?

Extensions and Variations

1. Pick an actual situation in your region or anywhere on the planet—with similar concepts.
2. Use a topographical map rather than a mural. Provide each person with copies of the map. Compare similarities and differences in solutions, all working from the same visual reference (the maps).
3. Represent the area in question in three dimensions using clay, papier mache', or even mud!

Evaluation

Define animal migration.

Name three animals that migrate. For each, describe a human activity that might interfere with migration.

Offer one or more suggestions for decreasing the negative impacts of human land use on animal migrations. Explain the reasoning behind your suggestions.

TO ZONE OR NOT TO ZONE

Objectives

Students will be able to: 1) identify social and ecological considerations where human uses of land conflict with each other and with wildlife habitat needs; and 2) describe the importance of land-use planning.

Method

Students role-play a meeting of a county commission pertaining to a land-use issue.

Background

This activity uses a role-play strategy for study of the importance of land-use planning. It emphasizes the complexities of decision-making where people of different points of view are involved.

The major purpose of this activity is for students to understand the importance as well as some of the complexities of land-use planning and decision-making.

Background for Students

Land use decisions affecting wildlife have become a familiar issue where housing developments are concerned. The following is an imaginary conflict that corresponds to some real life dilemmas:

Pleasant Valley is a ranching-logging community on the western slope of the Snow mountains. Silverton—a town of 20,000—is the trade center of the area. Cramer Lumber Company is expanding its operations. This will provide 250 new jobs,

but housing is very limited. A 200 home subdivision has been proposed for an 80 acre plot of undeveloped land on the south edge of town. This forested area is bordered by Rattlesnake Creek on the west. Rattlesnake Creek provides excellent fishing for rainbow trout. Fifty-three species of birds have been sighted in this area, including some rare species. In the spring and fall, the area is used by migrating waterfowl and deer feed in the area. Many nongame species such as ground squirrels and pocket gophers inhabit this land. This 80 acre plot is currently zoned for agriculture and forestry and would have to be rezoned as residential by a vote of the county commissioners. The subdivision would be on a central water system, but each home would have its own septic system.

Age: Grades 6-9
Subjects: Social Studies, Science, Environmental Problems, Language Arts, Speech
Skills: analysis, application, comparing similarities and differences, description, discussion, evaluation, generalization, public speaking, reporting, research, snythesis, writing
Duration: three 45-minute periods
Group Size: large group; depends on students assuming roles
Setting: indoors
Conceptual Framework Reference: I.D., II.A., II.B., II.C., II.C.2., II.C.3., II.D., II.D.1., II.D.2., II.D.3., II.E., II.E.1., II.E.2., II.E.3., II.F., IV.F.11., V.A.5., V.B., V.B.1., V.B.2., VI.A., VI.A.1., VI.A.2., VI.A.3., VI.A.4., VI.A.5., VI.B., VI.B.1., VI.B.2., VI.B.3., VI.B.4., VI.B.5., VI.B.6., VI.C., VI.C.1., VI.C.2., VI.C.6., VI.C.7., VI.C.12., VI.C.16., VI.D., VI.D.1., VII.A., VII.A.1., VII.A.2., VII.A.3., VII.A.4., VII.B., VII.B.1., VII.B.5., VII.B.6., VII.B.7.
Key Vocabulary: land-use planning

Materials
copies of role descriptions; props optional for role-play; room set up for hearing

Procedure

1. Provide the students with copies of the background information concerning this hypothetical land-use dilemma.

2. Thirteen students will be assigned (or volunteer) for roles as county commissioners, local residents, and business people—with each receiving a card describing his or her situation. The rest of the students will have roles as news reporters, outside experts, concerned citizens, etc. These students may ask questions of people testifying at the hearing. They can be required to write letters to the editor or one of the commissioners in support of a particular point of view; write news articles about the hearing or personal impact stories describing the potential consequences for local workers, residents, school children, etc.; prepare technical reports as researchers, etc. Every student should have a role—either as one of the 13 people preparing testimony for the hearing, or as active observers who prepare written questions, reports, or news articles.

3. To set the stage for the simulation, have each of the 13 participants read their personal data cards. The other students should select their role; they do not need personal data cards, although they may write their own. Students should then be given homework time to prepare their presentations as members of the inquiry; or questions, letters to the editor, and news stories as public observers. Students should be encouraged to improvise in developing their presentations and questions.

4. The day (or days) of the hearing, the chairperson of the commission is to run the meeting. It is up to him or her to maintain order. All participants must be recognized by the chairperson before they speak. After all those presenting prepared testimony have spoken and have been questioned—the reporters, researchers, and concerned citizens will be asked to read their statements (articles, reports, letters to the editor, etc.). This is an excellent way to start the final day of the simulation. After all testimony, questions, and statements, the commissioners vote and give the reasons for their decisions.

5. Suggested time line for this activity:

Day 1	Read background information and select roles (approximately 30—45 minutes)
homework	Prepare presentations
Day 2	Conduct hearing (approximately 30—45 minutes)
Day 3	Continue hearing, including reading of news items and letters to the editor; vote; discuss results

6. After the hearing and vote, discuss questions such as the following:

• What are some things we have learned about land-use decision making?

• What factors influence land-use decision making and planning?

• What differences and similarities were there between how decisions were made in this activity and how they happen in our community? Other areas? Other parts of the world?

• What responsibilities do we as citizens have in helping to make land-use decisions?

• Why are land-use decision making and land-use planning important for people, wildlife, and the environment?

Extensions and Variations

1. Have students identify a wildlife issue in their local area, gather data, and develop their own simulation.

2. Alter the role descriptions and repeat the simulation.

3. Use copies of a topographical map as common references for everyone.

4. Bring in real expert witnesses; e.g., local people who can add their perspectives and expertise. If you do, make an effort to get a balanced range of points of view rather than hearing from only one perspective on the issues involved.

5. Adapt this activity to a debate format.

Evaluation

What are the purposes of zoning laws? How are zoning laws passed? Give an example of how a zoning law might be good for wildlife. Describe how citizens can get their opinions considered in land-use decision making processes.

Personal Data Cards

LEN OR LINDA OLSEN, REALTOR (COUNTY COMMISSIONER)

You started your business in Silverton five years ago. Your business is doing well, but you have difficulty relating to the "old timers" like Thompson. Your real estate company is not developing this property. You have some question regarding the credibility of the developer, but you generally vote in favor of development.

DAVID OR WANDA DRESSER, MERCHANT (COUNTY COMMISSIONER)

You are 46 and own a furniture store. You would like to sell furniture to all the new home owners. You can also see the value of the 80 acres left in a natural and undeveloped condition. You are wondering if there might be another site for the development of this housing area.

JACK OR JANET THOMPSON, RANCHER (COUNTY COMMISSIONER)

You are the third generation to run the "Rolling T" Cattle Company. You are proud to tell people that your grandfather was one of the first to settle in this valley. Your spread covers 800 acres and you have grazing rights to surrounding U.S. Forest Service land. You resent the increase in population of the area and, although you are involved in community affairs, you resent individuals moving into the area who do not share your values. Last winter, snowmobiles cut your fences three times and in one case your cattle wandered onto the highway and caused a traffic accident.

BOB OR BETSY HENDERSON, FARMER (COUNTY COMMISSIONER)

You own and operate a large farm near the south edge of town and adjacent to the 80 acre plot in question. You have been interested in the possibility of buying the land to add to your family's agricultural operations. You've a keen interest in the environment, making efforts to employ agricultural practices that benefit wildlife and minimize damage to other natural resources. Since you are an adjacent landholder, you may need to disqualify yourself from participation as a Commissioner in this meeting.

ELMER OR BERTHA WILLAS, RESIDENT

You are a 68 year old "old timer" living on the land proposed for the subdivision. You have lived on Cornwall's land for 45 years, built a home there with Cornwall's permission, and have raised seven children. You raise bees and chickens out back and your garden covers one-half acre. You are settled in the middle of the area proposed for the housing development and there is no question that you will have to be evicted and your house torn down. You have no legal claim to any of the land, but have nowhere else to go.

JAMES OR ERMA "FROSTY" WHITE, SNOWMOBILER

You are 30 years old and have just been elected president of the "Rattlers," the local snowmobile club and you feel that you should defend their interests in the area. The cost of gas is high, and your club doesn't want to have to drive long distances to ride snowmobiles. You would like to open a snowmobile repair shop, but you might get a job at the new lumber mill.

TOM OR MARY BENNETT, PRESIDENT OF CHAMBER OF COMMERCE

This is your tenth year as president of the Chamber of Commerce. You own a grocery store in the middle of town. Your greatest concern is the weak business climate in your community. The Chamber recently hired Smith & Wittigen, a business consulting firm, to evaluate the retail potential of Pleasant Valley. Their findings indicate that the business community has overbuilt. Your profits and those of your fellow merchants have been steadily declining. You see this new lumber mill as the salvation of your business.

OSCAR OR JAN SPARROW, LOCAL AUDUBON PRESIDENT

You represent over 300 active Audubon members, and are director of the annual bird count competition. You have a list of 15 rare bird species found in the Rattlesnake Creek area. You are 37 years old, and work at the lumber mill.

GEORGE OR ALICE LONG WINGS, NATIVE AMERICAN INDIAN LEADER

You have an interest in the sanctity of the area in question as it is an ancient ceremonial site for your tribespeople.

CHARLIE OR CHARLOTTE JACKSON, HUNTER

You are a 53 year old "old timer" and an avid hunter and fisher. You have four boys and hunting has always been an important family activity. You are an influential member of Ducks Unlimited, and the 80 acres proposed for development contains one of the prime duck hunting areas close to town.

WALLACE OR WILMA CRAMER, LUMBER MILL OWNER

You own the nearby lumber mill. Operations have expanded and you need inexpensive housing for new employees coming to the area. The wood milled is used locally and transported throughout the state. It provides an important source of income to the town.

HARVEY OR GLADYS CROW, BANKER (COUNTY COMMISSIONER)

You are 50 years old, and, as a banker, are willing to finance new home loans. You are an art collector and former president of the local chamber of commerce. You also love birdwatching and fishing.

HAROLD OR CORNELIA CORNWALL, LAND OWNER

You are a 63 year old retired business person. You want to sell your land, move to Palm Springs, and live happily ever after under sunny skies. You want cash, but your asking price is very reasonable. You own 80 acres of prime wild land south of town. You are an active member of several animal welfare organizations, and are vocal in your opposition to hunting.

MARTIN OR ETHEL HIGGINS, DEVELOPER

You are a big time developer in the area and can afford to buy the land outright. You will make a substantial profit if the housing that is needed for the lumber mill employees is built. You are successful and fairly competent, but you have been criticized more than once for a lack of attention to landscape detail and design.

DEADLY LINKS

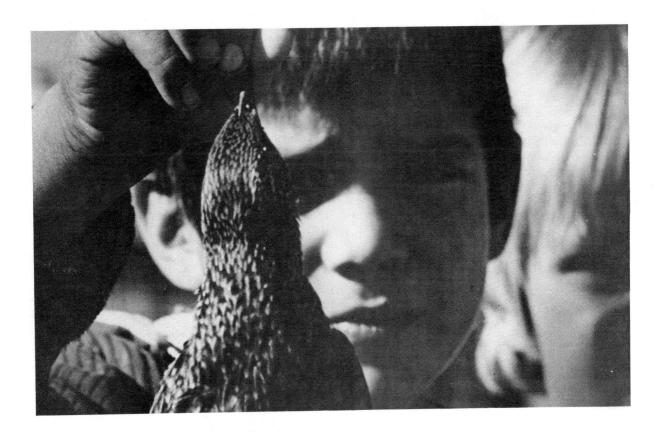

Objectives
Students will be able to: 1) give examples of ways in which pesticides enter food chains; and 2) describe possible consequences of pesticides entering food chains.

Method
Students become "hawks," "shrews," and "grasshoppers" in a highly-involving physical activity.

Background
People have developed pesticides to control organisms. Herbicides are used to control unwanted plants; insecticides to control unwanted insects, etc. When these pesticides involve use of poisons, the poisons frequently end up going where they are not wanted. Many toxic chemicals have a way of persisting in the environment, and often get concentrated in unexpected and undesirable places —from food and water supplies to wildlife and people, too.

For example, a pesticide (a chemical—frequently synthesized from inorganic compounds—used to kill something identified as a "pest" under some conditions) called DDT used to be applied regularly to crops as a means of controlling insects that were damaging the plants or trees. Then

Age: Grades 4-9
Subjects: Social Studies, Science, Physical Education
Skills: analysis, classification, comparing similarities and differences, computation, description, discussion, evaluation, generalization, kinesthetic concept development, synthesis
Duration: one 30-45 minute period
Group Size: minimum of ten students preferred
Setting: large playing area
Conceptual Framework Reference: I.C., I.C.3., I.C.4., I.D., II.B.2., II.B.3., II.B.4., III.B., III.B.1., III.B.2., IV.A.4., IV.C.3., VI.A., VI.A.2., VI.A.3., VI.A.4., VI.A.5., VI.B., VI.B.1., VI.B.2., VI.B.3. VI.C., VI.C.1., VI.C.6., VI.C.12., VI.C.13., VI.C.14., VI.C.15., VI.C.16., VI.D., VII.A.2., VII.A.4., VII.B., VII.B.1., VII.B.2., VII.B.3., VII.B.4., VII.B.5., VII.B.6., VII.B.7.
Key Vocabulary: pesticide, insecticide, herbicide, food chain, accumulate, toxic, chemicals, trade-offs, organic, inorganic

it was discovered that DDT entered the food chain with damaging results. For example, fish ate insects that were sprayed by the chemical; hawks, eagles, and pelicans ate the fish. The poisons became concentrated in the birds—sometimes weakening and killing them directly, and over time resulting in side effects like egg shells so thin that the eggs would not hatch, or were crushed by the parents in the nesting process. The impact on species, including the bald eagle and the brown pelican, has been well documented. Use of DDT has now been prohibited by law in the United States; however, at least one temporary waiver was granted in recent years to allow its limited use. It has not been prohibited worldwide, and therefore still enters the food chain.

settle into the soil, or stay on the crop, until it is washed by rain or irrigation into other water sources like groundwater, lakes, streams, rivers, and oceans. Testing the water after this has occurred typically does not show a particularly high concentration of these human-made chemicals—but testing the fish often does! Waterfowl and other species may also be affected—including human beings, if people eat contaminated fish or waterfowl, for example. In other words, wildlife and people become the concentrators of the pesticide because the chemicals do not pass out of their bodies but accumulate in their bodies over time.

The major purpose of this activity is for students to recognize the consequences of accumulation of some pesticides in the environment.

Damaging fertilizers as well as pesticides are used by many farmers as a part of the agricultural industry. Again, use of such chemicals—particularly the inorganic, synthesized compounds—has varying side effects. For example, a pesticide (either insecticide, to kill insects, or herbicide, to kill unwanted plants) may be sprayed or dusted on a crop. The pesticide may

Materials white pipe cleaners and colored pipe cleaners (two-thirds white, one-third colored); or white paper dots and colored paper dots (same proportion as above); or any other materials (two-thirds white, one-third colored) that can be picked up by students easily; 30 of these items per each student is recommended; one paper bag per grasshopper

Procedure

1. Tell the students that this is an activity about "food chains." If they are not familiar with the term, spend time in establishing a definition. (Food chain: a sequence or "chain" of living things in a community, based on one member of the community eating the member above it, and so forth; e.g., grasshopper eats plants like corn, shrews or other rodents eat grasshoppers, hawks eat rodents.)

2. Divide the students into three groups. In a class of 26 students, there would be two "hawks," six "shrews," and 18 "grasshoppers." (Work with approximately three times as many shrews as hawks, and three times as many grasshoppers as shrews.) Optional: Have grasshoppers, hawks, and shrews labelled so they can easily be identified; e.g., arm ties for grasshoppers, red bandannas for "red-tail hawks" and brown arm ties for shrews.

3. Hand each "grasshopper" a small paper bag or other small container. The container is to represent the "stomach" of whatever animal is holding it.

4. With the students' eyes closed, or otherwise not watching where you place the "food," distribute the white and colored paper dots (or whatever material you use) around in a large open space. Outside on a playing field if it is not windy, or on a gymnasium floor will work; a classroom will also work if chairs and tables or desks can be moved back.

5. Give the students their instructions. The grasshoppers are the first to go looking for food. The hawks and shrews are to sit quietly on the sidelines watching the grasshoppers; after all, the hawks and shrews are predators, and are watching their prey! At a given signal, the grasshoppers are allowed to enter the area to collect food and place the food in their stomachs (the bags). The grasshoppers have to move quickly to gather food. At the end of **30 seconds,** the grasshoppers are to stop collecting food.

6. The shrews are now allowed to hunt the grasshoppers. The hawks are still on the sidelines quietly watching the activity. The amount of time available to the shrews to hunt grasshoppers should take into account the size area you are working in. In a classroom, 15 seconds may be enough time; on a large playing field, 60 seconds may be better. Each shrew should have time to catch one or more grasshoppers. Any grasshopper caught by a shrew—that is, tagged or touched by the shrew, must give its bag of food to the shrew and then sit on the sidelines.

7. The next time period (from 15 to 60 seconds, or whatever time you set) is time for the hawks to hunt for food. The same rules follow. Any shrews still alive may hunt for grasshoppers; grasshoppers are hunting for the food chips that represent corn or other plants; and the hawks are hunting for the shrews. If a hawk catches a shrew, the hawk gets the food bag and the shrew goes to the sidelines. At the end of the designated time period, ask all the students to come together in a circle, bringing whatever food bags they have with them.

8. Ask the students who are "dead," having been consumed, to identify what animal they are and what animal ate them. (If they are wearing labels, this will be obvious.) Next ask the hawks to empty their food bags out onto the floor or on a piece of paper where they can count the number of food pieces they have. They should count the total number of white food pieces and the total number of multi-colored food pieces they have in their food sacks. List any grasshoppers and the total number of white and multi-colored food pieces each has; list the number of shrews left and the number of white and multi-colored pieces each has; and finally, list the two hawks and the number of white and multi-colored food pieces each has.

9. Inform the students that there is something called a "pesticide" in the environment. This pesticide was sprayed onto the crop the grasshoppers were eating, in order to prevent a lot of damage by the grasshoppers. If there was a lot of crop damage by the grasshoppers, the farmers would have less of their crop to sell, and some people and domestic livestock might have less of that kind of food to eat—or it might cost more to buy it because a smaller quantity was available. This particular pesticide is one that is poisonous, accumulates in food chains, and stays in the environment for a long time. In this activity, all of the multi-colored food pieces represent the pesticide. All of the grasshoppers that were not eaten by shrews may now be considered dead, **if they have any multi-colored food pieces in their food supply.** Any shrews for which half or more of their food supply was multi-colored pieces would also be considered dead. The one hawk with the highest number of multi-colored food pieces will not die at this time; however, it has accumulated so much of the pesticide in its body that the egg shells produced by it and its mate during the next nesting season will be so thin that the eggs will not hatch successfully. The other hawks are not visibly affected at this time.

10. Talk with the students about what they just experienced in the activity. Ask them for their observations about how the food chain seems to work, and how toxic substances can enter the food chain, with a variety of results. The students may be able to give examples beyond those of the grasshopper-shrew-hawk affected by the pesticide in this activity.

Extensions

1. Consider and discuss possible reasons for use of such chemicals. What are some of the trade-offs? What are some of the consequences?
2. Offer and discuss possible alternatives to uses of such chemicals in instances where it seems the negative consequences outweigh the benefits. For example, some farmers are successfully using organic techniques (e.g., sprays of organic, non-toxic substances; crop rotation; companion planting); biological controls (e.g., predatory insects); and genetic approaches (e.g., releasing sterile male insects of the "pest species") in efforts to minimize damages to their crops.
3. Find out what research is going on to develop and test effects of pest control efforts—from effects of possibly toxic chemicals, to non-toxic alternatives. With what impacts? Trade-offs? Potential?
4. Check newspapers for relevant local, national, or international examples of such issues.
5. Conduct the activity using different examples; e.g., people, shellfish.

Evaluation

Give three examples of ways in which pesticides could enter a food chain.

Discuss two possible consequences of pesticides entering the food chain for each of the examples you gave above.

An ecologist studied the presence of a toxic chemical in a lake. He found the water had one molecule of the chemical for every one billion molecules of water. This is called one part per billion (1ppb). The algae had one part per million (1ppm) of the toxic chemical. Small animals, called zooplankton, had 10 ppm. Small fish had 100 ppm. Large fish had 1,000 ppm. How do you explain this increase in this toxic chemical to 1,000 ppm for the large fish? Use a drawing to help support your answer.

The ecologist found the chemical was a pesticide which had been sprayed on cropland 100 miles away from the lake. How did so much of it get into the lake?

KEEPING SCORE

Objectives
Students will be able to: 1) describe cause and effect relationships that help and hinder wildlife in their community; and 2) recommend changes in their community that could benefit wildlife.

Method
Students investigate their neighborhoods for "cause and effect" relationships affecting wildlife; develop and use "community wildlife scorecards," and recommend actions to improve and/or maintain the quality of wildlife habitat in the community.

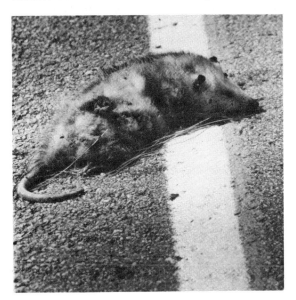

Background
There are pleasant surprises to be found in discovering and exploring some of nature's secrets—and these are available in our own schoolyards, backyards, neighborhoods, and communities. We sometimes forget that nature is all around us—in cities, suburbs, and agricultural areas—and not just in woods and lakes, high mountain meadows, deserts, rivers, skies, and oceans.

This activity is designed to assist students in searching out these surprises, as well as to make them aware of any problems that may exist for wildlife in their near surroundings, particularly as a result of human actions.

Some of us live in areas where limited wildlife is in evidence. However, many of us forget to see wildlife around us, even when it is there. Sometimes it is easy to take birds, butterflies, squirrels, and earthworms for granted! Frequently, we don't take into consideration the impact of our actions on the other living things around us. It is particularly easy to acquire a sort of "selective" vision that has us see aphids in our vegetable patch, for example, and not think about the impact on other life forms in the environment if we use a toxic spray to get rid of the aphids.

The major purpose of this activity is for students to increase their perceptions of cause and effect relationships affecting wildlife in their immediate communities, and to recommend some personal and community actions that could benefit wildlife.

Materials
dittoed or mimeographed scorecards; poster material; chalkboard or bulletin board for classroom display

Procedure
1. Ask the students to go home after school and look for "cause and effect" relationships in their neighborhood or community that seem to help or hurt wildlife—and some that seem not to affect wildlife at all. Ask every student to come back to school the next day prepared to share at least one example.

2. Get a sampling of information from the students in a brief discussion of what they found. Encourage them to explain their bases for

---

Age: Grades 4—8
Subjects: Science, Social Studies, Language Arts, Mathematics
Skills: analysis, application, classification, computation, description, discussion, evaluation, observation, problem-solving, reporting, small group work, synthesis, writing (limited)
Duration: two to three 30—45-minute periods; time after school working individually or in teams
Group Size: small groups and individual activity
Setting: indoors and outdoors
Conceptual Framework Reference: I.A.2., I.B., I.B.2., I.C., I.C.1., I.C.3., I.C.4., I.D., II.A., II.B., II.B.2., II.C., II.D., II.E., II.F., III.A.1., III.B.3., III.B.4., IV.C., IV.C.1., IV.C.3., IV.D., IV.D.4., IV.E., IV.E.4., V.A., V.A.5., VI.A., VI.A.2., VI.A.2., VI.A.4., VI.A.5., VI.B., VI.B.1., VI.B.2., VI.B.3., VI.C., VI.C.12., VI.C.13., VI.C.15., VI.C.16., VI.D., VII.A., VII.A.1., VII.A.2., VII.A.3., VII.A.4., VII.B., VII.B.1., VII.B.2., VII.B.3., VII.B.4., VII.B.5., VII.B.6., VII.B.9.
Key Vocabulary: cause, effect, habitat

identifying "cause and effect." Consider the following:

• What were some of the most surprising observations you made?

• What kinds of actions are people taking that directly affect wildlife? Which, if any, of these actions seem harmful to wildlife? Which, if any, of these actions seem helpful to wildlife? Which, if any, seem to have no effect?

• What, if any, problems affecting wildlife were identified? How do you know there are problems? If there are problems, are they apt to get better or worse in the future? Are there any actions that can be taken—by individuals and by the community—to reduce or get rid of these problems?

3. Next ask the students to work in small groups of four to six students. They should share what they identified as cause and effect relationships and whether the effect hurts or helps wildlife in their community. They can add examples of cause and effect relationships that could help or harm wildlife, even if they did not actually see them happening in their community. They should pool their ideas, eliminating duplicates, and putting their cause and effect relationships on one list representing their group's ideas. Ask one person to report for each group and turn in the group's list.

4. Either the teacher or a small group of students can pool the ideas from all the groups, putting together one master "Community Wildlife Scorecard."

5. Provide each student or team of students with a copy of the "Community Wildlife Scorecard." For example:

COMMUNITY WILDLIFE
SCORECARD

NAME _____

CAUSE	EFFECT	HURTS	HELPS	NEITHER	DAY
DOGS RUNNING FREE	SOMETIMES CHASE DEER AND KILL WILDLIFE	X			MONDAY WEDNESDAY
PERSON PLANTING TREES AND BUSHES	CAN CREATE FOOD AND SHELTER		X		SATURDAY

Read through the scorecard together, making sure the students are clear about what they are looking for in each situation.

6. Decide where the students will be doing their observing and "scorekeeping." It might be on the school grounds. The activity works very well if the students each take their scorecards home with them, making their observations to and from school, and after school in their own neighborhoods.

7. Ask the students to keep a score (tally) of each item they see—overnight, for a period of one week, or longer. (If a class cumulative scorecard is to be kept, prepare and post it in a conspicuous place—on a chalkboard, poster board, or bulletin board, for example.)

8. At the end of the week—or whatever record-keeping period is established—ask the students to tally and score their personal sightings. Subtract one point for every sighting of a cause and effect relationship that hurts wildlife; add one point for every sighting that helps wildlife; zero points for sightings with no impact.

9. Combine the personal scores and come up with a whole class score representing the "Community Wildlife Score."

10. Based on what they observed and recorded, ask the students what actions they think they could take as individuals and as a community to improve their "Community Wildlife Score." If the score is excellent already, what actions, if any, need to be taken to maintain the quality of their environment?

Evaluation

Identify and describe three kinds of wildlife habitat in your community, and list three kinds of wildlife which could live in each habitat. Describe three actions taken by members of your community that are helpful to wildlife.

Describe three actions taken by members of your community that are harmful to wildlife.

Describe three actions that might be taken in your community which could benefit wildlife, explaining what would happen, and why it would be helpful.

Identify what seems to be the greatest short-term problem for wildlife in your community, and the greatest long-term problem. Identify what might be done, if anything, to reduce or eliminate these problems.

COMMUNITY WILDLIFE SCORECARD

Cause/Effect Relationship	A Subtract 1	B Add 1	C No Impact
Subtotals			

(Subtract Column A from Column B for Total   Total Wildlife Score
Wildlife Score.)

PLANNING FOR PEOPLE AND WILDLIFE

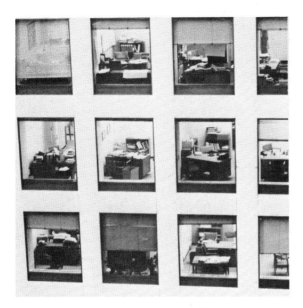

Objectives
Students will be able to: 1) describe considerations that are important in land-use planning for cities and other communities of people; 2) identify means by which negative impact on wildlife and other elements of the natural environment can be reduced in developing cities; and 3) describe actions that can be taken in some contemporary cities to enhance them as places in which both people and some wildlife can live.

Method
Students imagine and research what the area in which they live was like before a community was developed; design planned communities, and build and evaluate models of their community designs.

Background
NOTE: This activity is used effectively to culminate a unit on the importance of land-use planning; as well as issues affecting people, wildlife, and the environment.

Cities have developed as people have clustered together for purposes of meeting their needs— from shelter to food to a sense of community. They have typically developed as a hub of transportation and commerce, again serving as a means by which people meet their day-to-day survival needs. The development of cities, however, has been a mixed blessing. The large concentration of people in a given area has displaced plants and animals that lived there previously, and has given rise to problems unique to such crowded conditions. For example, varying forms of pollution accumulate in such centers, frequently with inadequate means for handling them—from products of industry to human waste.

Most cities are not the result of careful planning. Most have developed haphazardly, with attention to problems taking place when crises emerge. Crime, unemployment, poor housing, smog, contamination of water supplies by industrial and sewage waste disposal, energy consumption, transportation costs, and land-use sprawl are all among the serious problems facing contemporary cities today.

Age: Grades 4-12
Subjects: Social Studies, Art, Science
Skills: analysis, application, comparing similarities and differences, discussion, drawing, evaluation, invention, media construction, psychomotor development, problem-solving, synthesis, visualization
Duration: minimum of five 45-minute periods
Group Size: any
Setting: indoors
Conceptual Framework Reference: I.A., I.A.1., I.A.2., I.A.3., I.A.4., I.B., I.C., I.C.1., I.C.2., I.C.3., I.C.4., I.D., IV.A., IV.A.1., IV.A.2., IV.A.3., IV.A.4., IV.C., IV.D., IV.D.1., IV.D.2., IV.D.3., IV.D.4., IV.D.5., IV.D.6., IV.D.7., IV.E., IV.E.3., IV.E.4., IV.E.5., IV.E.7., IV.E.8., IV.E.10., IV.E.11., IV.F., IV.F.1., IV.F.2., IV.F.3., IV.F.4., IV.F.5., IV.F.6., IV.F.7., IV.F.8., IV.F.9., IV.F.11., V.A. V.B., V.B.1., V.B.2., VI.A., VI.A.2., VI.A.3., VI.A.4., VI.A.5., VI.B., VI.B.1., VI.B.2., VI.B.3., VI.B.4., VI.B.5., VI.B.6., VI.C., VI.C.1., VI.C.6., VI.C.12., VI.C.15., VI.C.16., VI.D., VI.D.1., VII.A., VII.A.1., VII.A.2., VII.A.3., VII.A.4., VII.B., VII.B.1., VII.B.2., VII.B.3., VII.B.4., VII.B.5., VII.B.6., VII.B.7.
Key Vocabulary: land-use planning, community, city

People today are faced with many important choices concerning how and where they will live. Many people in the United States are leaving the cities for suburban and rural life, bringing some of the same problems with them that encouraged them to leave the cities in the first place. New communities—large and small—are being developed. Some are the result of individual families moving into previously undeveloped areas; some are the result of business interests organizing to develop resources in an area, and creating entirely new cities in the process. This is happening in areas throughout the planet. Whole areas of some large and old cities are decaying as they are abandoned; in some cities, re-development projects are taking place to try to improve the habitability of the old and dying neighborhoods.

Ethical questions arise as people make decisions about where and how they will live. Any development or re-development of an area has an impact on the plants and animals who do and can live there, as well as on any people who might live there. Sometimes the development can be of benefit, and sometimes of long-term harm. When such decisions are made, it seems prudent to plan for the impact of our actions as carefully and thoughtfully as possible.

The major purpose of this activity is for students to consider the importance of land-use planning in community maintenance, improvement, and development. The concepts can be applied when considering re-development of old cities, as well as building of new cities and alternative communities in which people can live and work.

Materials
heavy cardboard or masonite; salt, flour and water to make salt clay for a model-building material; glue; toothpicks; natural materials like dried grass and construction paper for making buildings, roads, people, wildlife, and other components of community; tempera paint, brushes; and any other materials available and useful in model-building

Procedure

1. This is a "design a community" activity. Ask the students to close their eyes and visualize the community in which they live. If they live in a city, or if there is a city nearby, ask them to visualize how the city looks. Next ask them to try to visualize what that area might have looked like before the city or community was built in that spot. What plants were common to the area? What animals? Was there water in the area? What was the topography of the land?

2. Ask for a committee of volunteers to find out more precisely what the land, vegetation, wildlife, etc., was like in their area before their community was built. If the students live in a rural area where there is no city, ask them to find out this information for any city or community of their choice; e.g., the nearest big city. Ask the committee to report back to the rest of the students with this information in approximately one week. Sources could include province, state, city, or county historical societies, libraries, etc. City, regional, and state or province land-use planning offices may also have such information.

3. Ask the committee to report back to the rest of the students. The committee should report both visually and verbally. For example, they should list the descriptive characteristics of the vegetation in the area, and identify the kinds of wildlife and the food and water sources upon which that wildlife depended. Ask the committee to describe their findings thoroughly enough that the rest of the students can visualize a clear picture of what the area looked like before a community was developed there. Also ask the committee to leave a visual record of the major information they found for the rest of the students to use as a reference during the rest of this activity.

4. Next, ask all of the students, including the committee members who did the background research, to divide into working groups of from two to four students. Tell each group that it is their task to develop a community in this natural area, given the background information the committee has provided. In designing their community, they should aim to **develop a community in which people live and work with the least possible negative impact on the existing vegetation, air quality, water, soil, and wildlife,** at the same time that the needs of the people are met as well. In order to do this, the students should consider the following, as well as factors they identify:

• water sources, transportation, and treatment
• economic base; e.g., industry, small business
• kinds of housing, school, shopping areas, job sites
• ecological and recreational features; e.g., open space, green belts, parks
• sewage and waste disposal and treatment
• utilities
• food sources, transportation, and treatment
• aesthetics
• environmental safeguards
• means by which to effectively expand the number of people who can live in the community, if necessary, retaining minimum impact on the quality of the environment

5. Once each group has come up with a community development plan, review and discuss their plan with them.

6. Once their plans have been approved, provide the students with the necessary materials to build a model of their community. (See "Materials" above)

7. Once all the groups have developed their models of the communities they have designed, have a "Model Community Design Show," with each of the groups explaining the design features of their community.

8. Discuss the advantages and disadvantages of each community design in detail. For example, include, "What if" questions, like, "What if a new school had to be built?", "What if there is a drought or severe winter, would it be necessary to take special measures to assist the wildlife?"

9. Return to the models after two weeks to a month and ask the students to reflect upon whether they would make any changes in their community designs, as if they had had the opportunity to "live" in their communities for a while and might now see the need to do some things differently.

10. Ask a local architect, city planner, wildlife biologist or other resource manager to visit the class, in order to review and discuss the various model communities with the students who designed them.

Extensions and Variations

1. Show photos of actual cities. Look for advantages and disadvantages of city life, under a variety of circumstances.

2. Get a map showing a community (preferably yours!) 15, 25, 50, 75, 150 years ago. Evaluate the planning—or lack of—that seems to have taken place, with what results.

Evaluation

Name five important uses that must be considered for land in a human community.

For each of the previously mentioned considerations, list two ways that impact on the environment and wildlife can be reduced.

In most major cities, land-use planning has been non-existent or minimal. Describe five methods that might be used to enhance the existence of a city's people and wildlife, with explanations for the methods you choose.

RESPONSIBLE
HUMAN ACTIONS

ETHI-THINKING

Objectives
Students will be able to: 1) generate a list of activities done outside that are harmful to wildlife and the environment; 2) discuss reasons these activities are inappropriate; and 3) recommend alternative activities that are not harmful.

Method
Students list activities that might be harmful to wild plants and animals, and use photos or drawings to visualize, discuss, interpret, and evaluate these activities.

Background
Note: This activity can be used as an introduction to "Playing Lightly on the Earth."

The major purpose of this activity is for students to discriminate between outdoor activities that are harmful to wildlife and the environment, and those which are not.

Materials
art materials (crayons, construction paper, magazines for photos) to make discussion cards

Procedure
1. Ask students to help you make a list of activities people do that seem harmful to wild plants and animals. Ask them to think about things they've seen or know about that might be harmful. Some of these things could be:
- picking up baby wild animals in the environment (birds, fawns, etc.)
- carving initials in trees
- driving vehicles (cars, motorcycles) over fragile environments
- removing plants from environment, like digging up cactus

Age: Grades K—8
Subjects: Social Studies, Science, Art, Language Arts
Skills: analysis, application, description, discussion, drawing, evaluation, generalization, media construction, problem-solving, small group work, synthesis
Duration: one or two 20—40-minute periods
Group Size: any
Setting: indoors or outdoors
Conceptual Framework Reference: I.D., V.A., V.A.5., V.A.6., V.B.1., VI.A., VI.A.2., VI.A.3., VI.A.4., VI.A.5., VI.B., VI.B.1., VI.B.2., VI.B.3., VI.B.4., VI.B.5., VI.C., VI.C.1., VI.C.2., VI.C.12., VI.C.16., VII.A., VII.A.1., VII.A.2., VII.A.3., VII.A.4., VII.B., VII.B.1., VII.B.2., VII.B.3., VII.B.7.
Key Vocabulary: harm, wildlife

- destroying bird nests
- illegally killing, collecting, harassing, or possessing wildlife

2. Have students use cut-out photos or drawings to make these activities into cards showing pictures and describing what is happening. (Or, teacher can prepare cards in advance; laminate; and use again.) Or, older students can dramatize the situation in skits, "commercials," songs, poems, etc.

3. Collect the cards. Count students off to make groups of four each. Hand out one card to each group and ask them to discuss (or present the skits, poems, etc.):
- What is happening?
- Does it harm wildlife? How?
- Does it seem to be appropriate or inappropriate behavior? Why?
- Is the person doing it having fun?
- What else could he or she do that would satisy his or her needs and interests without harming wildlife or the environment?

4. Ask each group to report to everyone else about: a) their feelings concerning what is happening in the outdoor activity shown in the picture; and b) their recommendation for an alternative activity the people could do that would not be harmful.

Extensions

For Grades K—2:
Ask the students to draw pictures of things they know about or have seen happen that would hurt wild plants and animals. Ask them to describe what is happening in their drawing, and what could happen instead that would not be harmful.

For Older Students:
1. Choose something you or your family owns, like a car, television, refrigerator, etc. Imagine you are that object—and explore how you . . . from invention to garbage dump. . .affect wildlife!

2. Distinguish between actions that are harmful to individual plants and animals, and those which are harmful to large numbers of plants and animals. In what situations, if any, does it seem appropriate to harm a single animal or plant? In what situations, if any, does it seem appropriate to harm large numbers of animals or plants? In what situations, if any, does it seem inappropriate to harm a single animal or plant? In what situations, if any, does it seem inappropriate to harm large numbers of animals or plants? (Remember the definitions of wildlife and domesticated animals. Don't forget that wildlife includes, but is not limited to, insects, spiders, birds, reptiles, fish, amphibians, and mammals.)

3. Sometimes it is difficult to decide what is harmful and what is not. Usually if something is against the law, it is harmful in some way. Sometimes actions may be legal or there simply may be "no law against it", and people differ in their judgement as to whether the actions are harmful or not. Sometimes we may recognize that some of our actions are harmful in some ways—like some of our choices for housing, transportation, and consumer products in our daily lives—and we still take those actions because of our perceptions of the importance of our wants and needs. One way to examine wants and needs is to categorize them according to: Luxury, Useful But Not Necessary, and Necessary for Survival. We begin to get into the area of personal value judgements. Think about personal ethics. What are ethics? How do we each make responsible decisions in our daily lives? (See "Enviro-Ethics" for an activity aimed at identifying a "Personal Code of Environmental Ethics.")

Evaluation

Make a list of five things which people do that harm wildlife.

Make a list of five things which people do that harm wildlife habitat.

For each thing listed, describe what you can do about it.

Make a list of ten things which people do that help wildlife.

PLAYING LIGHTLY ON THE EARTH

Objectives
Students will be able to: 1) distinguish between games that are damaging and not damaging to the environment; and 2) invent games with a benign effect on the environment.

Method
Students look for evidence of games that harm the environment; and then invent and play games with a benign effect on the environment.

Background
Personal choices of all kinds can have an effect on the environment. Young people can look at the games they play outside—and choose those which have little or no damaging impact on the environment, rather than those which leave scars—aesthetically and ecologically.

The major purpose of this activity is for students to become actively aware of the choices they make each time they play a game outside, and to consciously experience games that have a benign effect on the environment. The activity is designed for students to experience success, at a personal and immediate level, in maintaining and improving the quality of their own environments.

Materials
access to going outside

Age: Grades K—8
Subjects: Social Studies, Physical Education, Science
Skills: analysis, comparing similarities and differences, evaluation, invention, psychomotor development, problem-solving, small group work, synthesis
Duration: one 30—45 minute period
Group Size: any
Setting: outdoors
Conceptual Framework Reference: I.D., VII.A., VII.A.1., VII.A.2., VII.A.3., VII.A.4., VII.B., VII.B.1., VII.B.2., VII.B.3., VII.B.7.
Key Vocabulary: game, harm

Procedure

1. Most of us like to play. In fact, playing is an important way to learn—as well as to have a good time. Ask the students to think of examples of ways to play outside that do no serious or permanent damage to the environment, and ways that are damaging. The damage might affect non-living things—like putting graffiti on cement walls. It might be damaging to plants and animals—like carving initials on tree trunks. Both are damage. Are there any games we can play that do no damage? There may not be, but we can think about how much damage, how permanent it is, and what it affects.

2. Go outside on the school grounds and look for evidence of games that have damaged the environment. Ask students what could have caused the damage and how it might have been prevented.

3. Introduce the concept of playing games that do not seriously harm the environment.

4. Ask the students to work together in small groups—from two to seven or eight—to **invent** a game that does no serious harm to the environment, including the plants and animals living there. The students could also try to invent games that could make this a **better** environment in some ways. Give the students about 15 minutes to invent their games.

5. Ask each group to present their game to the other students. Play each of the games. Ask the students to talk about their feelings about the importance of playing games that do little if any damage to the environment.

Extension

For older students: Analyze a variety of kinds of recreation for their impact on wildlife, vegetation, other natural resources, etc.

Evaluation

Keep a record of the games you play outside for one week. Identify which, if any, are harmful to the environment. For one week, or longer, play only games that do no harm to the environment.

WATER'S GOING ON?!

Objectives

Students will be able to: 1) record and interpret how much water they use in a day at school; and 2) make recommendations as to how they can save a significant percentage of that water.

Method

Students estimate and calculate water use in school, and then design and try ways to conserve water.

Background

Every molecule of water that was present when the earth's oceans were formed is still present today in one of water's three forms—as a gas, a liquid, or solid ice. Water molecules move at varying speeds through the water cycle; water in its gaseous form may remain in the atmosphere for about nine days, but it may stay frozen in the Antarctic ice cap for up to 10,000 years.

Most of the fresh water in the world is frozen in these polar ice caps. The largest part of what remains is groundwater—underground water that moves between layers beneath the earth's surface.

In the United States, approximately half of the water used is drawn from groundwater sources. This amounts to approximately 82 billion gallons a day of groundwater. Much of the groundwater used will not be returned to the groundwater system in the near future. Shallow groundwater may have a renewal rate of about 300 years, and deep groundwater (over 1,000 meters deep) may renew itself in about 4,600 years.

This causes an ever-increasing drain on the groundwater supply. As groundwater dries up, stream flows are reduced. Ponds and marshes dry up and plant species die out. The groundwater remaining may also become contaminated by saltwater intrusion or by pollution, rendering it unfit to drink. All these results have obvious effects on wildlife, people, and the environment.

A 1980 report from the Environmental Protection Agency states that groundwater depletion and contamination will be one of the major environmental problems of the 1980s.

Most of the world's fresh water is used for irrigation, but if a majority of Americans practiced personal water conservation and water quality practices, it would make a real difference.

The major purpose of this activity is for students to become aware of the amount of water they use and waste each day at school, and to make recommendations for ways to conserve the water both at school and at home.

Age: Grades 5—9
Subjects: Mathematics, Social Studies, Science, Home Economics
Skills: analysis, application, computation, discussion, evaluation, generalization, observation, problem-solving, synthesis
Duration: two 30—45-minute periods
Group Size: any
Setting: indoors
Conceptual Framework Reference: I.D., V.B., V.B.1., VI.A., VI.B., VI.C., VI.D., VII.A., VII.A.1., VII.A.2., VII.A.3., VII.A.4., VII.B., VII.B.1., VII.B.3., VII.B.7.
Key Vocabulary: conservation, water

Materials
chalkboard, paper and pencils

Procedure
1. Ask the students to estimate how much water each student uses each day in school. Have containers of different volumes for students to use for reference. Write their estimates on the chalkboard or on a chart. A chart may be made showing the class's estimates as follows:

gallons	2	4	6	8	10	12
	x	x	xxx	xxx	xxx	xxx
		x	xxx	xxx	xx	
		x	xxx			

2. Ask the students to monitor their use of water for a day. They can time their drinks of water and record them in a notebook. Ask them to do the same for handwashing. They should also record the number of times they use the restroom, etc.
3. As a class, calculate the amount of water used; e.g., run water from the fountain to a container for ten seconds and see how much water was used. Use this amount to calculate the amount per each drink that the students have recorded in seconds. Do the same for the sink faucets. Multiply the number of gallons used per flush by the number of trips to the restroom. Have each student come up with an individual number of gallons used.
4. Compare the **estimates** of water use to the **actual** water used.
5. Add all the individual gallons of water use to arrive at a total for the entire class. Divide this amount by the number of students in the class. In this way, individual students can compare their individual usage against a class average to see if they are above or below average in their water use.
6. Ask the students if it would be possible to reduce the amount of water used, and if so, how. For example, cups could be used at the drinking fountain to reduce the amount of water that goes down the drain.
7. Put the students' suggestions into practice for a day or two. Then ask the students how water conservation practices changed what they did. What materials did they use or buy? Did their attitude change? How? Which changes in their behavior will they keep, as part of their personal lifestyles?

Extensions
1. Where does our water come from? How does it get here? Does our finding, transporting, and using water affect wildlife in any way? If so, how? After a discussion of the effects of water depletion and conservation on wildlife, ask students to draw two murals—one showing the effects of depletion and another the effects of conservation.
2. Monitor water use at home (showers, dishes, clothes washing, lawn watering, etc.)
3. Use this activity for paper and energy use and conservation.
4. Incorporate use of elementary statistics in this activity!

Evaluation
Estimate the number of gallons of water you use each day personally.

What activity of yours requires the most water per year?

Describe and explain three ways you can decrease your use of water.

Describe and evaluate the seriousness of water problems you can identify which affect people and wildlife, now, and in the future.

WHAT DID YOUR LUNCH COST WILDLIFE?

Objectives

Students will be able to: 1) trace some foods back to their source, including the impact on wildlife and the environment along the way to the consumer; and 2) recommend, with explanations, some food habits that could benefit wildlife and the environment.

Method

Students trace food sources, diagram environmental impacts, and apply the knowledge they gain by making changes in some of their consumer choices.

Background

NOTE: Especially for younger students, this activity makes a nice summary companion to "What's For Dinner?"

Most of us make lifestyle choices each day that have some impact on wildlife and the environment. Many of those impacts are indirect, and therefore we are not as aware of them as we might be. The choice of foods we eat, for example, is an area with many implications for wildlife and the environment.

The places and ways in which foods are grown has impact. For example, we know that loss of habitat is one of the most critical problems facing wildlife. Habitat may be lost to agricultural use or development as well as to industrial, commercial, and residential uses. Given that people need food, the ways in which we grow that food —and the ways we care for the land in the process—are very important. Farmers can take measures to maintain and improve wildlife habitat as they grow and harvest their crops. They can pay attention to the impact of their growing practices. Both inorganic and organic fertilizers are commonly used in industrial agriculture. These compounds may run off or leach into water supplies. In lakes, for example, this run-off may contribute to a huge increase in the growth of plant nutrients such as algae.

This excess growth can act as a pollutant, poisonous to aquatic animal life such as fish, amphibians, arthropods, and insects.

Use of insecticides and herbicides also affects the environment, including wildlife. Obviously, if pesticides kill and eliminate the food source for wildlife, the wildlife either leaves or dies. Indirect effects can include accumulation of such pesticides in the bodies of animals—as in predatory birds, fish, and mammals, including people.

Age: Grades 4—12
Subjects: Social Studies, Language Arts, Science, Home Economics, Vocational Agriculture
Skills: analysis, application, classification, comparing similarities and differences, discussion, drawing, evaluation, media construction, problem-solving, synthesis, visualization, writing (limited)
Duration: one to three 45-minute periods
Group Size: any
Setting: indoors
Conceptual Framework Reference: I.D., III.B., III.B.1., III.B.2., IV.C., V.A., V.A.1., V.B., V.B.1., VI.A., VI.A.2., VI.A.3., VI.A.4., VI.B., VI.B.1., VI.B.2., VI.B.3., VI.C., VI.C.16., VI.D., VI.D.1., VII.A., VII.A.1., VII.A.2., VII.A.3., VII.A.4., VII.B., VII.B.1., VII.B.3., VII.B.7.
Key Vocabulary: organic, inorganic, source, renewable, nonrenewable, impact

Not all of the impact is due to some farmers' practices, however. Certainly, the transportation, processing, packaging, and marketing industries are involved as well. Questions about the natural resources involved in getting the food from its source of origin to the consumer are critically important. One example is increased exploration for and development of fossil fuels used to transport the food from growing site to consumer, used often to fuel the processing, and frequently used in the packaging, as in the case of fossil fuel-derived plastics.

Ethical considerations can also be raised concerning the impact upon individual animals and plants by the methods used to produce food for people, as well as choices of which foods to eat.

If the students have concern about adopting lifestyle habits that can be healthful to themselves at the same time they have less impact on wildlife and the environment, they can look at the food they eat as one place to begin. The major purpose of this activity is to provide a means for students to begin that process.

Materials writing and drawing materials

Procedure

1. Ask the students to generate a list of foods they either brought or bought for lunch. Be sure to include any packaging materials the foods came in.
2. Ask each student to pick one food to trace all the way back to its origins—including where and how it grew, was harvested, was transported, was packaged, and was made available to the consumer. . .the student. Ask the students to make simple flow diagrams of the path the food takes. (The students may want to do some research at this point to get some additional information.)
3. Next ask the students to add drawings of possible and likely impacts to wildlife and the environment along the path their food took to get to them.
4. Ask the students to report back to their classmates—using their diagrams as a visual aid as they describe the path taken by their food, and its impact to wildlife and the environment along the way.
5. Ask the students to discuss and summarize their findings.

6. Ask each student to think of one change he or she could make in his or her own lunch-time eating habits that would be likely to have a beneficial—or at least less harmful—effect on wildlife and the environment. Describe the reasoning for this change, and evaluate its consequences. If, after examination, each change seems in fact to be helpful, suggest that the students try making their changes for a week. At the end of the week, ask the students to report back. Were they able to stick with the change? What happened? If they didn't make the change, why not? Did they forget? If they did make the change, did they find themselves making or thinking about any other possible changes? If yes, what were they?

Extensions
1. Map the **energy** used to grow and get the food to you.
2. Include impact on other specified natural resources along the way.
3. Distinguish between renewable and nonrenewable resources.

Evaluation
Trace the possible course of a container of milk served in your school back to its probable source.

What impact does this journey have on wildlife?

Name three food habits that could reduce negative impacts to wildlife and the environment. Explain the reasoning behind your suggestions.

FLIP THE SWITCH FOR WILDLIFE!

Objectives

Students will be able to: 1) trace the route of electrical energy from source to use; 2) describe impacts on wildlife and the environment derived from various kinds of energy development and uses; and 3) evaluate the impact on wildlife and the environment as a result of their own energy-use practices.

Method

Students illustrate the route of energy from its sources to human use, including environmental impacts along its path; and then invent and try ways to make beneficial impacts on wildlife through their personal energy-use practices.

Background

The source of electrical energy in your area can come from one or a combination of the following sources: coal, hydroelectric, nuclear, fuel-oil, or natural gas fired generators. In the United States, about 60% of the electrical energy is produced from coal, 15% from hydroelectric sources, 15% from nuclear, and 10% from oil or natural gas.

In obtaining the energy to fuel our power plants, we affect wildlife in both positive and negative ways. We may build a hydroelectric dam that supplies energy and forms a lake good for fish, blocks runs of other fish, and in the process floods valuable wildlife habitat for land animals. A power line through a forest may improve the habitat for some species, and degrade it for others.

The major purpose of this activity is for students to compare the various sources of electrical energy, as well as learn the positive and negative impacts on wildlife for each of these sources, including those they use each day.

Materials

writing and drawing materials

Age: Grades 5—12
Subjects: Science, Social Studies, Language Arts
Skills: analysis, application, comparing similarities and differences, discussion, drawing, evaluation, media construction, problem-solving, reporting, research (hypothesis formation and testing), small group work, synthesis, visualization, writing (limited)
Duration: one to three 45-minute periods, depending on student prior knowledge of energy sources
Group Size: any
Setting: indoors
Conceptual Framework Reference: I.D., V.B., V.B.1., VI.A., VI.A.2., VI.A.3., VI.A.4., VI.A.5., VI.B., VI.C., VI.D., VII.A., VII.A.1., VII.A.2., VII.A.3., VII.A.4., VII.B., VII.B.1., VII.B.2., VII.B.3., VII.B.4., VII.B.5., VII.B.7.
Key Vocabulary: energy, development, generator, technology

Procedure

1. Ask the students the question, "What effects, if any, do we have on wildlife when we turn on a light switch?" Let them discuss the question and form an opinion. (Older students can generate hypotheses.) As a way of testing their ideas (or hypotheses), assign groups of three or four to research where their electricity comes from, identifying all steps from the light switch back to the land and how they think each step along the way might affect wildlife. Also assign groups to research alternative technologies (e.g., solar, geothermal, tidal, wind power). Note: This activity is excellent as an extension to energy source activities already underway with students.

2. Ask the students within each group to draw and label their "power pathway" on a large sheet of paper. For example, coal would travel from the strip mine or tunnel by truck to the processing plant, then by train to the power plant, over the electric power lines to their house and their light switch. Have the students label points along the way where wildlife could be positively or negatively affected.

3. When the students have completed their power paths, have them show them to the rest of the class. You can then discuss the following questions with them:

- What kind of effects on wildlife do we have when we turn on a light switch? Are they positive or negative? Can any of them reasonably be changed?
- Which type of fuel source do you think would have the greatest negative impact on wildlife? Which the least? Why? Which the greatest positive impact on wildlife? Why?
- How could we minimize the negative impacts?
- Why don't we use the source of power with the least impact to a greater degree?
- Which energy sources cost the least to develop and use? Which provide more jobs? Which seem to have the least negative overall impact on the environment?
- What trade-offs are involved? Are there any reasonable solutions? If yes, describe some possibilities. With what consequences?
- How can each of us help wildlife and the environment through our energy habits?

4. Ask each student to think of at least one constructive thing to do for wildlife that involves energy and its use—and do it!

Extensions

1. Create a large mural on butcher paper of a natural area complete with wildlife, trees, mountains, rivers, etc., but no human development. After completing the mural, brainstorm a list of things that would happen if a much needed energy source (e.g., coal, oil, uranium, water) was discovered in that area. Draw pictures of these activities and facilities with one picture for each item listed. When all the pictures are completed, place them in appropriate places on the mural. For example, put the pictures where you think they should go if you were an energy developer. You can pin, tack, or tape the pictures onto the paper. Discuss the positive and negative impacts the "new development" will have on the environment and wildlife, and create a list of these effects. Now, re-develop the energy source and see if you can come up with ways that the development can have less impact on the environment and still get the energy needed, at an affordable cost.

2. See if a similar situation exists in your area.

Evaluation

Trace energy from a burning light bulb back to the sun using two different pathways.

Describe two ways that wildlife and/or habitat might be affected by each of the following electric energy development and uses: hydroelectric dam, nuclear generating plant, coal generating plant, oil generating plant, wind generating plant, tidal generating plant, active or passive solar facility.

ETHI-REASONING

Objectives
Students will be able to: 1) examine their own values and beliefs related to wildlife and other elements of the environment; and 2) evaluate possible actions they might take that have impact on wildlife and the environment.

Method
Students read, discuss, make judgements, and write about hypothetical dilemmas concerning wildlife and/or natural resources.

Background
This activity is designed to give students the opportunity to examine their own values and beliefs as they relate to wildlife and other elements of the environment. It is not the intent of this activity to prescribe "right" and "wrong" answers for the students. One exception is in the areas where information about laws is conveyed.

There are variations from state to state in laws affecting wildlife and the environment. Each state has an official public agency which is legally responsible for caring for most wildlife within the state. This agency can be contacted in your state to request general information about laws affecting most wildlife in your area. For example, it is legal to hunt and fish for some animals in all states; however, what animals and under what conditions are specified by laws and regulations for which the state wildlife agency is responsible. There are also federal regulations affecting wildlife. The U.S. Fish and Wildlife Service can be contacted for information about such laws. For example, federal law protects all birds of prey—eagles, hawks, and owls—from shooting or any other intentional cause of death, injury, or harassment. All threatened and endangered species are protected by law. Songbirds are protected by law; that is, it is against the law to intentionally harm songbirds. It is also generally illegal to possess birds' nests, eggs, and feathers, even those found lying on the ground. It is generally against the law to pick up the carcass of an animal which has been killed by a vehicle along a highway or road. Instead, local wildlife authorities should be notified. In many cases, it is against the law to take an injured wild animal home to care for it. For example, birds of prey cannot be cared for by private citizens unless those citizens have a permit to do so. There are many laws, and they are complex. Again, it is useful and important to contact local authorities about the laws protecting and affecting wildlife in your area.

Whether right or wrong, questions of law can be separated from questions of ethics. At a personal level, an individual's choices as to what seem right or wrong for him or her in terms of values and behaviors may be described as a personal code of ethics. Hunting, for example, is controversial for some people from an ethical point of view. Some people say that even though hunting is legal, it is unethical, because a human being is taking the life of a wild animal. Others believe hunting to be a responsible and ethical form of recreation, acquiring food, or animal population control. These differences of belief may be sincerely held. Whether or not a person chooses to hunt is a personal choice dictated by one's personal ethics. Conflicts arise, however, when a person motivated by one set of ethics tries to force his or her ethics on others through activities such as arguments, harassment, or legislative action.

It is the major purpose of this activity to provide students with an opportunity to come to their own judgements about what they think are the most responsible and appropriate actions to take in situations affecting wildlife and the environment.

Age: Grades 5—12
Subjects: Social Studies, Science, Language Arts
Skills: analysis, application, discussion, evaluation, problem-solving, small group work, synthesis, writing
Duration: one 30—45-minute period
Group Size: any; small groups of two to four students recommended
Setting: indoors or outdoors
Conceptual Framework Reference: I.D., V.A., V.B., V.B.1., VI.B., VI.B.1., VI.B.2., VI.B.4., VI.B.5., VI.C., VI.C.1., VI.C.2., VI.C.7., VI.C.12., VI.C.16., VII.A., VII.A.1., VII.A.2., VII.A.3., VII.A.4., VII.B., VII.B.1., VII.B.2., VII.B.3., VII.B.4., VII.B.7.
Key Vocabulary: dilemma, responsibility

Materials
copies of "dilemma cards"

Procedure

1. From the attached pages the teacher should copy and cut up the dilemma cards. Other dilemmas could be written that are more specific to problems in your area. Students could also be involved in the process of creating the dilemma cards, with each student responsible for one card. Dilemmas can be left entirely open-ended, with no options suggested for consideration.

2. Divide the class into groups of four, and give each group a stack of dilemma cards. Place them face down at the center of the group.

3. The first student draws a card from the top of the stack. The student studies the situation, decides what he or she should do, and formulates his or her reasons.

4. When the student is ready—typically in less than two minutes—the student reads the situation and the options aloud to the rest of the group. The student gives the decision he or she has chosen, and briefly describes the reasoning involved. In turn, each of the other members of the group is invited to comment on the dilemma, and what he or she would do in the situation. The discussion of each dilemma by the members of the group should take about five minutes. The person whose dilemma is being discussed should have the opportunity to ask questions of the other members of the group, and to offer clarification about his or her decision. The discussion gives the students experience in having ideas examined by peers, and is intended to remind the students of the need to take personal responsibility for decision-making. It is not necessary and may not be desirable for the students to reach consensus; there are legitimately ranging views of the most appropriate and responsible actions to take in many situations. The purpose is to provide students with an opportunity to examine, express, clarify, and take responsibility for their own reasoning.

5. The card is then returned to the bottom of the stack and the next student selects a card from the top of the stack. Continue this process until all students have had the opportunity to express their decision and rationale about a dilemma.

Extensions and Variations

1. Here are a few other general topics, around which dilemma cards could be created: abandoning pets to fend for themselves to try to find new homes; impact of pets on wildlife, like cats catching wild birds, and dogs chasing deer; use of pesticides in gardens; live Christmas trees versus artificial; acid rain; picking wild flowers and fruit; feeding wildlife around your home, etc.

2. Adapt this to a debate format!

3. Write and discuss you own dilemmas!

Evaluation

Choose a dilemma. Write a short paragraph on the positive and negative effects of all the options listed for that dilemma. Indicate what additional information, if any, is needed in order to make a responsible and informed decision. Identify what seems, in your judgement, to be the most responsible decision—and explain your reasoning.

Dilemma Card

You are president of a large corporation. You are very interested in pollution control and have had a task force assigned to study the pollution your plant is creating. The task force reports that you are barely within the legal requirements. The plant is polluting the community. To add the necessary equipment to reduce pollution would cost so much that you have to fire 50 employees. Should you:

- add the equipment and fire the employees
- not add the equipment
- wait a few years to see if the cost of the equipment will drop
- hire an engineering firm to provide further recommendations
- other

Dilemma Card

You are a member of a country club that has recently voted to build a game farm to raise animals for members to hunt. You are not a hunter, you think that hunting is only okay to do in the wild, and you are opposed to the building of the game farm. Should you:

- stay in the club and do nothing
- stay in the club and speak out strongly against the subject
- resign from the club
- other

Dilemma Card

A deer herd has grown so large during the past ten years that many of the deer appear to be starving. The herd is severely damaging the habitat, eliminating much of the vegetation that the animals use for food or shelter. There is a disagreement within your community as to what course of action is best to take. You are personally opposed to hunting. A limited legal hunt has been proposed in order to reduce the size of the herd in this area. Should you:

- investigate and consider the situation to see what, in your judgement, seems to be the most humane and reasonable solution, including the feasibility of options such as moving some of the deer to other areas, understanding that they still may not survive
- organize a protest to bring people opposed to hunting out the recreation area at the time the legal hunt is to begin
- allow the habitat degradation to continue and the deer to starve
- leave it to the state wildlife agency to work with the land holder to arrive at a solution
- other

Dilemma Card

You are fishing at a secluded lake and have caught seven fish during your first day at the lake. Now, on the second day, the fishing has been great and you have caught five fish in the first hour, all of which are bigger than yesterday's fish. The law allows you to possess 12 fish. Should you:

- continue to fish and keep all the fish
- dispose of the smaller fish you caught yesterday and keep the big ones to stay within your limit
- have fish for lunch
- quit fishing and go for a hike
- other

Dilemma Card

You are the head of a task force created to select the best course of action to attempt to preserve the California condor. There are apparently 22 condors left in a steadily declining population. Left to their own, it is probable they will all die. Some members of your task force would like you to authorize capturing some of the condors and sending them to zoos to try to propagate them in captivity. Should you:

- leave them in their natural environment
- capture some of them for zoos
- launch an education campaign about causes of endangerment of species, focusing specifically on the condor
- other

Dilemma Card

You are finally able to build the home your family has dreamed about. After reviewing the plans for your home, you realize that you cannot include all of the features you had planned for, due to rising construction costs. You must decide which one of the following you will include:

- solar heating
- recreation room with fireplace
- hot tub and sauna
- greenhouse
- other

Dilemma Card

You love children and would like to have a large family. You are aware, however, of the world's population projections for the future. Should you:

- plan to have a large family anyway
- decide not to have children
- limit yourself to one or two children
- other

Dilemma Card

You have found a young screech owl which you have managed to raise to maturity. You have been told that you cannot keep the owl any longer because keeping it without the proper permit is in violation of state and federal laws. Should you:

- offer it to your local zoo
- keep it as a pet
- call the fish and wildlife agency and ask their advice
- determine whether it could survive in the wild and, if it appears it could, release it in a suitable area
- other

Dilemma Card

You are walking in the woods and come upon a young fawn. There is no sign of the fawn's mother. Should you:

- leave it where it is
- move it to a sheltered area
- take it home
- other

Dilemma Card

You are out in the woods with a friend when you spot a hawk perched on a high limb. Before you realize what is happening, your friend shoots the hawk. An hour later, you are leaving the woods and are approached by a state wildlife officer, who tells you a hawk has been illegally shot and asks if you know anything about it. Should you:

- deny any knowledge of the incident
- admit your friend did it
- make up a story implicating someone else
- say nothing, but call the fish and wildlife office later with an anonymous phone tip
- other

Dilemma Card

You have purchased a beautiful ten acre property in the mountains to build a summer home. One hillside of the property has a beautiful view of the valley and lake below and is your choice for your homesite. However, you discover there is an active bald eagle nest site on that hillside. The bald eagle is sensitive to disturbance around its nest tree and is a protected species. Bald eagles are highly selective in choosing nest sites and usually return to the same nest year after year. Should you:

- select a different site on the property to build your home
- sell the property
- chop down the tree and build your home
- other

Dilemma Card

You are on a field trip with your class to the zoo. Although you know that feeding of the animals by zoo visitors is prohibited, some of your friends are feeding marshmallows to the bears. Should you:

- tell them that feeding marshmallows may harm the bears and ask them to stop
- report their behavior to the nearest zoo keeper
- ask the teacher to ask them to stop
- not do anything
- other

Dilemma Card

You are an influential member of the community. On your way home from work, you are stopped by a police officer and cited for having excessive auto emmissions. Should you:

- use your influence to have the ticket invalidated
- sell the car to some unsuspecting person
- work to change the law
- get your car fixed and pay the ticket
- other

Dilemma Card

You are on a picnic with your family and you see another family leaving to go home, without having picked up their own trash. It is clear the other family is going to leave litter all around. Should you:

- move quickly and ask them to pick up their trash before they leave.
- wait for them to leave and pick up the trash for them
- do nothing
- other

Dilemma Card

You are a farmer. You've been studying and hearing about farming practices like leaving edge areas for wildlife and organic pest control. Although these practices may improve your long-term benefits, they may reduce your short-term profits. You are already having trouble paying you. taxes and keeping up with expenses. Should you:

- sell the farm
- keep studying farming practices but make no changes for now
- try a few methods on some of you acreage and compare the results with other similar areas on your land
- other

CAN DO!

Objectives

Students will be able to: 1) identify a problem involving wildlife on their own school grounds; 2) suggest and evaluate alternative means by which to either solve the problem or at least improve the situation; 3) successfully undertake the project; and 4) analyze and describe the process by which they successfully solved the problem or improved the situation.

Method

Students select a school environmental project; conduct research; make plans; and follow procedures to accomplish the project.

Background

Each of us can make constructive contributions to improving the environment in which we live. Sometimes our actions can improve the environment for people, sometimes for wildlife, and sometimes for both. Sometimes our effectiveness can be improved if we work with other people—sharing ideas, information, and skills.

A working knowledge of the following terms will be useful to students in this activity:

Problem—a difficult situation to be improved, or an opportunity to make things better. Problems can't always be "solved," but situations can usually be improved.

Authority—an individual or group of people with the power to make changes.

Compromise—a way to settle a problem in which both "sides" usually give a little.

Given that it is important for young people to learn that they "can do" for people, wildlife, and the environment—use your judgement in the course of this activity to assist students in selecting a project that is realistic, constructive, and possible. If not, the students may experience an activity that contributes to their thinking that they "can't do."

The major purpose of this activity is to provide students an opportunity to experience success in taking constructive actions to improve the environment for people and wildlife.

NOTE: See "The Monday Group: From Awareness to Action" for descriptions of successful community projects undertaken by older students, but still relevant as examples of what can be done.

Materials

writing materials

Age: Grades 2—9
Subjects: Social Studies, Language Arts, Science
Skills: analysis, application, description, discussion, evaluation, invention, listing, public speaking, problem-solving, small group work, synthesis, writing
Duration: minimum of three 45-minute periods
Group Size: any
Setting: outdoors and indoors
Conceptual Framework Reference: I.D., IV.A., IV.A.1., IV.A.2., IV.A.3., IV.A.4., IV.C., IV.D., IV.D.1., IV.D.2., IV.D.3., IV.D.4., IV.D.5., IV.D.6., IV.E., IV.E.4., IV.E.5., IV.E.9., IV.E.10., IV.F.11., VI.B.7., VII.A., VII.A.2., VII.A.3., VII.B., VII.B.1., VII.B.5., VII.B.6.
Key Vocabulary: problem, authority, compromise, constructive, realistic, effective, alternatives

Procedure

1. Ask the students to think of some ways in which they could improve areas of the school grounds as a home for wildlife. They might generate a list of activities on their school grounds that have a negative impact on wildlife. The list might include litter that poses a hazard for some kinds of wildlife; a muddy area that birds use for water but that has been recommended for blacktopping to minimize dust and mud; a proposed pesticide spraying that will not only kill the "pest" but perhaps affect other plants and animals; removal of a tree that presently helps contribute to cleaning the air, produces oxygen, and serves as a food and shelter source for varying kinds of wildlife, etc.

2. Looking at the list of possible problems and suggestions for ways to improve wildlife habitat at school—ask the students to select one they think they could realistically handle and do something constructive about. If there is difficulty in deciding which one, and reasonable support has been offered for each, the students might vote to decide. Students could also make speeches in support of the project they want to tackle, in hopes of swaying the class vote.

3. Once the project has been selected, ask the students to work alone or in small groups to begin to generate ideas for possible solutions to the problem and ways to implement the project. Each individual or small group could come up with a plan, including a written description and illustrations or sketches of how it will work, and how it can be accomplished.

4. Ask the groups to present their plans to the rest of the students. Students may ask questions for clarification. Once all the plans have been presented, ask the students to select the plan that seems most: a) constructive; b) realistic; c) helpful to wildlife; and d) apt to make a lasting contribution.

5. Also ask the students to select one or more alternative plans, in case their first choice is not acceptable to authorities at the school.

6. Once a plan, with alternatives for "back up," has been selected—ask the students to select a delegation to present their proposal to the school principal or whomever the appropriate authority would be. Remember janitors, groundskeepers, school board, etc.—anyone who would be physically and/or officially involved. A practice session before the students and any interested parents or other groups of students would be helpful. At the practice session, the student delegation would make their presentation as they plan to before the principal, janitor, etc.—responding to any questions from their audience that might be raised.

7. The students should make an appointment to present their proposal, make the presentation, and report back to their classmates. If their plan is accepted, they should make sure they know who to contact next in order to successfully complete their project. Making sure they have all necessary permissions secured, the students should proceed to successfully accomplish their project.

8. Once accomplished, ask the students to analyze their results. Did things work out like they wanted them to? Were there any surprises? Any unforeseen problems? How might they have been any more effective?

Evaluation

A nature trail near you is being vandalized. People are shooting at squirrels, taking bird nests from trees, and using knives to destroy interpretive signs. Name three things you and your class could do to help reduce this problem.

IMPROVING WILD-LIFE HABITAT IN THE COMMUNITY

Objectives

Students will be able to: 1) apply their knowledge of wildlife by describing essential components of habitat in an arrangement appropriate for the wildlife they identify; and 2) evaluate compatible and incompatible uses of an area by people and specified kinds of wildlife.

Method

Students design and accomplish a project to improve wildlife habitat in their community.

Background

NOTE: See "Can Do." Its scope is the school; the scope of "Improving Wildlife Habitat" is the community. "Keeping Score" can be helpful in identifying community needs for habitat improvement, used prior to this activity.

This activity provides an opportunity for students to evaluate and apply much of what they have learned about wildlife and its needs.

The major purpose of this activity is to provide students with experience in looking at their own communities; applying knowledge and skills they have acquired; evaluating; and experiencing the possibilities of enhancing their communities as places within which both people and wildlife can live suitably.

NOTE: See "The Monday Group: From Awareness to Action" for descriptions of successful community projects undertaken by students.

Materials

writing and drawing materials, poster or butcher paper OR, model-making materials, like plaster of Paris, clay, small replicas of animals, etc.

Procedure

1. Ask students whether their community could benefit from improved areas for wildlife habitat. If yes, this activity provides a process for helping to make such improvements. If a need is identified, the scope of such a project is a major decision. Habitat improvement projects can be large or small. If a project from this activity is actually to be implemented:
- It should be within the scope and means of the students to experience success with it; and,
- It should clearly be of benefit to wildlife and the community.

2. After general discussion, ask the students to divide into groups of four or five. Give each group the task of beginning a design for a habitat improvement project. The project should involve

---

Age: Grades 4—12
Subjects: Science, Social Studies, Art, Mathematics, Language Arts
Skills: analysis, application, description, discussion, drawing, evaluation, invention, media construction, problem-solving, small group work, synthesis, visualization
Duration: one or two 45-minute class periods if hypothetical; much more time if project is to be implemented
Group Size: any
Setting: indoors (and outdoors, optional)
Conceptual Framework Reference: I.D., IV.A., IV.A.1., IV.A.2., IV.A.3., IV.A.4., IV.C., IV.C.1., IV.C.2., IV.C.4., IV.D., IV.D.1., IV.D.2., IV.D.3., IV.D.4., IV.D.5., IV.D.6., IV.E., IV.E.4., IV.E.5., IV.E.7., IV.E.8., IV.E.9., IV.E.10., IV.E.11., IV.F.11., V.A., V.B., V.B.1., V.B.2., VII.A., VII.A.1., VII.A.2., VII.A.3., VII.A.4., VII.B., VII.B.1., VII.B.2., VII.B.3., VII.B.5., VII.B.6., VII.B.7.
Key Vocabulary: habitat, improvement

native plants and animals, and make a contribution to the community. Provide time for the students to discuss and make decisions about:
• What will be its purpose?
• What animals will it serve? Will people be able to visit? Will it be for plants and animals only? What plants and what animals? If people can visit, what will they be allowed to do? What won't they be allowed to do?
• What positive contributions might this improved wildlife habitat area make to the community? What possible problems could arise, if any?
• What costs will be involved? Who will pay? How?
• Where will the area be? How large will it be?
• What are the habitat needs of any animals who will live there? What species of animals can live in the size land area that is available? (Some animals need more room than others and if you are to have a self-sustaining system, you will need a population in an area large enough for successful breeding over time.)
• What herbivores and carnivores might be needed? Predators? Prey? What specific kinds of plants (herbs, shrubs, trees, grasses, etc.) are needed and in what arrangement?
• What will be the water sources? How will air and water quality be maintained?
• What kinds of programs, if any, will be necessary to maintain the area once it has been improved?
• Who must be contacted in order for this project to be undertaken? What permissions would be needed? From whom?
• In balance, is it a good idea . . . for wildlife, the environment, and the people who live in this community?
Optional: Make a site visit.
3. Ask each of the groups to prepare the following: a) a written description of their habitat improvement project, including its location, characteristics, inhabitants, and purposes; and b) a map or model to scale of the area. The map or model can include:
• habitat components for various species
• wildlife living in the area, in their appropriate locations
• bodies of water, natural or made by people
• major areas of vegetation and a key to type
• major landmarks; e.g., rock outcropping, roosts for birds, bare ground, meadows, brush, low trees, high trees

• major food sources and types; e.g., berry patch for birds, prairie dog village for coyotes or birds of prey
• areas developed for human access
• etc.
4. Ask each group to display their plans. After all the students have had an opportunity to read the background information and see the map or model of each habitat improvement project, ask the students to talk about what they learned in the process of creating these designs. They can include discussion of problems they encountered, what seemed realistic and what did not, etc. In discussion—and based on their observations of the various proposed projects—ask the students to summarize what seemed to be the most important things to remember about designing such an area (e.g., size appropriate to wildlife, diversity, native elements, appropriateness to community wants and needs).

Extension
Consider the feasibililty of designing and implementing one or more of these projects for your community. Do have a local wildlife specialist, and appropriate local officials, e.g., landowners, zoning authorities, critique and cooperate with any proposed project before you get underway with it. Make sure the project is worthy, feasible, and legal—and then proceed!

Evaluation
Rate the following uses of an area as either compatible or incompatible for people and wildlife: houses being built 200 feet from a heron rookery; picnic tables set up in an area heavily populated by squirrels; snowmobile trails through a deciduous forest; swimming beach at a local lake. Think of your own examples. What could be done to make each of these uses more compatible for people and wildlife?

ENVIRO-ETHICS

Objectives
Students will be able to: 1) distinguish between actions that are harmful and beneficial to the environment; and 2) evaluate the appropriateness and feasibility of making changes in their own behaviors related to the environment.

Method
Students develop and use a "Personal Code of Environmental Ethics."

Background
The major purpose of this activity is to provide students with the encouragement and opportunity to look at their own lifestyles in light of their impact on natural resources and the environment.

Materials
none needed

Procedure
1. Involve the students in discussion about the impact each of us has each day on aspects of the environment—from using electricity to make breakfast to putting on clothes that were derived from some natural resources and transported to us by some means, to use of the varied products we choose and employ each day, to our choices of recreation and entertainment. We are consumers, and our impact is formidable.

Age: Grades 6—12
Subjects: Language Arts, Social Studies, Science, Home Economics
Skills: analysis, application, comparing similarities and differences, description, discussion, evaluation, invention, problem-solving, reporting, synthesis, writing (optional)
Duration: one or two 30—45-minute periods
Group Size: any
Setting: indoors or outdoors
Conceptual Framework Reference: I.D., V.A., V.B.1., VI.A., VI.B., VI.B.2., VI.B.3., VI.B.4., VI.B.5., VI.C., VII.A., VII.A.1., VII.A.2., VII.A.3., VII.A.4., VII.B., VII.B.1., VII.B.2., VII.B.3., VII.B.6., VII.B.7.
Key Vocabulary: ethics, responsibility, lifestyle

codes, keeping track of how easy or difficult it is for them to live by them. "Progress reports" are appropriate, again in the spirit of each person paying attention to his or her own actions, and bearing responsibility for them.

Variations and Extensions

1. Reflect for a few minutes on your daily life. In fact, close your eyes and follow yourself through a typical day. What natural resources do you use? What choices do you make that have an impact on the environment? What choices do you make that have an impact on wildlife and its habitat? What choices do you make that have an impact on other people, here and elsewhere on the planet? If you could, what things—if any—would you change about your daily life in order to have a more beneficial, or less harmful, impact on the environment? What things—if any—do you already do that you think are helpful, or at least not harmful, to the environment? Brainstorm ten words that come to mind when you think of actions and behaviors you value. Create a sentence, paragraph, or poem that might capture the essence of your own "Personal Code of Environmental Ethics."

2. Develop a "life map." It could include where you want to live, whether you want a family, what kind of home, transportation, food sources, job, recreation, etc. Look at the costs and benefits of your choices—for you personally, other people in your community, wildlife, other natural resources, etc.

2. Ask each student to work alone to devise a "Personal Code of Environmental Ethics." This code may be written or not. Emphasize the importance of the code being for the person who creates it. The code should take into consideration daily actions that are harmful to the environment, and those which are beneficial; the students should consciously create their code based on actions they believe are beneficial, or at least not harmful, to elements of the environment. We will always have some impact; we can make choices about the kinds of impacts we make, their extensiveness, etc.

3. Ask for any volunteers to share their "Personal Code of Environmental Ethics." They might share the entire code, or a segment of it. They might describe the thinking that went into the decisions they made in constructing their code. Students might illustrate a part of their code—if they chose not to write it—to convey a major idea. Encourage the students to ask each other questions about the codes, in the spirit of learning more about each person's priorities, but not in a judgemental approach. The purpose is for each student to evaluate his or her own priorities, in a responsible consideration of day-to-day actions that affect the environment, but not to be actively critical of another student's approach to the same problem. In this way, each student is simply encouraged to take responsibility for his or her own actions.

4. Encourage the students to try using their

Evaluation

List five environmental issues.

List one way that you directly or indirectly contribute to an environmental problem.

Identify, describe, and evaluate one way you could lessen your role in contributing to an environmental problem.

Make at least one change in your lifestyle that will reduce your role in contributing to an environmental problem.

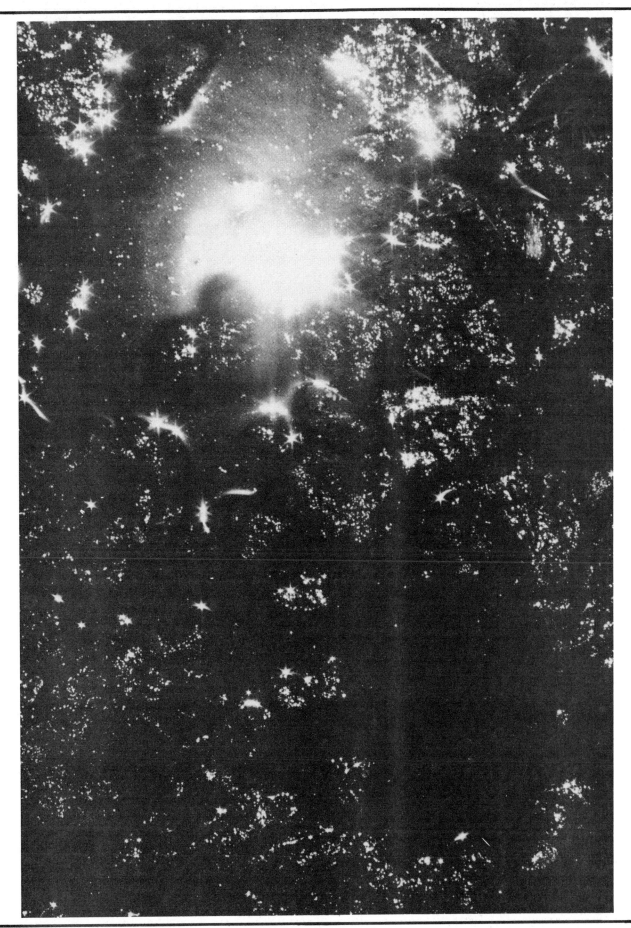

LIST OF AGENCIES AND ORGANIZATIONS

The following list is not intended to be comprehensive. It includes federal agencies with responsibilities involving wildlife which are referenced in Project WILD activities. State wildlife agencies may be contacted directly in each state. The organizations are also listed in one or more Project WILD activities, tend to have national memberships or scope, and can be contacted for information. The organization list as a whole represents a range of views concerning wildlife-related issues. Project WILD encourages teachers and students to contact a **range** of organizations, supporting instruction for informed decision making. It is recommended that requests be as specific as possible, be mailed on behalf of a class rather than each individual student submitting a request, and be sent with a stamped self-addressed envelope for return of materials. Only ask for what you think you want and will use—and try to allow two to three weeks time for a response.

Federal Agencies

Bureau of Land Management
Washington, D.C. 20240

National Marine Fisheries Service
U.S. Department of Commerce
N.O.A.A.
Washington, D.C. 20235

National Park Service
Interior Building
Washington, D.C. 20240

Soil Conservation Service
P.O. Box 2890
Washington, D.C. 20013

U.S. Department of Agriculture
14th St. and Jefferson Dr. S.W.
Washington D.C. 20250

U.S. Fish and Wildlife Service
18th and C Streets N.W.
Washington, D.C. 20240

U.S. Forest Service
P.O. Box 2417
Washington, D.C. 20013

Organizations

American Cetacean Society
P.O. Box 4416
San Pedro, CA 90731

American Fisheries Society
5410 Grosvenor Lane
Bethesda, MD 20014

American Humane Association
9725 East Hampden
Denver, CO 80231

Animal Protection Institute of America
P.O. Box 22505
Sacramento, CA 95822

Animal Welfare Institute
P.O. Box 3650
Washington, D.C. 20007

Cousteau Society
777 Third Avenue
New York, NY 10017

Defenders of Wildlife
1244 19th St. N.W.
Washington, D.C. 20036

Ducks Unlimited
P.O. Box 66300
Chicago, IL 60666

Elsa Wild Animal Appeal
P.O. Box 4572
North Hollywood, CA 91607

Friends of the Earth
529 Commercial St.
San Francisco, CA 94111

Fund For Animals
140 W. 57th St.
New York, NY 10019

Greenpeace
Building E, Fort Mason
San Francisco, CA 94123

Humane Society of the United States
2100 L St. NW
Washington, D.C. 20037

International Association of Fish And Wildlife Agencies
1412 16th St. N.W.
Washington, D.C. 20036

International Whaling Commission
The Red House, 135 Station Road
Histon, Cambridge CB4 4NP
England

Izaak Walton League of America
1800 North Kent St., Suite 806
Arlington, VA 22209

National Audubon Society
950 Third Avenue
New York, NY 10022

National Rifle Association
1600 Rhode Island Avenue NW
Washington, D.C. 20036

National Wildlife Federation
1412 16th St. NW
Washington, D.C. 20036

Nature Conservancy
1800 N. Kent St., Suite 800
Arlington, VA 22209

Safari Club International
5151 East Broadway, Suite 1680
Tucson, AZ 85711

Sierra Club
530 Bush St.
San Francisco, CA 94108

Sport Fishing Institute
1010 Massachusetts Avenue NW
Washington, D.C. 20001

Whale Center
3929 Piedmont Avenue
Oakland, CA 94611

The Wilderness Society
1901 Pennsylvania Avenue, N.W.
Washington, D.C. 20006

Wildlife Management Institute
1000 Vermont Avenue. N.W.
Washington, D.C. 20005

The Wildlife Society
5410 Grosvenor Lane
Bethesda, MD 20814

GLOSSARY

abiotic: a non-living factor in an environment; e.g., light, water, temperature.

adapted, adaptation: the process of making adjustments to the environment. For example, forests develop only where soil types, moisture, and sunlight are balanced to the proper degree. Desert plants have made adjustments so as to be able to live under intense sunlight, on poor quality soils, and with much reduced water supply.

aerate: to supply with air or oxygen; to supply the blood with oxygen as in the function of lungs; to supply running water with additional oxygen as when a stream runs over falls or rapids, or when wind creates waves on a lake.

aesthetic: relating to or dealing with the beautiful. An aesthetic value relates to the value placed on beauty.

aestivation: dormancy, typically seasonal

amphibian: an animal that typically lives in an aquatic habitat breathing by gills as young, and primarily in a terrestrial habitat breathing by lungs and through moist glandular skin as adult, e.g., frog.

anadromous fish: those fish which spend the greater share of their lives in salt water, but migrate into fresh water streams for reproduction; salmon, shad, bass, and others that migrate from the sea up a river to spawn.

animal community: animals of various species living within a certain habitat, each occupying a specific position in this particular environment; directly parallel and related to plant communities. For example, in a desert area, a coyote, jackrabbit, gopher, snake, elf owl, gecko, scorpion, and cactus wren may be part of an animal community.

annual: a plant that completes its life cycle from seedling to mature seed-bearing plant during a single growing season, and then dies.

annual turnover: the rate of replacement of individual animals in a population. Birds, such as quail, may have a 70 percent turnover annually. This means that only 30 percent of the birds alive at the beginning of one year are still alive at the end of the year. The reproductive capability of a species will match the mortality, or turnover, rate.

anthropomorphism: the attribution of human characteristics to non-humans, especially animals. Biologists recognize that animals may exhibit emotions and behavior patterns resembling those of humans. Anthropomorphism is generally used to refer to a fictionalized portrayal of animals found in many children's books, cartoons, etc.

aquatic: growing, living in, or frequenting water.

arboreal: tree dweller.

bag limit: the maximum number of animals allowed to be taken by an individual in regulated fishing or hunting. For example, an angler may catch ten fish; a deer hunter may kill one deer per year. These are bag limits.

behavior: what an animal does.

biennial: a plant that lives for two growing seasons, producing only leaves during the first season, flowers and seeds during the second.

big game: a term designating larger hunted species, such as deer, elk, moose, bear, and bighorn, as opposed to "small game," such as rabbits, woodchucks, squirrels, doves, and quail, or "nongame," such as songbirds and birds of prey. In many states, species are legally designated as big game, small game, or nongame.

biodegradable: the property of a substance that permits it to be broken down by microorganisms into simple, stable compounds such as carbon dioxide and water.

biologist: a person who studies living organisms and their relationship to one another.

biome: a large geographic area with somewhat uniform climatic conditions; a complex of communities characterized by a distinctive type of vegetation and maintained under the climatic conditions of the region.

biosphere: the part of the earth's crust, water, and atmosphere where living organisms can subsist.

biota: the animal and plant life of a region or period.

biotic community: commonly the living organisms in a given community. It includes all plant and animal life within the community. The non-living parts are considered the abiotic parts of the community.

biotic potential: the capacity of a population of animals or plants to increase in numbers under optimum environmental conditions.

blind: a hiding place for observing.

bounty: a reward or payment for removing certain species of animals felt to be harmful. Use of bounties is slowly going out of practice.

breeding: a series of complex behavioral interactive patterns from courtship to rearing of young which are necessary for the continuation of a species.

broadleaf: the term describing a plant with widebladed leaves, such as an oak or maple; generally refers to flowering trees in contrast to conifers.

brood: the offspring of a bird or mammal.

browse: a general term, commonly used in wildlife management to signify brushy plants utilized by deer, elk, or cattle as feed; to eat the twigs and leaves of woody plants.

burrowing: spending a portion of life under ground.

canopy: layer formed by the leaves and branches of the forest's tallest trees.

carnivore: a meat eater.

carrion: the bodies of dead animals, usually found in nature in the process of decay; not "fresh" meat.

carrying capacity: a wildlife management term for the total number of any species that a given area of habitat will support at any given time; the ability of a given unit of habitat to supply food, water, cover or shelter, and necessary space to a wildlife species; the number of organisms of a given species and quality that can survive in a given ecosystem without causing deterioration; the largest population the unit can support on a year-round basis, or during the most critical season. Carrying capacity varies throughout the year. The population number varies from year to year, dependent upon conditions within the habitat such as rainfall, competition from domestic animals, etc.

chaparral: in wildlife work, the term describing brushy areas where manzanita, ceanothus, cliffrose, scrub oak, skunk brush, and others are the predominant vegetative types. The term originates from the Spanish, and referred to thorny bushes and is also the source of the word "chaps," a part of the cowboy costume. Chaps were originally called "chaparreras," with the word later shortened by Anglo cowboys.

climatic: the average condition of the weather as defined by temperature, precipitation, and wind velocities; the environmental conditions relating to weather.

climax: the final stage of plant or animal succession; when environmental conditions have been stable long enough for an area to develop a semi-permanent biome. For example, rock crumbles, and pioneering plants begin to grow in the sandy soil. As they add mulch and humus, other plants follow--from grasses to shrubs to pine forest. If climatic conditions and soil types are appropriate, the climax species could be the pine forest. Animal types would follow this pattern of succession, ending perhaps with squirrels, porcupines, and Stellar's jays as climax species.

coloration: a genetically-controlled pattern or markings which protects an individual organism.

community: an association of organisms--plant and animal--each occupying a certain position or ecological niche, inhabiting a common environment, and interacting with each other; all the plants and animals in a particular habitat that are bound together by food chains and other interrelations.

competition: when two or more organisms have the potential for using the same resource. May be inter- or intra-specific.

conifer: a plant that bears its seeds in cones; usually refers to needleleaf trees, although some needleleaf, such as yew, do not bear cones.

coniferous: refers to cone-bearing. A coniferous forest is one composed of pines, firs, or spruces.

conservation: the use of natural resources in a way that assures their continuing availability to future generations; the wise and intelligent use or protection of natural resources. (See "preservation.")

consumer: the first part of an ecosystem is the nonliving substance; the second part consists of those organisms which are called "producers," or food makers; part three of this system is called the "consumer" because it utilizes the producer for its food; it may in turn be used as food by a secondary consumer. A rabbit is a primary consumer. A fox would be a secondary consumer.

consumptive use: in general terms related to wildlife, any use which involves activity resulting in the loss of wildlife. Examples may be the death of an individual animal, as in hunting, fishing, and trapping. Consumptive use may include indirect impacts of activities such as habitat loss or alteration. (See "non-consumptive use.")

courtship: a behavior pattern which ensures mating with a suitable partner of the correct species at the correct time.

cover: the vegetation, debris, and irregularities of the land that provide concealment, sleeping, feeding, and breeding areas for wildlife.

covey: a small flock or group, often a family group, of birds such as quail.

crepuscular: active at dawn and dusk.

dabbling ducks: ducks which frequent shallow marshes, ponds, and rivers and "tip up" to feed. They feed with body above water and take off vertically when startled; also called "puddle ducks." (See "diving ducks.")

deciduous: referring to trees, those that annually shed their leaves; regarding animal teeth, those commonly called "milk teeth."

decomposer: those organisms (bacteria, fungi) which convert dead organic materials into inorganic materials; a plant or animal that feeds on dead materials and causes its mechanical or chemical breakdown.

depradation: the act of preying upon, usually in relation to wildlife damage to people's crops or animals.

desert scrub: arid environments with irregular winter rainfall, summer rainfall, or biseasonal rainfall; highly varied plantlife, with leafless, drought deciduous, or evergreen species of trees, shrubs, herbs and grasses, yuccas, agaves, and cacti.

display: an observable behavioral pattern that carries a specific message. The message may be inter- or intra-specific.

diurnal: active by daylight; the opposite of nocturnal.

diversity: variety

diving ducks: ducks which prefer deep water as in lakes and bays. They feed by diving below the surface and take wing from a running start.

domesticated: referring to animals, those which humans have tamed, kept in captivity, and bred for special purposes. All domesticated animals have their origins in wild ancestors. Cattle used for food and other products; sheep for wool and other products; as well as dogs, cats, birds, and fish commonly kept as pets are all examples of domesticated animals.

dominant species: plant or animal species which exert major controlling influence on the community. Removal of dominant species results in important changes in the community. Generally, dominants have the greatest total biomass. (biomass: total numbers or weight)

ecological niche: the special place in a community occupied by a given organism; where an organism lives, where it gathers food, where it seeks shelter, who are its "friends and enemies," what it gives to the community, what it takes from the community, how it is affected by its environment, and how the environment is affected by it. These determine the niche or place in society of an organism.

ecologist: a scientist who studies the interrelations of living things to one another and their environment.

ecology: the study of the relation of organisms or groups of organisms to their environment; or the science of the interrelations between living organisms and their environment.

ecosystem: a natural unit that includes living and nonliving parts interacting to produce a stable system in which the exchange of materials between the living and nonliving parts follows closed paths; all living things and their environment in an area of any size, with all linked together by energy and nutrient flow.

edge effect: the tendency of wildlife to use the areas where two vegetative types come together forming an edge; where rabbits, for example, concentrate in an area where brush land and meadow land meet because of the diversity of food, shelter, and other habitat components provided by the edge.

endangered: an "endangered" species is one which is in danger of extinction throughout all or a significant portion of its range. (A "threatened" species is one that is likely to become endangered.)

environment: the total of all of the surroundings--air, water, vegetation, human element, wildlife--that has influence on you and your existence, including physical, biological, and all other factors; the surroundings of a plant or animal including other plants and animals, climate, and location.

ethics: a personal or social moral code.

eutrophication: enrichment of soils and water due to fertilization, sewage, effluent, or other waters that carry a high plant-nutrient component.

evergreen: a plant that does not lose all of its leaves at one time. Among trees, some broadleaf species, such as live oak, remain green all year, but most North American evergreens are coniferous.

exotic: in conservation language, this refers to a foreign plant or animal--one that has been introduced into a new area. Examples could be the "wild' burro or the ring-necked pheasant.

extinction: the condition of having been removed from existence. An animal or plant facing extinction is one in danger of vanishing from our world.

feral: used in wildlife as referring to domesticated animals gone wild; e.g., wild burros, goats, cats, dogs.

finite: having bounds or limits; capable of being counted or measured; the opposite of infinite.

flyway: fly routes established by migratory birds.

food chain: the transfer of food energy from the source in plants through a series of animals, with repeated eating and being eaten. For example, a green plant, a leaf-eating insect, and an insect-eating bird would form a simple food chain. Any one species is usually represented in several or many food chains.

food web: an interlocking pattern of food chains.

forage: refers to vegetation taken naturally by herbivorous animals, both wild and domesticated.

forbs: an important part of wildlife habitat. In wildlife usage, forbs are weeds and herbs; low-growing, annual or perennial, herbaceous plants.

forest: a complex community of plants and animals in which trees are the most conspicuous members.

forest floor: the layer of decomposing material that covers the soil in a forest.

forest management: the practical application of scientific, economic, and social principles to the administration of a forest for specified objectives.

forest region: an extensive area of a continent in which the climax forest associations are closely similar. The major forest regions of North America are West Coast Forest, Western Forest, Central Hardwood Forest, Tropical Forest, Northern Forest, and Southern Forest.

game animal: legal designation for animals which may be managed and hunted only under regulation.

grassland: a vegetative community in which grasses are the most conspicuous members.

grazer: a herbaceous organism that consumes primarily grasses.

habitat: the arrangement of food, water, shelter or cover, and space suitable to animals' needs. It is the "life range' which must include food and water, as well as escape cover, winter cover, cover to rear young, and even cover in which to play.

hardwood: a deciduous or broadleaf tree; the wood from such trees.

harvest: the intentional gathering of plants, animals, and other natural resources for use, especially renewable resources; a human intervention in a life cycle in order to use a resource. In wildlife management, hunting is considered a form of harvest in which individual animals are killed.

herb: any flowering plant or fern that has a soft, rather than woody, stem.

herb layer: the layer of soft-stemmed plants growing close to the forest floor.

herbivore: a plant eater.

hibernation: the act of passing the winter, or a portion of it, in a state of sleep; a torpid or resting state.

home range: the area in which an animal travels in the scope of normal activities; not to be confused with territory.

hunter: a person or animal who searches for wildlife with the intent of catching or killing it.

hunting: the act of a person or animal who hunts.

hunting pressure: the numbers, amount, or concentration of hunters in a specific area and upon a specific animal.

indigenous: a naturally occurring species.

inorganic: not living.

insectivorous: refers to insect eaters.

interaction: the relationship of one organism to another; the action of one population affecting the growth or death rate of another population. One population may eat members of the other populations, compete for food, excrete harmful wastes, or otherwise interfere with the other population. Some interactions are positive, some negative, and some are completely neutral.

interdependencies: the interrelationships of wildlife with one another and with the various elements of their environment.

invade: to enter, to encroach upon, to spread over into. In wildlife usage, this usually refers to when an organism is removed from a community and another organism spreads over into this community.

inventory: in wildlife terms, the process of identifying and counting animals.

key plant species: those plant species which are used to indicate the general condition of a habitat. For example, when plants show overuse, the animals may have exceeded the carrying capacity of the habitat.

license: in wildlife terms, a legal permit, e.g., to hunt, fish, trap, transport, keep captive wildlife, or perform taxidermy.

lichen: algae and fungus growing together in a symbiotic relationship.

life cycle: the continuous sequence of changes undergone by an organism from one primary form to the development of the same form again.

limiting factors: influences in the life history of any animal, population of animals, or species; e.g., food, water, shelter, space, disease, predation, climatic conditions, pollution, hunting, poaching, and accidents. When one or more of these exceeds the limit of tolerance of that animal, population of animals, or species, it then becomes a limiting factor; it then directly affects the well-being of that animal and may result in the animal or animals' death. Limiting factors may result from causes in nature as well as human activities.

litter: the number of young born per birthing.

management: in general terms related to wildlife, the intentional manipulation or non-manipulation of habitat and/or the organisms within the habitat. (See "wildlife management.')

microclimates: the climates of specific small areas. Microclimates are the tiny contrasts to the general climate of the area. A deep, narrow, shadowed canyon--cool and damp--might be a microclimate within a desert mountain range. The shady side of a huge boulder, or the area immediately surrounding a tiny spring, or the north side of a city building would be classified as microclimates.

microhabitat: a small habitat within a larger one in which environmental conditions differ from those in the surrounding area. A hole in a tree trunk or an animal carcass is a microhabitat within the forest.

microorganism: an organism microscopic in size, observable only through a microscope.

migratory: in wildlife usage, birds or other animals which make annual migrations; i.e., travel distances in seasonal movements. Migrations may be great, or very short, depending upon the species.

mitigate: to make up for; to substitute some benefit for losses incurred.

mixed forest: a forest that includes both coniferous and deciduous trees.

monoculture: the raising of a crop of a single species, generally even-aged.

mortality rate: the death rate; usually expressed in deaths per thousand.

mulching: to add materials to soil in order to protect from cold, to reduce evaporation, to control weeds, or to enrich the soil. Common materials could be sawdust, bark, leaves.

multiple-use: a term referring to a system of management in which lands and waters are used for a variety of purposes. The uses are not necessarily simultaneous but are intended to be compatible. For example, a tract of forest land can serve as a home for wildlife, provide clean air and water, be a place for recreation, be used to grow and harvest trees for products, and be aesthetically pleasing, all at the same time.

multiple-use forestry: any practice of forestry fulfilling two or more objectives of management.

mutualism: a close association between two different species whereby each species derives some benefit. The yucca plant and the yucca moth each benefit from their relationship.

natal: related to birth or being born.

natural selection: a process in nature resulting in the survival and perpetuation of only those forms of plant and animal life having certain favorable characteristics that enable them to adapt best to a specific environment.

needleleaf: bearing needlelike leaves.

niche: see "ecological niche."

nitrogen-fixation: the conversion of elemental nitrogen from the atmosphere to organic combinations or to forms readily utilizable in biological processes; normally carried out by bacteria, living symbiotically in legumes or by free-living soil bacteria.

nocturnal: active by night; the opposite of diurnal.

non-consumptive use: in general terms related to wildlife, any use which does not directly kill wildlife, e.g., most forms of birdwatching, photography, hiking, and other pursuits involving activity as well as vicarious forms such as movie, television, and gallery viewing of wildlife. (See "consumptive use.")

nongame: all wildlife species which are not commonly hunted, killed, or consumed by humans, such as songbirds and raptors.

nonrenewable resource: nonliving resources such as rocks and minerals; resources which do not regenerate themselves; substances such as petroleum, coal, copper, and gold which, once used, cannot be replaced--at least not in this geological age. (See "renewable resource.")

omnivore: an animal which eats both plant and animal materials.

organic matter: chemical compounds of carbon combined with other chemical elements, and generally manufactured in the life processes of plants and animals. Most organic compounds are a source of food for bacteria and are usually combustible.

organism: a living thing; a form of life composed of mutually dependent parts that maintain various vital processes.

parasite: an organism that lives by deriving benefit from another organism, usually doing harm to the organism from which it derives benefit.

parasitic: to be a parasite on. Mistletoe is a parasite growing on trees.

pelage: body covering on a mammal.

perennial: a plant that lives for several years and usually produces seeds each year.

pesticide: any chemical preparation used to control populations of organisms, including plants and animals, perceived to be injurious.

pinch period: that period of an annual cycle when the factors necessary for life are least favorable.

plankton: those organisms suspended in an aquatic hab?n movements; usually microscopic, including bacteria, algae, protozoans, rotifers, larvae, and small crustaceans. Phytoplankton are the plant plankton; zooplankton are the animal species.

plant communities: an association of plants, each occupying a certain position or ecological niche, inhabiting a common environment, and interacting with each other. Dominant plants usually define the community, e.g., a spruce-fir community.

pollution: harmful substances deposited in the air or water or land, leading to a state of dirtiness, impurity, unhealthiness, or hazard.

population: the number of a particular species

in a defined area.

population inventory: a measure of the current density of a species of animal or plant.

prairie: a grassland community.

predaceous: a predaceous animal is a predator who kills and eats other animals.

predation: the act of preying upon.

predator: an animal that kills and eats other animals.

prescribed burning: the planned application of fire to natural fuels with the intent to confine the burning to a predetermined area.

preservation: protection which emphasizes non-consumptive values and uses, including no direct use by humans, contrasted with conservation which emphasizes both consumptive and non-consumptive values and uses. (See "conservation.")

prey: animals that are killed and eaten by other animals.

primary producers: green plants which are able to manufacture food from simple organic substances.

rain shadow: an area on the leeward side of a mountain barrier that receives little rainfall.

range: see "home range"; the land upon which animals live; an area grazed by livestock and/or wildlife.

rangeland: all lands, including forest land, that produce native forage in contrast to land cultivated for agricultural crops or carrying a dense forest.

raptor: pertaining to eagles, hawks, and owls; birds which are predatory, preying upon other animals.

rare: referring to wildlife species not presently in danger, but of concern because of low numbers.

recreation: entertainment, frequently implying activity in the out-of-doors.

reintroduction of species: a wildlife management technique, where a species is reintroduced into historic range; replanting of animals in areas where they had become extinct.

renewable resource: living resources, such as plants and animals, which have the capacity to renew themselves when conditions for survival are favorable. (See "nonrenewable resource.")

resident wildlife: animals which are residents to a specific area on a year-round basis, as opposed to migratory.

resource: a portion of an environment upon which people have placed or assigned value, or see as being available for use.

savanna: a parklike grassland with scattered trees or clumps of trees.

scavenger: an organism that habitually feeds on refuse or carrion. A coyote is a part-time scavenger; a dermestid beetle is a full-time scavenger.

scrub: low, woody vegetation composed principally of shrubs.

season: a period of time, usually when something specific occurs; for example, any of four times of year characterized by differences or changes, as in plant growth and temperature. In wildlife management or conservation terms, that time when hunting, fishing, or trapping is permitted for a particular species.

sere: the series of communities that follow one another in a natural succession, as in the change from a bare field to a mature forest.

shelter: cover; cover from elements, for natal activity, to travel in, for breeding, for bedding, etc.; varies depending upon species.

skink: any of a family of small, smooth-scaled lizards.

slough: an inlet from a river; backwater; tideflat; a creek in a marsh.

small game: a term designating smaller hunted species, such as rabbits, woodchucks, squirrels, doves, and quail, as opposed to big game such as deer, elk, moose, bear, and bighorn, or "nongame" such as songbirds and birds of prey. In many states, species are legally designated as big game, small game, or nongame.

snag: a standing dead tree from which the leaves and most of the branches have fallen; typically important as wildlife habitat.

social limits: the saturation point of a species in an environment; how much crowding an individual will accept; varies widely with species.

softwood: a coniferous tree; a common but not strictly accurate term; the wood of many conifers is harder than that of some so-called hardwood trees.

spawning: the act of producing or depositing eggs; usually refers to fish.

species: a population of individuals that are more or less alike, and that are able to breed and produce fertile offspring under natural conditions; a category of biological classification immediately below the genus or subgenus.

state wildlife agency: the state agency that has the legal responsibility for management of some or all wildlife, including habitat protection, restoration, and alteration; planning; land acquisition; research; education; information; endangered species; consumptive uses; non-consumptive programs; regulations; and usually law enforcement.

static: showing little change, usually used in reference to a population or to a condition of habitat.

stewardship: related to the environment, the concept of responsible caretaking; based on the premise that we do not own resources, but are managers of resources and are responsible to future generations for their condition.

stress: usually thought of as a physical factor that applies to detrimental pressure to an organism or population. A drought period would apply a stress to a plant community and thereby to an animal population, and this would perhaps inhibit reproduction rather than eliminating the species.

succession: the orderly, gradual, and continuous replacement of one plant or animal by another.

symbiosis: a close living relationship between organisms.

symbiotic: the characteristic of symbiosis.

terrestrial: ground dweller

territory: the concept of "ownership" or dominance over a unit of habitat; an area defended by an animal against others of the same species; used for breeding, feeding, or both. Many species of wildlife are territorial. Best known are certain birds and wolves.

territorial imperative: the instinctive compulsion to gain and defend a territory. Many zoologists believe this drive to be more compelling and persuasive than the sexual urge.

threatened: in wildlife terms, a species present in its range but in danger because of a decline in numbers.

tree: a woody plant 12 or more feet (four or more meters) tall with a single main stem (trunk) and a more or less distinct crown of leaves.

transplant: In wildlife terms, an animal moved to a new area.

understory: the layer of plants growing under another higher layer of plants, e.g., grass, weeds, and brush under forest trees.

vegetation: the mass of plants that covers a given area. Flora, a term often wrongly used interchangeably with vegetation, is a list of the species of plants that compose the vegetation.

veldt: South African grassland, with scattered trees.

variable: cabable of living, growing, and developing.

waterfowl: water birds, usually ducks, but including shore and wading birds, geese, etc.

wild: not tamed or domesticated, living in a basically free condition. A wild animal provides for its own food, shelter, and other needs in an environment that serves as a suitable habitat.

wildlife: animals that are not tamed or domesticated; may be small organisms only visible to humans if seen through a microscope, or as large as a whale. Wildlife includes, but is not limited to, insects, spiders, birds, reptiles, fish, amphibians, and mammals, if non-domesticated.

wildlife manager: a person who manages wildlife habitat, and/or other related human acitivites.

wildlife management: the application of scientific knowledge and technical skills to protect, preserve, conserve, limit, enhance, or extend the value of wildlife and its habitat.

woodland: a wooded area in which the trees are often small, short bowled, and open grown; farm woodland—any wooded area that is part of a farm.

yard up: to gather in a sheltered area in winter; used typically in reference to deer, moose, etc.

zero population growth: the maintenance or holding of population numbers at a fixed level so as to obviate increase.

This glossary is primarily designed for reference and background information. Occasionally, terms are defined within an activity and are not repeated here. Key vocabulary for activities is usually defined here, especially if it is specific to wildlife and understanding of natural systems. This "Glossary" is compiled from four principal sources. The majority of the terms and definitions are reprinted with few changes from Multidisciplinary Wildlife Teaching Activities, developed and edited by William R. Hernbrode. (Columbus, Ohio: ERIC Clearinghouse for Science, Mathematics, and Environmental Education, 1978.) The next largest group of entries is derived from the "Glossary" which appears in the Project Learning Tree Supplementary Actitity Guide for Grades K through 6, and Grades 7 through 12. (Washington D.C.: American Forest Institute, 1977.) A number of entries are adapted or reprinted from "Wildlife Aid" No. 2. (Portland, Oregon: U.S. Forest Service, R-6, June 1965.). Additional entries are based on the contributions of the Project WILD Steering Committee, staff, and reviewers.

All "Glossary" materials derived from previously published sources are adapted and/or reprinted with the permission of the copyright holder. We extend our thanks to those organizations and individuals for their assistance.

ACTIVITIES BY GRADE

Activities are listed by grade level in the order they appear in the book.

Kindergarten
What's Wild?
Color Crazy
Wildlife Is Everywhere!
Everybody Needs A Home
Make A Coat!
What Bear Goes Where?
Forest In A Jar
The Thicket Game
Seeing Is Believing
Surprise Terrarium
Classroom Carrying Capacity
Wildwork
First Impressions
Saturday Morning Wildlife Watching
Learning To Look, Looking To See
Too Close For Comfort
Ethi-Thinking
Playing Lightly On The Earth

Grade 1
What's Wild?
Color Crazy
Wildlife Is Everywhere!
Everybody Needs A Home
Make A Coat!
What Bear Goes Where?
Forest In A Jar
The Thicket Game
Seeing Is Believing
Surprise Terrarium
Classroom Carrying Capacity
Wildwork
First Impressions
Saturday Morning Wildlife Watching
Learning to Look, Looking To See
Too Close For Comfort
Ethi-Thinking
Playing Lightly On The Earth

Grade 2
What's Wild?
Color Crazy
Grasshopper Gravity

Wildlife Is Everywhere!
The Beautiful Basics
Everybody Needs A Home
Habitracks
What's That, Habitat?
Make A Coat!
What Bear Goes Where?
Graphananimal
Forest In A Jar
The Thicket Game
Surprise Terrarium
Polar Bears In Phoenix?
Classroom Carrying Capacity
Wildwork
First Impressions
And The Wolf Wore Shoes
Saturday Morning Wildlife Watching
Learning To Look, Looking To See
Too Close For Comfort
Ethi-Thinking
Playing Lightly On The Earth
Can Do!

Grade 3
What's Wild?
Ants On A Twig
Color Crazy
Grasshopper Gravity
Wildlife Is Everywhere!
Everybody Needs A Home
Habitracks
What's That, Habitat?
What's For Dinner?
Museum Search For Wildlife
Environmental Barometer
Make A Coat!
What Bear Goes Where?
Graphananimal
Forest In A Jar
The Thicket Game
Seeing Is Believing
Surprise Terrarium
Polar Bears In Phoenix?
Classroom Carrying Capacity
How Many Bears Can Live In This Forest?
Owl Pellets
Wildwork
First Impressions
And The Wolf Wore Shoes
Saturday Morning Wildlife Watching
Learning To Look, Looking To See
Too Close For Comfort
Ethi-Thinking
Playing Lightly On The Earth
Can Do!

Grade 4

Animal Charades
Bearly Born
Ants On A Twig
Color Crazy
Grasshopper Gravity
Microtrek Scavenger Hunt
Stormy Weather
Habitat Lap Sit
Habitracks
Habitat Rummy
What's For Dinner?
Litter We Know
Tracks!
Wild Words
Animal Poetry
Museum Search For Wildlife
Let's Go Fly A Kite
Environmental Barometer
Make A Coat!
Graphananimal
Urban Nature Search
Good Buddies
Forest In A Jar
Pond Succession
The Thicket Game
Adaptation Artistry
Seeing Is Believing
Polar Bears In Phoenix?
Quick Frozen Critters
Classroom Carrying Capacity
Muskox Maneuvers
How Many Bears Can Live In This Forest?
Visual Vocabulary
Owl Pellets
Wildwork
Oh Deer!
Who Lives Here?
Planting Animals
Smokey The Bear Said What?
Lobster In Your Lunch Box
First Impressions
And The Wolf Wore Shoes
Saturday Morning Wildlife Watching
Wildlife In National Symbols
Learning To Look, Looking To See
Too Close For Comfort
Shrinking Habitat
Migration Barriers
Deadly Links
Keeping Score
Planning For People And For Wildlife
Ethi-Thinking
Playing Lightly On The Earth
What Did Your Lunch Cost Wildlife?
Can Do!
Improving Wildlife Habitat In The Community

Grade 5

Animal Charades
Bearly Born
Ants On A Twig
Color Crazy
Interview A Spider
Grasshopper Gravity
Microtrek Scavenger Hunt
Stormy Weather
Habitat Lap Sit
Habitracks
Habitat Rummy
My Kingdom For A Shelter
What's For Dinner?
Litter We Know
Tracks!
Wild Words
Animal Poetry
Museum Search For Wildlife
Let's Go Fly A Kite
Seed Need
Environmental Barometer
Make A Coat!
Graphananimal
Urban Nature Search
Good Buddies
Forest In A Jar
Pond Succession
The Thicket Game
Adaptation Artistry
Seeing Is Believing
Polar Bears In Phoenix?
Quick Frozen Critters
Classroom Carrying Capacity
Muskox Maneuvers
How Many Bears Can Live In This Forest?
Visual Vocabulary
Owl Pellets
Wildwork
Oh Deer!
Here Today, Gone Tomorrow
Who Lives Here?
Planting Animals
Smokey The Bear Said What?
The Hunter
Lobster In Your Lunch Box
First Impressions
And The Wolf Wore Shoes
Saturday Morning Wildlife Watching
Wildlife In National Symbols
Changing Attitudes
Learning To Look, Looking To See
Too Close For Comfort
Shrinking Habitat
Migration Barriers
Deadly Links
Keeping Score

Planning For People And For Wildlife
Ethi-Thinking
Playing Lightly On The Earth
Water's Going On?!
What Did Your Lunch Cost Wildlife?
Flip The Switch For Wildlife
Ethi-Reasoning
Can Do!
Improving Wildlife Habitat In The Community

Grade 6
Animal Charades
Bearly Born
Ants On A Twig
Color Crazy
Interview A Spider
Grasshopper Gravity
Microtrek Scavenger Hunt
Stormy Weather
Habitat Lap Sit
Habitat Rummy
My Kingdom For A Shelter
What's For Dinner?
Litter We Know
Tracks!
Wild Words
Animal Poetry
Museum Search For Wildlife
Let's Go Fly A Kite
Eco-Enrichers
Seed Need
Make A Coat!
Graphananimal
Urban Nature Search
Good Buddies
Forest In A Jar
Pond Succession
The Thicket Game
Adaptation Artistry
Seeing Is Believing
Polar Bears In Phoenix?
Quick Frozen Critters
Classroom Carrying Capacity
Muskox Maneuvers
How Many Bears Can Live In This Forest?
Visual Vocabulary
Rainfall And The Forest
Owl Pellets
Wildwork
Oh Deer!
Here Today, Gone Tomorrow
Who Lives Here?
Planting Animals
Smokey The Bear Said What?
Checks And Balances
No Water Off A Duck's Back

The Hunter
Lobster In Your Lunch Box
First Impressions
Saturday Morning Wildlife Watching
Cartoons And Bumper Stickers
Does Wildlife Sell Cigarettes?
The Power Of A Song
Wildlife In National Symbols
Changing Attitudes
Learning To Look, Looking To See
Too Close For Comfort
Shrinking Habitat
Migration Barriers
To Zone Or Not To Zone
Deadly Links
Keeping Score
Planning For People And For Wildlife
Ethi-Thinking
Playing Lightly On The Earth
Water's Going On?!
What Did Your Lunch Cost Wildlife?
Flip The Switch For Wildlife
Ethi-Reasoning
Can Do!
Improving Wildlife Habitat In The Community
Enviro-Ethics

These are suggested grade levels, reflecting the grades at which the activities were tested; however, you are encouraged to use and adapt the activities with younger and older students as well as special audiences.

ACTIVITIES BY SUBJECT

This is intended only as a guide for finding activities by subject. It is not a comprehensive listing of the subject areas within which a Project WILD activity may be used. Please be encouraged to incorporate and adapt activities for use in subject areas not listed.

Anthropology
Wildlife In National Symbols

Art
What's Wild?
Color Crazy
Everybody Needs A Home
What's That, Habitat?
My Kingdom For A Shelter
Litter We Know
Tracks!
Museum Search For Wildlife
Let's Go Fly A Kite
Make A Coat!
What Bear Goes Where?
Pond Succession
Adaptation Artistry
Seeing Is Believing
Rainfall And The Forest
Planting Animals
Smokey The Bear Said What?
Wildlife In National Symbols
Learning To Look, Looking To See
Planning For People And For Wildlife
Ethi-Thinking
Improving Wildlife Habitat In The Community

Business Education
Does Wildlife Sell Cigarettes?

Career Education
Wildwork
Checks And Balances
What Did Your Lunch Cost Wildlife?

Drama
Animal Charades
Visual Vocabulary

Environmental Problems
To Zone Or Not To Zone

Geography
Wildlife In National Symbols

Government
Wildlife In National Symbols

Health
The Beautiful Basics
What's For Dinner?
Lobster In Your Lunch Box

History
Wildlife In National Symbols

Home Economics
Make A Coat!
No Water Off A Duck's Back
Water's Going On?!
What Did Your Lunch Cost Wildlife?
Enviro-Ethics

Language Arts
What's Wild?
Color Crazy
Interview A Spider
Grasshopper Gravity
Wildlife is Everywhere
Microtrek Scavenger Hunt
Stormy Weather
The Beautiful Basics
Everybody Needs A Home
Habitracks
What's That, Habitat?
What's For Dinner?
Litter We Know
Wild Words
Animal Poetry
Museum Search For Wildlife
Make A Coat!
Graphananimal
Urban Nature Search
Good Buddies
Pond Succession
The Thicket Game
Adaptation Artistry
Seeing Is Believing
Surprise Terrarium
Polar Bears In Phoenix?
Classroom Carrying Capacity
Visual Vocabulary
Wildwork

Here Today, Gone Tomorrow
Who Lives Here?
Planting Animals
Smokey The Bear Said What?
No Water Off A Duck's Back
The Hunter
Lobster In Your Lunch Box
First Impressions
And The Wolf Wore Shoes
Saturday Morning Wildlife Watching
Cartoons And Bumper Stickers
Does Wildlife Sell Cigarettes?
The Power Of A Song
Changing Attitudes
Learning To Look, Looking To See
Too Close For Comfort
To Zone Or Not To Zone
Keeping Score
Ethi-Thinking
What Did Your Lunch Cost Wildlife?
Flip The Switch For Wildlife
Ethi-Reasoning
Can Do!
Improving Wildlife Habitat In The Community
Enviro-Ethics

Mathematics
Bearly Born
Grasshopper Gravity
Litter We Know
Let's Go Fly A Kite
Seed Need
Environmental Barometer
Make A Coat!
Graphananimal
How Many Bears Can Live In This Forest?
Oh Deer!
Checks And Balances
No Water Off A Duck's Back
The Hunter
Lobster In Your Lunch Box
Keeping Score
Water's Going On?!
Improving Wildlife Habitat In The Community

Music
The Power Of A Song

Physical Education
The Thicket Game
Quick Frozen Critters
Muskox Maneuvers
How Many Bears Can Live In This Forest?
Oh Deer!
Deadly Links
Playing Lightly On The Earth

Reading
And The Wolf Wore Shoes

Science
What's Wild?
Animal Charades
Bearly Born
Ants on A Twig
Color Crazy
Interview A Spider
Grasshopper Gravity
Wildlife Is Everywhere!
Microtrek
Scavenger Hunt
Stormy Weather
The Beautiful Basics
Everybody Needs A Home
Habitat Lap Sit
Habitracks
What's That, Habitat?
Habitat Rummy
My Kingdom For A Shelter
What's For Dinner?
Litter We Know
Tracks!
Animal Poetry
Let's Go Fly A Kite
Eco-Enrichers
Seed Need
Environmental Barometer
Make A Coat!
What Bear Goes Where?
Graphananimal
Urban Nature Search
Good Buddies
Forest In A Jar
Pond Succession
The Thicket Game
Adaptation Artistry
Seeing Is Believing
Surprise Terrarium
Polar Bears In Phoenix?
Quick Frozen Critters
Classroom Carrying Capacity
Muskox Maneuvers
How Many Bears Can Live In This Forest?
Visual Vocabulary
Rainfall And The Forest
Owl Pellets
Wildwork
Oh Deer!
Here Today, Gone Tomorrow
Who Lives Here?
Planting Animals
Smokey The Bear Said What?
Checks And Balances

No Water Off A Duck's Back
The Hunter
Lobster In Your Lunch Box
First Impressions
And The Wolf Wore Shoes
Saturday Morning Wildlife Watching
Wildlife In National Symbols
Learning To Look, Looking To See
Too Close For Comfort
Shrinking Habitat
Migration Barriers
To Zone Or Not To Zone
Deadly Links
Keeping Score
Planning For People And For Wildlife
Ethi-Thinking
Playing Lightly On The Earth
Water's Going On?!
What Did Your Lunch Cost Wildlife?
Flip The Switch For Wildlife
Ethi-Reasoning
Can Do!
Improving Wildlife Habitat In The Community
Enviro-Ethics

Social Studies
Grasshopper Gravity
Microtrek Scavenger Hunt
Stormy Weather
Habitracks
What's That, Habitat?
Litter We Know
Museum Search For Wildlife
Seed Need
Environmental Barometer
Make A Coat!
Urban Nature Search
Polar Bears In Phoenix?
Classroom Carrying Capacity
How Many Bears Can Live In This Forest?
Rainfall And The Forest
Wildwork
Oh Deer!
Here Today, Gone Tomorrow
Smokey The Bear Said What?
No Water Off A Duck's Back
The Hunter
Saturday Morning Wildlife Watching
Cartoons And Bumper Stickers
Does Wildlife Sell Cigarettes?
The Power Of A Song
Wildlife In National Symbols
Changing Attitudes
Learning To Look, Looking To See
Too Close For Comfort
Shrinking Habitat

Migration Barriers
To Zone Or Not To Zone
Deadly Links
Keeping Score
Planning For People And For Wildlife
Ethi-Thinking
Playing Lightly On The Earth
Water's Going On?!
What Did Your Lunch Cost Wildlife?
Flip The Switch For Wildlife
Ethi-Reasoning
Can Do!
Improving Wildlife Habitat In The Community
Enviro-Ethics

Speech
To Zone Or Not To Zone

Vocational Agriculture
Checks And Balances
What Did Your Lunch Cost Wildlife?

CROSS REFERENCE BY SKILLS

The following is a listing of major skills which Project WILD activities have been designed to teach or develop. The list is not intended to be comprehensive; most activities teach additional skills. Activities may also be adapted to emphasize additional and different skills.

Analysis

Bearly Born; Ants On A Twig; Grasshopper Gravity; Wildlife Is Everywhere!; Microtrek Scavenger Hunt; The Beautiful Basics; Everybody Needs A Home; Habitracks; What's That, Habitat?; Habitat Rummy; What's For Dinner?; Litter We Know; Tracks!; Museum Search For Wildlife; Eco-Enrichers; Seed Need; Environmental Barometer; Make A Coat!; What Bear Goes Where?; Graphananimal; Urban Nature Search; Forest In A Jar; Pond Succession; The Thicket Game; Adaptation Artistry; Seeing Is Believing; Polar Bears In Phoenix?; Quick Frozen Critters; Classroom Carrying Capacity; Muskox Maneuvers; How Many Bears Can Live In This Forest?; Rainfall And The Forest; Owl Pellets; Here Today, Gone Tomorrow; Planting Animals; Smokey The Bear Said What?; Checks And Balances; No Water Off A Duck's Back; The Hunter; Lobster In Your Lunch Box; First Impressions; And The Wolf Wore Shoes; Saturday Morning Wildlife Watching; Cartoons And Bumper Stickers; Does Wildlife Sell Cigarettes?; The Power Of A Song; Wildlife In National Symbols; Changing Attitudes; Migration Barriers; To Zone Or Not To Zone; Deadly Links; Keeping Score; Planning For People And Wildlife; Ethi-Thinking; Playing Lightly On The Earth; Water's Going On?!; What Did Your Lunch Cost Wildlife?; Flip The Switch For Wildlife; Ethi-Reasoning; Can Do!; Improving Wildlife Habitat; Enviro-Ethics

Application

Microtrek Scavenger Hunt; Habitat Rummy; My Kingdom For A Shelter; Wild Words; Museum Search For Wildlife; Eco-Enrichers; What Bear Goes Where?; Urban Nature Search; Good Buddies; Forest In A Jar; Pond Succession; The Thicket Game; Adaptation Artistry; Seeing Is Believing; Surprise Terrarium; Polar Bears In Phoenix?; Classroom Carrying Capacity; Visual Vocabulary; Rainfall And The Forest; Oh Deer!; And The Wolf Wore Shoes; Migration Barriers; To Zone Or Not To Zone; Keeping Score; Planning For People And Wildlife; Ethi-Thinking; Water's Going On?!; What Did Your Lunch Cost Wildlife?; Flip The Switch For Wildlife; Ethi-Reasoning; Can Do!; What Bear Goes Where?; Urban Nature Search; Good Buddies; Forest In A Jar; Pond Succession; The Thicket Game; Adaptation Artistry; Seeing Is Believing; Surprise Terrarium; Polar Bears In Phoenix?; Classroom Carrying Capacity; Visual Vocabulary; Oh Deer!; And The Wolf Wore Shoes; Migration Barriers; To Zone Or Not To Zone; Keeping Score; Planning For People And Wildlife; Ethi-Thinking; Water's Going On?!; What Did Your Lunch Cost Wildlife?; Flip The Switch For Wildlife; Ethi-Reasoning; Can Do!; Improving Wildlife Habitat; Enviro-Ethics

Classification

What's Wild; Ants On A Twig; Grasshopper Gravity; Microtrek Scavenger Hunt; The Beautiful Basics; Habitracks; Habitat Rummy; What's For Dinner?; Litter We Know; Eco-enrichers; Seed Need; Environmental Barometer; Make A Coat!; What Bear Goes Where?; Graphananimal; Urban Nature Search; Good Buddies; Seeing Is Believing; Here Today, Gone Tomorrow; Who Lives Here?; Smokey The Bear Said What?; Lobster In Your Lunch Box; And The Wolf Wore Shoes; Saturday Morning Wildlife Watching; Does Wildlife Sell Cigarettes?; Deadly Links; Keeping Score; What Did Your Lunch Cost Wildlife?;

Comparing Similarities And Differences

Bearly Born; Ants On A Twig; Grasshopper Gravity; Stormy Weather; The Beautiful Basics; Everybody Needs A Home; Habitracks; What's That, Habitat?; Habitat Rummy; Tracks!; Eco-Enrichers; Seed Need; Environmental Barometer; What Bear Goes Where?; Urban Nature Search; Forest In A Jar; Pond Succession; Seeing Is Believing; Polar Bears In Phoenix?; Classroom Carrying Capacity; Rainfall And The Forest; Owl Pellets; Oh Deer!; Smokey The Bear Said What?; The Hunter;

First Impressions; And The Wolf Wore Shoes; Saturday Morning Wildlife Watching; Wildlife In National Symbols; Changing Attitudes; Shrinking Habitat; Migration Barriers; To Zone Or Not To Zone; Deadly Links; Planning For People And Wildlife; Playing Lightly On The Earth; What Did Your Lunch Cost Wildlife?; Flip The Switch For Wildlife; Enviro-Ethics

Computation

Bearly Born; Grasshopper Gravity; Litter We Know; Eco-Enrichers; Environmental Barometer; Graphananimal; How Many Bears Can Live In This Forest?; Checks And Balances; No Water Off A Duck's Back; Lobster In Your Lunch Box; Deadly Links; Keeping Score; Water's Going On?!

Description

Ants On A Twig; Color Crazy; Interview A Spider; Grasshopper Gravity; Microtrek Scavenger Hunt; Stormy Weather; My Kingdom For A Shelter; Wild Words; Animal Poetry; Eco-Enrichers; Seed Need; Make A Coat!; What Bear Goes Where?; Urban Nature Search; Forest In A Jar; Pond Succession; The Thicket Game; Adaptation Artistry; Seeing Is Believing; Quick Frozen Critters; Classroom Carrying Capacity; Muskox Maneuvers; Wildwork; Oh Deer!; Who Lives Here?; Smokey The Bear Said What?; The Hunter; First Impressions Learnning To Look, Looking To See; Shrinking Habitat; Migration Barriers; To Zone Or Not To Zone; Deadly Links; Keeping Score; Ethi-Thinking; Can Do!; Improving Wildlife Habitat; Enviro-Ethics

Discussion

Bearly Born; Ants On A Twig; Interview A Spider; Grasshopper Gravity; Wildlife Is Everywhere!; Microtrek Scavenger Hunt; The Beautiful Basics; Everybody Needs A Home; Habitat Lap Sit; Habitracks; What's That, Habitat?; What's For Dinner?; Litter We Know; Wild Words; Museum Search For Wildlife; Let's Go Fly A Kite; Eco-Enrichers; Environmental Barometer; Make A Coat!; What Bear Goes Where?; Urban Nature Search; Forest In A Jar; Pond Succession; The Thicket Game; Adaptation Artistry; Seeing Is Believing; Surprise Terrarium; Polar Bears In Phoenix?; Quick Frozen Critters; Classroom Carrying Capacity; Muskox Maneuvers; How Many Bears Can Live In This Forest?; Rainfall And The Forest; Wildwork; Oh Deer!; Here Today, Gone Tomorrow; Who Lives Here?; Planting Animals; Smokey The Bear Said What?; No Water Off A Duck's Back; The Hunter; Lobster In Your Lunch Box; And The Wolf Wore Shoes; Saturday Morn-

ing Wildlife Watching; Cartoons And Bumper Stickers; Does Wildlife Sell Cigarettes?; The Power Of A Song; Learning To Look, Looking To See; Shrinking Habitat; To Zone Or Not To Zone; Deadly Links; Keeping Score; Planning For People And Wildlife; Ethi-Thinking; Water's Going On?!; What Did Your Lunch Cost Wildlife?; Flip The Switch For Wildlife; Ethi-Reasoning; Can Do!; Improving Wildlife Habitat; Enviro-Ethics

Drawing

Bearly Born; Color Crazy; Everybody Needs A Home; What's That, Habitat?; What's For Dinner?; Wild Words; Forest In A Jar; Pond Succession; Adaptation Artistry; Polar Bears In Phoenix?; No Water Off A Duck's Back; Migration Barriers; Planning For People And Wildlife; Ethi-Thinking; What Did Your Lunch Cost Wildlife?; Flip The Switch For Wildlife; Improving Wildlife Habitat

Evaluation

Litter We Know; Environmental Barometer; Make A Coat!; Polar Bears In Phoenix?; Quick Frozen Critters; Classroom Carrying Capacity; Muskox Maneuvers; How Many Bears Can Live In This Forest?; Who Lives Here?; Smokey The Bear Said What?; Checks And Balances; The Hunter; Saturday Morning Wildlife Watching; Cartoons And Bumper Stickers; Does Wildlife Sell Cigarettes?; The Power Of A Song; Wildlife In National Symbols; Changing Attitudes; Too Close For Comfort; Shrinking Habitat; Migration Barriers; To Zone Or Not To Zone; Deadly Links; Keeping Score; Planning For People And Wildlife; Ethi-Thinking; Playing Lightly On The Earth; Water's Going On?!; What Did Your Lunch Cost Wildlife?; Flip the Switch For Wildlife; Ethi-Reasoning; Can Do!; Improving Wildlife Habitat; Enviro-Ethics

Generalization

Bearly Born; Ants On A Twig; Color Crazy; Interview A Spider; Grasshopper Gravity; Wildlife Is Everywhere!; Microtrek Scavenger Hunt; Stormy Weather; Everybody Needs A Home; Habitat Lap Sit; Habitracks; What's That, Habitat?; Museum Search For Wildlife; Eco-Enrichers; What Bear Goes Where?; Urban Nature Search; Forest In A Jar; The Thicket Game; Seeing Is Believing; Surprise Terrarium; Quick Frozen Critters; Muskox Maneuvers; How Many Bears Can Live In This Forest?; Rainfall And The Forest; Owl Pellets; Oh Deer!; Who Lives Here?; No Water Off A Duck's Back; First Impressions; Shrinking Habitat; Migration Barriers; To Zone Or Not To Zone; Deadly Links; Ethi-Thinking; Water's Going On?!

Inference

Seeing Is Believing; Classroom Carrying Capacity; Too Close For Comfort

Interview

Interview A Spider; Changing Attitudes

Invention

Color Crazy; Animal Poetry; Let's Go Fly A Kite; Make A Coat!; Forest In A Jar; Adaptation Artistry; Seeing Is Believing; Polar Bears In Phoenix?; Visual Vocabulary; Planning For People And Wildlife; Playing Lightly On The Earth; Can Do!; Improving Wildlife Habitat; Enviro-Ethics

Kinesthetic Concept Development

Animal Charades; Ants On A Twig; Habitat Lap Sit; Eco-Enrichers; Seed Need; Graphananimal; Urban Nature Search; The Thicket Game; Quick Frozen Critters; Classroom Carrying Capacity; Muskox Maneuvers; How Many Bears Can Live In This Forest?; Visual Vocabulary; Oh Deer!; Shrinking Habitat; Deadly Links

Listening

The Power Of A Song

Listing

Grasshopper Gravity; Microtrek Scavenger Hunt; The Beautiful Basics; What's For Dinner?; Seed Need; What Bear Goes Where?; Graphananimal; Urban Nature Search; Classroom Carrying Capacity; How Many Bears Can Live In This Forest?; Wildwork; Here Today, Gone Tomorrow; Smokey The Bear Said What?; Lobster In Your Lunch Box; First Impressions; And The Wolf Wore Shoes; Learning To Look, Looking To See; Can Do!

Mapping

Habitracks

Media Construction

What's Wild; Bearly Born; Color Crazy; Habitat Rummy; My Kingdom For A Shelter; What's For Dinner?; Litter We Know; Wild Words; Let's Go Fly A Kite; Make A Coat!; What Bear Goes Where?; Graphananimal; Forest In A Jar; Pond Succession; Adaptation Artistry; Seeing Is Believing; Planting Animals; Smokey The Bear Said What?; Lobster In Your Lunch Box; Wildlife In National Symbols; Migration Barriers; Planning For People And Wildlife; Ethi-Thinking; What Did Your Lunch Cost Wildlife?; Flip The Switch For Wildlife; Improving Wildlife Habitat

Observation

What's Wild; Animal Charades; Ants On A Twig; Color Crazy; Grasshopper Gravity; Wildlife Is Everywhere!; Microtrek Scavenger Hunt; Habitracks; My Kingdom For A Shelter; Litter We Know; Wild Words; Museum Search For Wildlife; Eco-Enrichers; Seed Need; Environmental Barometer; Make A Coat!; What Bear Goes Where?; Graphananimal; Urban Nature Search; Pond Succession; The Thicket Game; Adaptation Artistry; Seeing Is Believing; Surprise Terrarium; Polar Bears In Phoenix?; Quick Frozen Critters; Classroom Carrying Capacity; Muskox Maneuvers; How Many Bears Can Live In This Forest?; Visual Vocabulary; Oh Deer!; No Water Off A Duck's Back; And The Wolf Wore Shoes; Saturday Morning Wildlife Watching; Cartoons And Bumper Stickers; Does Wildlife Sell Cigarettes?; Learning To Look, Looking To See; Shrinking Habitat; Migration Barriers; Keeping Score; Water's Going On?!

Problem Solving

Microtrek Scavenger Hunt; Litter We Know; Let's Go Fly A Kite; Adaptation Artistry; Polar Bears In Phoenix?; Visual Vocabulary; Keeping Score; Planning For People And Wildlife; Ethi-Thinking; Playing Lightly On The Earth; Water's Going On?!; What Did Your Lunch Cost Wildlife?; Flip The Switch For Wildlife; Ethi-Reasoning; Can Do!; Improving Wildlife Habitat; Enviro-Ethics

Psychomotor Development

Tracks!; Let's Go Fly A Kite; Eco-Enrichers; Make A Coat!; What Bear Goes Where?; Graphananimal; Forest In A Jar; The Thicket Game; Seeing Is Believing; Quick Frozen Critters; Muskox Maneuvers; How Many Bears Can Live In This Forest?; Visual Vocabulary; Oh Deer!; Planting Animals; Planning For People And Wildlife; Playing Lightly On The Earth

Public Speaking

Changing Attitudes; Can Do!

Reading

Bearly Born; Color Crazy; Interview A Spider; Grasshopper Gravity; Microtrek Scavenger Hunt; The Beautiful Basics; Habitracks; What's That, Habitat?; Habitat Rummy; Graphananimal; Visual Vocabulary; Who Lives Here?; And The Wolf Wore Shoes; Cartoons And Bumper Stickers; Does Wildlife Sell Cigarettes?

Reporting

Eco-Enrichers; Good Buddies; Adaptation Artistry; Who Lives Here?; First Impressions; Saturday Morning Wildlife Watching; Changing Attitudes; Migration Barriers; To Zone Or Not To Zone; Keeping Score; Flip The Switch For Wildlife; Enviro-Ethics

Research

Interview A Spider; My Kingdom For A Shelter; Eco-Enrichers; Good Buddies; Forest In A Jar; Who Lives Here?; Planting Animals; Smokey The Bear Said What?; First Impressions; Wildlife In National Symbols; Changing Attitudes; To Zone Or Not To Zone; Flip The Switch For Wildlife

Small Group Work

Ants On A Twig; Microtrek Scavenger Hunt; Habitat Lap Sit; Habitracks; Habitat Rummy; Litter We Know; Good Buddies; Pond Succession; Seeing Is Believing; Muskox Maneuvers; Visual Vocabulary; Smokey The Bear Said What?; First Impressions; Saturday Morning Wildlife Watching; And The Wolf Wore Shoes; Migration Barriers; Keeping Score; Ethi-thinking; Playing Lightly On The Earth; Flip The Switch For Wildlife; Ethi-Reasoning; Can Do!; Improving Wildlife Habitat

Synthesis

Habitracks; Litter We Know; Tracks!; Animal Poetry; Make A Coat!; What Bear Goes Where?; Pond Succession; Adaptation Artistry; Seeing Is Believing; Polar Bears In Phoenix?; Visual Vocabulary; Rainfall And The Forest; Wildwork; Here Today, Gone Tomorrow; Planting Animals; Smokey The Bear Said What?; Saturday Morning Wildlife Watching; Wildlife In National Symbols; Shrinking Habitat; Migration Barriers; To Zone Or Not To Zone; Deadly Links; Keeping Score; Planning For People And Wildlife; Ethi-Thinking; Playing Lightly On The Earth; Water's Going On?!; What Did Your Lunch Cost Wildlife?; Flip The Switch For Wildlife; Ethi-Reasoning; Can Do!; Improving Wildlife Habitat; Enviro-Ethics

Visualization

Stormy Weather; Everybody Needs A Home; Wild Words; Animal Poetry; Pond Succession; Polar Bears In Phoenix?; Visual Vocabulary; Planting Animals; Smokey The Bear Said What?; Migration Barriers; Planning For People And Wildlife; What Did Your Lunch Cost Wildlife?; Flip The Switch For Wildlife; Improving Wildlife Habitat

Writing

Bearly Born; Ants On A Twig; Color Crazy; Interview A Spider; Grasshopper Gravity; Microtrek Scavenger Hunt; What's That, Habitat?; Habitat Rummy; What's For Dinner?; Wild Words; Animal Poetry; Eco-Enrichers; Seed Need; Graphan-animal; Urban Nature Search; Adaptation Artistry; Planting Animals; Lobster In Your Lunch Box; First Impressions; Changing Attitudes; To Zone Or Not To Zone; Keeping Score; What Did Your Lunch Cost Wildlife?; Flip The Switch For Wildlife; Ethi-Reasoning; Can Do!

TOPIC INDEX

The following is an alphabetical listing of topics included in Project WILD activities. This is not a comprehensive listing; that is, it does not list every possible topic. It does however include topics that might be included in an elementary course of study in a variety of subject areas.

Activities are listed generally in the order they appear in the guide, not according to the degree to which they emphasize the topic.

We hope this serves to assist in your curriculum planning as you integrate Project WILD activities into existing courses of study and other instructional programs.

Adaptation
Tracks!; What Bear Goes Where?; The Thicket Game; Adaptation Artistry; Seeing Is Believing; Surprise Terrarium; Polar Bears In Phoenix?; Quick Frozen Critters, Muskox Maneuvers; Rainfall And The Forest; Owl Pellets; Here Today, Gone Tomorrow (indirect); Who Lives Here? (indirect); Too Close For Comfort (indirect)

Advertising
Does Wildlife Sell Cigarettes?; The Power Of A Song

Aesthetic Values of Wildlife
Wild Words; Animal Poetry; Museum Search For Wildlife; Let's Go Fly A Kite; Here Today, Gone Tomorrow (extension); First Impressions; Cartoons And Bumper Stickers; Does Wildlife Sell Cigarettes?; The Power Of A Song; Wildlife In National Symbols; Too Close For Comfort; Shrinking Habitat; Migration Barriers; To Zone Or Not To Zone; Planning For People And For Wildlife

Agriculture
Deadly Links; What Did Your Lunch Cost Wildlife?

Basic Survival Needs
Bearly Born; Ants On A Twig; Stormy Weather; The Beautiful Basics; Everybody Needs A Home; Habitat Lap Sit; Habitracks; What's That, Habitat?; Habitat Rummy; My Kingdom For A Shelter; What's For Dinner?; What Bear Goes Where?; Polar Bears In Phoenix?; Quick Frozen Critters; Classroom Carrying Capacity; How Many Bears Can Live In This Forest?; Rainfall And The Forest; Oh Deer!; Here Today, Gone Tomorrow;

Who Lives Here? (indirect); Planting Animals (indirect); Checks And Balances; Lobster In Your Lunch Box; Too Close For Comfort; Shrinking Habitat; Migration Barriers; Deadly Links; Planning For People And For Wildlife (indirect); Water's Going On (indirect); Flip The Switch For Wildlife; Improving Wildlife Habitat

Camouflage
Surprise Terrarium; The Thicket Game; Quick Frozen Critters

Career Education
Wildwork

Carrying Capacity
Classroom Carrying Capacity; How Many Bears Can Live In This Forest?; Rainfall And The Forest; Oh Deer!; Here Today, Gone Tomorrow (indirect); Who Lives Here? (indirect); Planting Animals; Checks And Balances; The Hunter (indirect); Too Close For Comfort; Shrinking Habitat; Planning For People And For Wildlife (indirect); Flip The Switch For Wildlife (indirect); Improving Wildlife Habitat

Change
Eco Enrichers; Forest In A Jar; Pond Succession; Classroom Carrying Capacity; How Many Bears Can Live In This Forest?; Oh Deer!; Who Lives Here?; Planting Animals; Smokey The Bear Said What?; Checks And Balances; Shrinking Habitat; To Zone Or Not To Zone; Deadly Links; Planning For People And For Wildlife; Flip The Switch For Wildlife; Improving Wildlife Habitat

Commensalism
Good Buddies

Commercial Values of Wildlife
Make a Coat; Here Today, Gone Tomorrow (indirect); The Hunter (indirect); Lobster In Your Lunch Box; First Impressions; Does Wildlife Sell Cigarettes?; The Power Of A Song; Wildlife In National Symbols; Too Close For Comfort (indirect); Shrinking Habitat (indirect); Migration Barriers (indirect); To Zone Or Not To Zone (indirect); Planning For People And For Wildlife (indirect)

Communications
Checks And Balances; First Impressions; And The Wolf Wore Shoes; Saturday Morning Wildlife

Watching; Cartoons And Bumper Stickers; Does Wildlife Sell Cigarettes?; The Power Of A Song; Wildlife In National Symbols; Changing Attitudes; Too Close For Comfort (indirect); Migration Barriers; To Zone Or Not To Zone; Planning For People And For Wildlife; What Did Your Lunch Cost Wildlife?; Ethi-Reasoning; Can Do!; Improving Wildlife Habitat; Enviro-Ethics

Community Attitudes
The Hunter; Changing Attitudes; Shrinking Habitat; To Zone Or Not To Zone; Keeping Score (indirect); Planning For People And For Wildlife (indirect); Ethi-Thinking; Water's Going On; What Did Your Lunch Cost Wildlife?; Flip The Switch For Wildlife; Ethi-Reasoning; Can Do!; Improving Wildlife Habitat; Enviro-Ethics

Components Of Habitat
Ants On A Twig; The Beautiful Basics; Everybody Needs A Home: Habitat Lap Sit; Habitracks; What's That, Habitat?; Habitat Rummy; What Bear Goes Where?; Polar Bears in Phoenix?; Rainfall And The Forest; Oh Deer! (indirect); Improving Wildlife Habitat (application)

Concept Review
Visual Vocabulary

Conflicting Points Of View Regarding Natural Resource Issues
Smokey The Bear Said What?; Checks And Balances; No Water Off A Duck's Back; The Hunter; Saturday Morning Wildlife Watching; Cartoons And Bumper Stickers; Does Wildlife Sell Cigarettes?; The Power Of A Song; Changing Attitudes; Too Close For Comfort (indirect); Shrinking Habitat; Migration Barriers; To Zone Or Not To Zone; Keeping Score (indirect); Planning For People And For Wildlife (indirect); What Did Your Lunch Cost Wildilfe?; Ethi-Reasoning; Improving Wildlife Habitat

Conservation
Here Today, Gone Tomorrow; Who Lives Here? Planting Animals; Smokey The Bear Said What?; Checks And Balances; No Water Off A Duck's Back; The Hunter; Lobster In Your Lunch Box; Cartoons And Bumper Stickers; Does Wildlife Sell Cigarettes?; To Close For Comfort; Shrinking Habitat; Migration Barriers; To Zone Or Not To Zone; Deadly Links; Keeping Score; Planning For People And For Wildlife; Ethi-Thinking; Playing Lightly On The Earth; Water's Going On; What Did Your Lunch Cost Wildlife?; Flip The Switch For Wildlife; Ethi-Reasoning; Can Do!; Improving Wildlife Habitat; Enviro-Ethics

Crowding
Too Close For Comfort; Shrinking Habitat; Planning For People And For Wildlife

Cycles
Forest In A Jar; Pond Succession; Rainfall And The Forest; Oh Deer!; Smokey The Bear Said What?; Checks And Balances; Deadly Links

Definitions Of Wild And Domesticated Animals
What's Wild?; Animal Charades; Interview A Spider; Lobster In Your Lunch Box

Dependence On Plants
What's For Dinner?; Eco-Enrichers; Rainfall And The Forest; Oh Deer!; Smokey The Bear Said What?; Checks And Balances; Lobster In Your Lunch Box; Shrinking Habitat; Deadly Links; What Did Your Lunch Cost Wildlife?; Improving Wildlife Habitat

Ecological Values Of Wildlife
Eco—Enrichers; Seed Need; Environmental Barometer; Good Buddies; Pond Succession; Here Today, Gone Tomorrow (extension); Who Lives Here?; Planting Animals; Lobster In Your Lunch Box; First Impressions; Too Close For Comfort; Shrinking Habitat; Migration Barriers; To Zone Or Not To Zone; Planning For People And For Wildlife

Economics
What's For Dinner?; Make A Coat; Wildwork; Checks And Balances; No Water Off A Duck's Back; The Hunter (indirect); Saturday Morning Wildlife Watching (indirect); Does Wildlife Sell Cigarettes?; The Power Of A Song; Shrinking Habitat; Migration Barriers; To Zone Or Not To Zone; Planning For People And For Wildlife; Water's Going On; What Did Your Lunch Cost Wildlife?; Flip The Switch For Wildlife; Improving Wildlife Habitat; Enviro-Ethics (indirect)

Endangered (Rare, Threatened, And Extinct) Species
Here Today, Gone Tomorrow; Who Lives Here? (indirect); Planting Animals; No Water Off a Duck's Back (indirect); Cartoons And Bumper Stickers (indirect); Too Close For Comfort; Migration Barriers (indirect); Deadly Links; Water's Going On (indirect); Flip The Switch For Wildlife (indirect)

Energy
Lobster In Your Lunch Box; Migration Barriers; Keeping Score (indirect); Planning For People And For Wildlife; Water's Going On; What Did Your

Lunch Cost Wildlife?; Flip The Switch For Wildlife; Enviro-Ethics (indirect)

Evidence Of Wildlife
Tracks!; Environmental Barometer; Graphan-animal; Urban Nature Search; Surprise Terrarium; Owl Pellets; Too Close For Comfort; Keeping Score

Environmental Impact Statement
Migration Barriers

Fire
Smokey The Bear Said What?

Food Chain
Owl Pellets; Shrinking Habitat; Deadly Links; Keeping Score (indirect); What Did Your Lunch Cost Wildlife?

Habitat (application; see Components Of Habitat for introduction)
Classroom Carrying Capacity; How Many Bears Can Live In This Forest?; Rainfall And The Forest; Oh Deer!; Here Today, Gone Tomorrow; Who Lives Here?; Planting Animals; Checks And Balances; Shrinking Habitat; Migration Barriers; To Zone Or Not To Zone; Deadly Links; Keeping Score; Planning For People And For Wildlife; Ethi-Thinking; What Did Your Lunch Cost Wildlife?; Flip The Switch For Wildlife; Can Do!; Improving Wildlife Habitat

Habitat Improvement
Environmental Barometer; Here Today, Gone Tomorrow (indirect); Who Lives Here? (indirect); Planting Animals (indirect); Smokey The Bear Said What?; Checks And Balances; Shrinking Habitat; Keeping Score; Planning For People And For Wildlife; Flip The Switch For Wildlife; Can Do!; Improving Wildlife Habitat

Habitat Loss
My Kingdom For A Shelter; Environmental Barometer (indirect); Polar Bears In Phoenix? (indirect); Classroom Carrying Capacity; How Many Bears Can Live In This Forest?; Oh Deer!; Here Today, Gone Tomorrow (indirect); Who Lives Here? (indirect); Planting Animals; Smokey The Bear Said What?; Checks And Balances; No Water Off A Duck's Back; Lobster In Your Lunch Box (indirect); Too Close For Comfort; Shrinking Habitat; Migration Barriers; To Zone Or Not To Zone; Keeping Score; Planning For People And For Wildlife; Flip The Switch For Wildlife; Improving Wildlife Habitat

Herbivores, Carnivores, Omnivores
Owl Pellets; Shrinking Habitat; Deadly Links (if terms introduced)

Historical Values Of Wildlife
Museum Search For Wildlife; Make A Coat; Here Today, Gone Tomorrow (extension); The Hunter; Lobster In Your Lunch Box; First Impressions; Cartoons And Bumper Stickers; The Power Of A Song; Wildlife In National Symbols; Changing Attitudes; Too Close For Comfort; Shrinking Habitat; Migration Barriers; To Zone Or Not To Zone; Planning For People And For Wildlife

Human Responsibilities And Wildlife
Grasshopper Gravity (introductory); Litter We Know; Polar Bears In Phoenix?; Here Today, Gone Tomorrow (indirect); Planting Animals; Smokey The Bear Said What?; Checks And Balances; No Water Off A Duck's Back; The Hunter; Lobster In Your Lunch Box; First Impressions; Saturday Morning Wildlife Watching; Cartoons And Bumper Stickers; Does Wildlife Sell Cigarettes?; The Power Of A Song; Changing Attitudes; Too Close For Comfort; Shrinking Habitat; Migration Barriers; To Zone Or Not To Zone; Deadly Links; Keeping Score; Planning For People And For Wildlife; Ethi-Thinking; Playing Lightly On The Earth; What Did Your Lunch Cost Wildlife?; Flip The Switch For Wildlife; Ethi-Reasoning; Can Do!; Improving Wildlife Habitat; Enviro-Ethics

Humor
Saturday Morning Wildlife Watching; Cartoons And Bumper Stickers; The Power Of A Song (indirect)

Hunting
Classroom Carrying Capacity; How Many Bears Can Live In This Forest? (indirect); Oh Deer! (indirect); Checks And Balances; The Hunter; Changing Attitudes; To Zone Or Not To Zone (indirect); Ethi-Reasoning

Interdependence
Good Buddies; Urban Nature Search (extension); Forest In A Jar; Pond Succession; The Thicket Game; Polar Bears In Phoenix?; Quick Frozen Critters; How Many Bears Can Live In This Forest?; Rainfall And The Forest; Owl Pellets; Oh Deer!; Here Today, Gone Tomorrow (indirect); Who Lives Here?; Planting Animals; Smokey The Bear Said What?; Checks And Balances; No Water Off A Duck's Back; Too Close For Comfort; Shrinking Habitat; Migration Barriers; To Zone Or Not To

Zone; Deadly Links; Keeping Score; Planning For People And For Wildlife; Water's Going On; What Did Your Lunch Cost Wildlife?; Flip The Switch For Wildlife; Can Do!; Improving Wildlife Habitat; Enviro-Ethics

Intrinsic Value
Grasshopper Gravity; Wild Words: A Journal-Making Activity (indirect); Animal Poetry (indirect); Museum Search for Wildlife (indirect); Let's Go Fly A Kite (indirect); Make A Coat; Here Today, Gone Tomorrow; The Hunter; Wildlife In National Symbols (indirect); To Zone Or Not To Zone (indirect); Keeping Score

Introduced Species
Who Lives Here?; Planting Animals, Lobster In Your Lunch Box (extension)

Land Development
Shrinking Habitat; Migration Barriers; To Zone Or Not To Zone; Planning For People And For Wildlife; Flip The Switch For Wildlife

Land Use
Too Close For Comfort; Shrinking Habitat; Migration Barriers; To Zone Or Not To Zone; Keeping Score; Planning For People And For Wildlife; Playing Lightly On The Earth; What Did Your Lunch Cost Wildlife?; Flip The Switch For Wildlife; Can Do!; Improving Wildlife Habitat

Land Use Planning
Shrinking Habitat; Migration Barriers; To Zone Or Not To Zone; Planning For People And For Wildlife; Flip The Switch For Wildlife (indirect); Can Do!; Improving Wildlife Habitat

Limiting Factors
Quick Forzen Critters; Muskox Maneuvers; How Many Bears Can Live In This Forest?; Rainfall And The Forest; Oh Deer!; Here Today, Gone Tomorrow; Who Lives Here? (indirect); Planting Animals; Checks And Balances; The Hunter; Too Close For Comfort; Shrinking Habitat; Migration Barriers (indirect); Deadly Links; Planning For People And For Wildlife (indirect); Water's Going On (indirect); What Did Your Lunch Cost Wildlife? (indirect); Flip The Switch For Wildlife (indirect); Improving Wildlife Habitat

Literature
Wild Words; Animal Poetry; The Hunter; First Impressions (indirect); And The Wolf Wore Shoes

Management Of Habitat
Classroom Carrying Capacity; How Many Bears Can Live In This Forest? (indirect); Oh Deer! (indirect); Here Today, Gone Tomorrow; Who Lives Here?; Planting Animals; Smokey The Bear Said What?; Checks And Balances; No Water Off A Duck's Back; The Hunter; Cartoons And Bumper Stickers; Too Close For Comfort; Shrinking Habitat; Migration Barriers; To Zone Or Not To Zone; Deadly Links; Planning For People And For Wildlife; What Did Your Lunch Cost Wildlife?; Flip The Switch For Wildlife; Can Do!; Improving Wildlife Habitat

Management Techniques
Planting Animals; Smokey The Bear Said What?; Checks And Balances; No Water Off A Duck's Back; The Hunter; What Did Your Lunch Cost Wildlife? (indirect); Cartoons And Bumper Stickers; Too Close For Comfort; Shrinking Habitat; Migration Barriers; To Zone Or Not To Zone; Deadly Links; Planning For People And For Wildlife; Flip The Switch For Wildlife (indirect); Can Do!; Improving Wildlife Habitat

Migration
Migration Barriers

Music
Power Of A Song

Mutualism
Good Buddies

National Symbols
Wildlife In National Symbols

Native/Non-Native Species
Here Today, Gone Tomorrow; Who Lives Here?; Planting Animals; Lobster In Your Lunch Box (extension)

Newspaper
Interview A Spider; Cartoons And Bumper Stickers; Does Wildlife Sell Cigarettes?

Occupation/Vocation
Wildwork; Checks And Balances, Smokey The Bear Said What?

Parasitism
Good Buddies

People And Wildlife Sharing Environments
Wildlife Is Everywhere; Microtrek Scavenger Hunt; Stormy Weather; Litter We Know; Here Today, Gone Tomorrow (indirect); Who Lives Here? (indirect); Planting Animals; Checks And Balances; No Water Off A Duck's Back; The Hunter;

Too Close For Comfort; Shrinking Habitat; Migration Barriers; To Zone Or Not To Zone; Deadly Links; Keeping Score; Planning For People And For Wildlife; Ethi-Thinking; Playing Lightly On The Earth; Water's Going On; What Did Your Lunch Cost Wildlife?; Ethi-Reasoning; Can Do!; Improving Wildlife Habitat; Enviro-Ethics

Pesticides
Deadly Links; What Did Your Lunch Cost Wildlife?

Politics
To Zone Or Not To Zone; Planning For People And For Wildlife; Flip The Switch For Wildlife; Can Do!; Improving Wildlife Habitat

Pollution
Litter We Know; Here Today, Gone Tomorrow (indirect); Checks And Balances; No Water Off A Duck's Back; Too Close For Comfort; Shrinking Habitat (indirect); Deadly Links; Keeping Score (indirect); Planning For People And For Wildlife (indirect); Ethi-Thinking (indirect); Playing Lightly On The Earth (indirect); What Did Your Lunch Cost Wildlife?; Flip The Switch For Wildlife (indirect)

Predator/Prey Relationships
The Thicket Game; Quick Frozen Critters, Muskox Maneuvers; Owl Pellets; Who Lives Here? (indirect); The Hunter

"Real" And "Make-Believe"
And The Wolf Wore Shoes; Saturday Morning Wildlife Watching; Cartoons And Bumper Stickers (indirect); Does Wildlife Sell Cigarettes? (indirect); Wildlife In National Symbols

Recreational Value Of Wildlife
The Hunter; First Impressions; Too Close For Comfort; Shrinking Habitat; Migration Barriers (indirect); To Zone Or Not To Zone; Planning For People And For Wildlife; Playing Lightly On The Earth

Renewable And Nonrenewable Natural Resources
Make A Coat; The Hunter; What Did Your Lunch Cost Wildlife?

Resource Agencies And Organizations
Here Today, Gone Tomorrow (indirect); Planting Animals; Smokey The Bear Said What?; Checks And Balances; The Hunter; Cartoons And Bumper Stickers (indirect); Does Wildlife Sell Cigarettes? (indirect); Too Close For Comfort (indirect); Migration Barriers; To Zone Or Not To Zone; Deadly Links (indirect); Flip The Switch For Wildlife

Responsible Human Actions
Litter We Know; Polar Bears In Phoenix?; Here Today, Gone Tomorrow (extension); Smokey The Bear Said What?; Checks And Balances; No Water Off A Duck's Back; The Hunter; First Impressions; Saturday Morning Wildlife Watching; Does Wildlife Sell Cigarettes?; The Power Of A Song; Too Close For Comfort; Shrinking Habitat; Keeping Score; Planning For People And For Wildlife; Ethi-Thinking; Playing Lightly On The Earth; Water's Going On; What Did Your Lunch Cost Wildlife?; Flip The Switch For Wildlife; Ethi-Reasoning; Can Do!; Improving Wildilfe Habitat; Enviro-Ethics

Seed Dispersal
Seed Need

Similarities And Differences Between People, Wildlife, And Domesticated Animals
Bearly Born, Ants On A Twig; Stormy Weather; The Beautiful Basics; Everybody Needs A Home; Habitat Lap Sit; Habitracks; What's That, Habitat?; What's For Dinner? (similarities); How Many Bears Can Live In This Forest?; And The Wolf Wore Shoes; Saturday Morning Wildlife Watching; Too Close For Comfort; Shrinking Habitat; Deadly Links; Improving Wildlife Habitat (indirect)

Soil
Eco Enrichers

Stereotype
First Impressions, And The Wolf Wore Shoes; Saturday Morning Wildlife Watching; Cartoons And Bumper Stickers (indirect); Does Wildlife Sell Cigarettes?; Wildlife In National Symbols

Succession
Forest In A Jar; Pond Succession

Symbiosis
Good Buddies

Television
Saturday Morning Wildlife Watching; Does Wildlife Sell Cigarettes?

Toxic Substances
No Water Off A Duck's Back; Deadly Links; What Did Your Lunch Cost Wildlife?

Variety Of Wildlife

Bearly Born; Ants On A Twig; Color Crazy; Interview A Spider; Grasshopper Gravity; My Kingdom For a Shelter; Tracks!; Animal Poetry; Museum Search For Wildlife; Eco Enrichers; Environmental Barometer; What Bear Goes Where? Graphananimal; Adaptation Artistry; Seeing Is Believing; Surprise Terrarium; Polar Bears In Phoenix?; Muskox Maneuvers; How Many Bears Can Live In This Forest?; Rainfall And The Forest; Owl Pellets; Here Today, Gone Tomorrow; Lobster In Your Lunch Box; And The Wolf Wore Shoes; Wildlife In National Symbols; Keeping Score; Improving Wildlife Habitat

Water

Rainfall And The Forest; Water's Going On; What Did Your Lunch Cost Wildlife? (indirect); Flip The Switch For Wildlife (indirect)

Wildlife As An Indicator Of Environmental Quality

Litter We Know; Environmental Barometer; Here Today, Gone Tomorrow (indirect); Who Lives Here? (indirect); No Water Off A Duck's Back; Too Close For Comfort; Shrinking Habitat; Migration Barriers (indirect); Deadly Links; Keeping Score; Planning For People And For Wildlife (indirect)

Zoos

Polar Bears In Phoenix?

INDOORS OR OUTDOORS

Most activities can be conducted outdoors. However, this listing is designed to indicate those activities tending to require an outdoor setting or at least a large open area.

Indoors

What's Wild; Animal Charades; Bearly Born; Color Crazy; Interview A Spider; Grasshopper Gravity; Stormy Weather; The Beautiful Basics; Everybody Needs A Home; Habitat Lap Sit; What's That, Habitat?; Habitat Rummy; My Kingdom For A Shelter; What's For Dinner?; Animal Poetry; Museum Search For Wildlife; Eco-Enrichers; Make A Coat!; What Bear Goes Where?; Graphananimal; Good Buddies; Forest In A Jar; Pond Succession; Adaptation Artistry; Seeing Is Believing; Surprise Terrarium; Polar Bears In Phoenix?; Classroom Carrying Capacity; Visual Vocabulary; Rainfall And The Forest; Owl Pellets; Wildwork; Here Today, Gone Tomorrow; Who Lives Here?; Planting Animals; Smokey The Bear Said What?; Checks And Balances; No Water Off A Duck's Back; The Hunter; Lobster In Your Lunch Box; First Impressions; And The Wolf Wore Shoes; Saturday Morning Wildlife Watching; Cartoons And Bumper Stickers; Does Wildlife Sell Cigarettes?; The Power Of A Song; Wildlife In National Symbols; Changing Attitudes; Too Close For Comfort; Migration Barriers; To Zone Or Not To Zone; Planning For People And Wildlife; Ethi-Thinking; Water's Going On?!; What Did Your Lunch Cost Wildlife?; Flip The Switch For Wildlife; Ethi-Reasoning; Can Do!; Improving Wildlife Habitat; Enviro-Ethics

Outdoors

Ants On A Twig; Wildlife Is Everywhere!; Microtrek Scavenger Hunt; Habitracks; My Kingdom For A Shelter; Litter We Know; Tracks!; Wild Words; Let's Go Fly A Kite; Seed Need; Environmental Barometer; Urban Nature Search; The Thicket Game; Quick Frozen Critters; Muskox Maneuvers; How Many Bears Can Live In This Forest?; Oh Deer!; Learning To Look, Looking To See; Shrinking Habitat; Deadly Links; Keeping Score; Playing Lightly On The Earth

CONCEPTUAL FRAMEWORK

This framework serves as the conceptual basis for activities in Project WILD. Each activity in the materials is designed to correspond to one or more points in this outline. Sometimes the correspondence is direct; that is, the activity is designed to teach the underlying concepts. In other instances, the relationship is indirect; that is, the reference to the conceptual framework is made to provide additional background information for the instructor.

I. **Awareness and Appreciation of Wildlife**

    A. Humans and wildlife have similar basic needs.
        1. All forms of life depend upon water, oxygen, nutrients, and/or sunlight in some combination.
        2. All living things are affected by and interact with their environment.
        3. Either directly or indirectly, plants support nearly all forms of animal life, including humans.
        4. Wildlife has habitat needs that are much like those of humans, although these needs are satisfied in different ways.

    B. Humans and wildlife share environments.
        1. Wildlife is present in or on nearly all areas of the earth's surface.
        2. Over a period of time, humans and wildlife must adjust or adapt to the environment, alter the environment, or perish.
        3. Wildlife is all around us even though we may not actually see, hear, or otherwise sense its presence.
        4. Wildlife varies from microscopic forms to those over 100 feet in length and occurs in a variety of forms, colors, and shapes.

    C. Humans and wildlife are subject to many of the same environmental conditions.
        1. Both humans and wildlife depend on their habitats.
        2. Habitat is composed of many integrated components including food, water, shelter or cover, space, and the arrangement of these in relation to each other.
        3. The health and well-being of both humans and wildlife are dependent upon the quality of the natural environment.
        4. Environmental change in its various forms affects all life.

    D. Humans have far greater ability to alter or adjust to environments than does wildlife; thus, humans have a responsibility to consider effects of their activities on other life forms.

II. **Human Values and Wildlife**

    A. Wildlife has aesthetic and spiritual values.
        1. The aesthetic and spiritual values humans place on wildlife vary from person to person and culture to culture.
        2. Human and wildlife relationships are expressed through myths, religious teachings and writings, symbols, ceremonies, and other activities.
        3. Humans may find peace and inspiration through study and observation of wildlife, or simply through knowledge of its existence.
        4. Human appreciation of wildlife is often expressed through art, music, drama, dance, literature, photography, and other means of creative expression.

B. Wildlife has ecological and scientific values.
   1. Wildlife interacts with its environment and thereby affects the functioning of the ecological system.
   2. Wildlife may be used as a barometer of overall environmental quality.
   3. Study of the interaction of wildlife and its environment, past and present, helps humans to better understand ecological systems and the effect of human activities on those systems.
   4. Study of the physiology, behavior, and needs of wildlife can yield insight into some of the physiology, behavior, and needs of humans.

C. Wildlife has social and political values.
   1. Historically, wildlife affected the development, movement, and size of human societies.
   2. Wildlife questions and issues have influenced alliances and conflicts between and within communities, societies, states, and nations.
   3. Wildlife issues can affect national, regional, and local political activities.

D. Wildlife has commercial and economic values.
   1. The distribution and abundance of wildlife can affect the economy of an area.
   2. Throughout history, humans have utilized wildlife for food, shelter, clothing, and other products.
   3. Human use of wildlife directly and indirectly creates job opportunities for people.
   4. Some wildlife provides products of commercial value to humans.

E. Wildlife has consumptive and non-consumptive recreational values.
   1. Wildlife-based recreation is of major importance to many millions of Americans.
   2. Consumptive wildlife-based activities, such as hunting and fishing, provide U.S. and Canadian citizens with millions of days of outdoor recreation each year.
   3. Non-consumptive activities, such as wildlife photography, painting, feeding, and observation also provide millions of days of recreation annually.

F. Wildlife has intrinsic value, although humans often only recognize values based upon human wants and needs.

III. **Wildlife and Ecological Systems**

A. Each environment has characteristic life forms.
   1. The environment, created and shaped by natural forces and modified by humans, determines what life forms can occupy it.
   2. Each species occupies a niche within the range of environments in which it is found.
   3. All life forms show adaptations to the environments in which they live.

B. All living elements of an ecological system are interdependent.
   1. Plants and animals in ecological systems live in a web of interdependence in which each species contributes to the functioning of the overall system.
   2. Food webs and energy chains illustrate the interrelationships of all living things.
   3. In a naturally functioning ecosystem, life forms and environmental factors interact to keep wildlife populations in a long-term dynamic equilibrium with each other and with their habitats.
   4. Diverse plant communities tend to support diverse wildlife communities.
   5. Some wildlife populations exhibit cyclic patterns over time.
   6. Natural laws are ultimately as binding on human populations as on wildlife.

C. Variation and change occur in all ecological systems.

1. All forms of life, including wildlife, are affected by changes in their environments.
2. Wildlife numbers and species compositions are not static but are constantly changing.
3. There is a trend of continuous replacement of one natural community of life by another.
4. Natural events and human activities affect the rate and direction of succession.

D. Adaptation is continuous within all ecological systems.
1. Each habitat is suitable only to those life forms that have adapted, over a number of generations, to its ecological conditions.
2. Wildlife adapts to its environment in ways that enable it to survive and maintain its numbers.
3. Wildlife species differ in their ability to adapt to changes in their habitat.
4. Species with very specific habitat requirements tend to be less able to adjust to environmental change.
5. Isolated ecosystems such as lakes or islands may develop specialized life forms, thus making these systems more vulnerable to environmental change.

E. Living things tend to reproduce in numbers greater than their habitat can support.
1. A population tends to increase in size until limited by one or more factors.
2. Various mortality factors, such as disease, predation, climatic conditions, pollution, accidents, and shortages of life's necessities, will cause a percentage of any population to die each year.

F. Each area of land or water, and ultimately the planet, has a carrying capacity of plants and animals.
1. Carrying capacity is determined by climatic, geological, biological, and/or behavioral factors along with human activities.
2. Carrying capacity may vary from season to season and year to year.
3. Carrying capacity affects and is affected by wildlife behavior.
4. The numbers, health, and distribution of wildlife are related to carrying capacity.
5. Carrying capacity limitations can result in competition between and among domestic animals, wildlife, and humans.

IV. **Wildlife Conservation**

A. Management of resources and environments is the application of scientific knowledge and technical skills to protect, preserve, conserve, limit, enhance, or extend the value of a natural resource, as well as to improve environmental quality.
1. All resource and environmental management practices are limited in their scope and effectiveness.
2. Wise resource and environmental management can improve the quality of life for wildlife and humans.
3. Wildlife management practices are limited in their ability to benefit wildlife.
4. Philosophies, objectives, and practices of various types of resource management are sometimes incompatible with each other, and therefore conflicts and trade-offs may occur.

B. Wildlife is one of our basic natural resources, along with water, air, minerals, soil, and plant life.
1. Nonrenewable natural resources are those which are available on a finite basis, such as minerals and fossil fuels.
2. Wildlife and other renewable natural resources can replenish themselves independently or with human assistance.

C. Good habitat is the key to wildlife survival.
1. Wildlife is affected by changes in the quality, quantity, and distribution of its habitat.
2. For a wildlife population to sustain itself there must be suitable habitat to support a viable breeding population, not just a few individuals.
3. Most species that are endangered or threatened became so from natural or human-caused changes in their habitat and their inability to adapt or adjust to such changes.
4. Successful reintroduction of wildlife into formerly occupied range may be possible but only if suitable habitat is available.

D. Wildlife resources can be managed and conserved.
1. Wildlife can be managed to alter its value to humans.
2. Humans have learned management principles by observing natural forces and events through experimentation and research.
3. Conservation of wildlife involves wise and varied uses as well as protection.
4. The diversity and numbers of wildlife present in an area often reflect the nature of human use of that habitat.
5. Habitat management is often the best way to help threatened or endangered species.
6. Management of one species will affect other species in a community.
7. For management purposes, wildlife has often been divided into categories such as game, nongame, endangered, threatened, furbearers, and commercial.

E. Wildlife conservation practices depend on a knowledge of natural laws and the application of knowledge from many disciplines.
1. Wildlife management practices generally developed in a progressive sequence, beginning with regulations, followed by predator control, creation of refuges, stocking programs, and habitat management.
2. Systematic inventory of wildlife populations did not become a common practice until the 1930s, although journals of early explorers reflect considerable variation in historic population levels.
3. Nongame species have recently begun to receive greater and more specific management attention.
4. Scientific knowledge of all aspects of wildlife, including biological and social, is limited but growing.
5. Wildlife managers use a variety of techniques in management programs, such as information, education, and regulations involving people; as well as inventory, damage control, habitat management, stocking, artificial propagation, transplanting, and direct manipulation of wildlife populations.
6. Regulated harvest of some wildlife is a management technique.
7. Regulations are necessary for wildlife conservation but cannot substitute for good habitat or maintain a species whose habitat has been depleted or destroyed.
8. Some wildlife species are not native but have been introduced to the area they presently occupy. Such introductions create changes ranging from beneficial to harmful.
9. Adding members to a community or subtracting members from it affects other members of the community.
10. Acquisition, protection, improvement, and restoration of habitat are considered to be the most beneficial long-range management techniques for wildlife.
11. Wildlife management programs are based on both biological and social-political considerations.

F. In the United States, wildlife is considered to be a public resource. Ownership of land or water alone does not secure ownership of wildlife on that land or in that water as it does in some other countries.
   1. Primary responsibility for most wildlife conservation programs in the U.S. is delegated to governmental agencies.
   2. States are generally considered to have a greater responsibility for wildlife conservation programs than the federal government.
   3. State wildlife agencies are legally responsible for managing most wildlife on public and private lands within their geographic jurisdictions.
   4. Federal agencies, in cooperation with state agencies, are legally responsible for managing wildlife affecting national interest such as most threatened and endangered species and migratory wildlife.
   5. Private organizations, industrial interests, and individual citizens also conduct wildlife conservation activities.
   6. Privately owned lands continue to provide significant amounts of habitat for wildlife.
   7. Funds provided by consumptive users, not general tax dollars, are the primary source of income for most state wildlife management programs and some federal programs.
   8. Most wildlife exists on land or in waters that are not directly controlled by state or federal wildlife management agencies.
   9. Wildlife agencies manage not only wildlife but also the activities of people who use wildlife.
   10. Wildlife agencies employ persons with a variety of scientific training and vocational skills. Competition for jobs in the wildlife field is very keen, and applicants must usually have a college degree.
   11. Citizens can become involved in the management of wildlife, habitat, and the environment by direct participation in the political process or through local, state, national, or international organizations.

V. Cultural and Social Interaction With Wildlife

A. Human cultures and societies, past and present, affect and are affected by wildlife and its habitat.
   1. All livestock and pet animals were domesticated and developed from wildlife species as humans sought to provide themselves with food, shelter, medicines, and companionship and to satisfy other needs or wants.
   2. Human societies and cultures developed in various ways partly because environmental factors produced different types of plants and animals in different places.
   3. Members of some cultures still depend on wildlife to supply a portion of their requirements for food, shelter, and clothing.
   4. Creative portrayal of wildlife through art, literature, dance, music, and drama is an historic as well as contemporary means of expressing human relationships with wildlife.
   5. Societies and subgroups within a society may have different attitudes toward wildlife and its uses, formed and transmitted by family, community, and other social groups in a variety of ways.
   6. Social attitudes toward wildlife and habitat are affected by the content of various communications media such as books, television, radio, movies, and magazines.

B. Societies develop programs and policies relating to wildlife and its habitat through a variety of social mechanisms.
  1. Some of the values, ethics, and historical traditions of societies are reflected in their treatment of wildlife and other resources.
  2. Wildlife management programs and policies are developed largely through political, social, economic, and scientific processes.
  3. Other nations and governments have different policies and philosophies relating to wildlife ownership and protection and to habitat management.

VI. **Wildlife Issues and Trends: Alternatives and Consequences**

A. Human impacts on wildlife and its habitat are increasing worldwide.
  1. Demand for wildlife tends to be greater than the supply available.
  2. Human intervention in the environment continues to change plant and animal distribution, diversity, and abundance.
  3. Increasing human populations and technologies often require space and activities that are detrimental to wildlife and its habitat.
  4. Loss and degradation of habitat is considered the greatest problem facing wildlife today.
  5. Human activities are accelerating the rate at which wildlife becomes threatened, endangered, and extinct.

B. Issues involving wildlife and its habitat are a product of social and cultural trends.
  1. Cultural differences and priorities continue to cause conflicts concerning wildlife.
  2. Modernization continues to separate people from direct contact with the natural world. This affects their actions and attitudes toward wildlife.
  3. Economic trends plus increased human population and mobility have important influences on wildlife and its habitat.
  4. Recreational trends affect wildlife and its habitat.
  5. More leisure time and growing pursuit of outdoor activities are increasing the pressures on wildlife and habitat.
  6. Political trends affect wildlife and other natural resources.

C. Current wildlife issues and trends are complex and involve alternatives and consequences.
  1. Public interest and involvement in wildlife continues to grow.
  2. Many wildlife issues involve conflicts between different interest groups.
  3. Historically when conflict between recreational and commercial harvest of a wildlife species became severe, the commercial use has been eliminated.
  4. Native American Indians and other groups at times disagree over certain uses of and rights to wildlife.
  5. Charging an access fee to hunt, fish, camp, recreate, or trap on private land is becoming a more common practice.
  6. Wildlife interest groups are making increasing use of the judicial, legislative, and regulatory systems in seeking their objectives.
  7. Whether uses of wildlife should be consumptive or non-consumptive is of concern to increasing numbers of people.
  8. Among consumptive groups, conflicts often involve how, when, and how much wildlife populations are used.
  9. Funding for state wildlife agencies historically has been derived from consumptive user fees.
  10. The levels and methods by which wildlife interest groups should fund wildlife programs are continuing issues.
  11. Recent concerns are that policies are influenced by funding sources rather than from a wider constituency.

12. Various groups interested in wildlife represent a wide range of philosophies and ethics concerning wildlife and how best to ensure its long range health and viability.

13. Questions exist concerning efforts to save endangered species for their present and future scientific, biological, aesthetic, economic, social, and intrinsic values.

14. Controversy exists between some state and federal agencies over the responsibility for management of various wildlife species.

15. Philosophies and practices in wildlife management have been both supported and criticized by individuals as well as public and private organizations.

16. The value placed on wildlife is commonly an issue in resource management decisions because value is often intangible and varies from person to person.

D. Many problems, issues, and trends involving wildlife in other parts of the world are similar to those in this country.

1. Wildlife habitat loss as a result of natural trends or human activities is a condition common among nearly all nations.

2. Consumptive uses of wildlife have been excessive in some settings and continue as a persistent problem in parts of the world.

3. Commercial sale of wildlife and wildlife products is controversial and has worldwide implications.

4. Many wildlife species regularly move across national boundaries, making adoption of international agreements necessary along with formation of international agencies and organizations to ensure protection and management of these species.

VII. Wildlife, Ecological Systems, and Responsible Human Actions

A. Each person as an individual and as a member of society affects the environment.

1. Individual and community lifestyle decisions, including recreational choices, transportation options, housing selections, vocation, food, clothing, and energy use, affect wildlife directly and indirectly.

2. Personal and community conservation practices, plus social, cultural, and economic values, affect environmental programs and activities.

3. Wildlife depletion and habitat destruction can be changed by the development and adoption of alternative human lifestyles and social expectations.

4. In determining responsible and ethical actions in relation to wildlife and the environment, individuals must separate desires from actual needs.

B. Responsible environmental actions are the obligation of all levels of society, starting with the individual.

1. Human activities increasingly determine which species of plants and animals will flourish and which will decline or disappear.

2. All users of wildlife must respect the rights and property of others, consider effects on the habitat, and observe rules and regulations relating to wildlife.

3. It is the responsibility of citizens, government, and industry to avoid waste and destructive exploitation of natural resources, including wildlife.

4. Prosecution for violations relating to wildlife and other natural resources often reflects the community's perception of the importance of those resources.

5. Public decisions that affect wildlife and the environment are made through social and political processes designed to represent the wishes of the society.

6. Individuals can influence public processes by voting, demonstrating, lobbying, seeking office, and supporting compatible interest groups.

7. Private decisions that affect wildlife and the environment are made through personal judgements. Each person makes such decisions on a daily basis, including use of time and energy, consumer choices, vocational and leisure time activities.

METRIC CONVERSION CHART*

Symbol	When You Know	Multiply by	To Find	Symbol
		LENGTH		
in	inches	2.5	centimeters	cm
ft	feet	30	centimeters	cm
yd	yards	0.9	meters	m
mi	miles	1.6	kilometers	km
		AREA		
in^2	square inches	6.5	square centimeters	cm^2
ft^2	square feet	0.09	square meters	m^2
yd^2	square yards	0.08	square meters	m^2
mi^2	square miles	2.6	square kilometers	km^2
	acres	0.4	hectares	ha
		MASS (weight)		
oz	ounces	28	grams	g
lb	pounds	0.45	kilograms	kg
	short tons (2,000 pounds)	0.9	tonnes	t
		VOLUME		
tsp	teaspoons	5	milliliters	ml
Tbsp	tablespoons	15	milliliters	ml
fl oz	fluid ounces	30	milliliters	ml
c	cups	0.24	liters	l
pt	pints	0.47	liters	l
qt	quarts	0.95	liters	l
gal	gallons	3.8	liters	l
ft^3	cubic feet	0.03	cubic meters	m^3
yd^3	cubic yards	0.76	cubic meters	m^3
		TEMPERATURE (exact)		
°F	Fahrenheit temperature	5/9 (after subtracting 32)	Celsius temperature	°C

METRIC CONVERSION CHART*

LENGTH

symbol	unit	number of meters
km	kilometer	1,000
hm	hectometer	100
dkm	decameter	10
m	meter	1
dm	decimeter	0.1
cm	centimeter	0.01
mm	millimeter	0.001

AREA

symbol	unit	number of square meters
km^2	square kilometer	1,000,000
ha	hectare	10,000
a	are	100
ca	centare	1
cm^2	square centimeter	0.0001

MASS (weight)

symbol	unit	number of grams
t	metric ton or tonne	1,000,000
kg	kilogram	1,000
hg	hectogram	100
dkg	decagram	10
g	gram	1
dg	decigram	0.1
cg	centigram	0.01
mg	milligram	0.001

VOLUME

symbol	unit	number of cubic meters
cm^3 (or cc)	cubic centimeters	0.000001

CAPACITY

symbol	unit	number of liters
kl	kiloliters	1,000
hl	hectoliter	100
dkl	decaliter	10
l	liter	1
dl	deciliter	0.1
cl	centiliter	0.01
ml	milliliter	0.001

TEMPERATURE
Celsius scale

°C	degree Celsius
0°C	freezing point of water
100°C	boiling point of water

This chart is reprinted with permission from the **Project Learning Tree Supplementary Activity Guide for Grades K—6** (Washington. D.C.: American Forest Institute, 1977).

THE MONDAY GROUP: FROM AWARENESS TO ACTION

By Bill Hammond
Director, Environmental Education
Lee County Schools
Fort Myers, Florida

The following is a testimony to "the possible." It shows us what young people can do, given the opportunity. Of profound importance in these times, Bill Hammond's leadership and clarity provide solid guidance for those of us who work with young people. Bill offers a structure that works for creating environments in which students truly can use their knowledge and skills in order to move, "from awareness to action" in conscientious, thorough, and responsible ways. Thanks to Bill, the young people of Ft. Myers, and their community for this opportunity to share in their learning—and to apply that learning, in our own ways, in our own lives and communities.

The Editors.

NOTE: This article is based on the activities of a group of senior high school students. Even so, the background may be of use to elementary school teachers. Structural changes would be necessary in most elementary schools; however, the spirit behind the accomplishments of the students is equally applicable to elementary as well as older-age young people. Grade school youth can move from "awareness to action." This article offers suggestions for some possibilities.

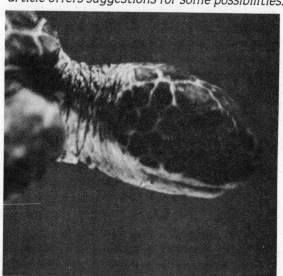

BACKGROUND

The concept that later established the High School Environmental Education Seminar was born in 1970. It was the height of the Earth Day consciousness. A group of high school students who had been in the Lee County Schools advanced track science program—some of whom had published in international scientific journals—were able to organize a system of ecology clubs in each of the middle and high schools in Lee County.

As one of the many projects that the students undertook in their ecology club system, an organized litter march down U.S. Highway 41 involved close to 2000 students. After careful planning and a day of collecting truckloads of litter from the highway and the adjacent canals—followed by a public speaking rally in one of the downtown bank parking lots in Fort Myers—the students found themselves surprised at the public support they received from the business community. Recognizing this support, the students wanted to continue their public campaign to effect environmental changes—the underlying purpose of their ecology clubs.

The students initiated a planning process. As they planned, their discussion focused on what their followup to this successful "litter campaign" would be. This led them to the idea of hanging two of the Lee County Commissioners, whom they thought to be environmentally insensitive, in effigy from the oak tree in front of the old Courthouse.

As their discussion progressed, twinges of concern passed through their advisor. I asked the students what they really knew about those County Commissioners. In the discussion, the "aha," or light bulb, phenomenon occurred. It became very clear that—despite their unusual sophistication and understanding of the scientific problems as well as the ecological relationships and applications in this community—the students actually had little knowledge and few skills for resolving conflicts or implementing the things that they felt strongly about in this community. They did not know how to use the democratic process. As a result, they repeatedly sought solutions based on emotion rather than a skillful application of facts, data, and skills.

It was this situation that proved the impetus to initiate "The Monday Group"—the High School Environmental Education Seminar class program. The program goal: to help students acquire and refine skills through practical experience in addressing significant community problems. The program was to emphasize political and personal skills—from lobbying, to use of mass media, to empathizing with politicians and other community change agents, to acquiring insight into differing values and attitudes, to studying and describing varying points of view and the rationales underlying those views, to learning and practicing the skills of effective political advocacy within the democratic system.

ORGANIZING THE PROGRAM

The first step was to seek out current and potential high school leaders. Interested leaders in student councils and other school organizations were among those initially enlisted. In the process of freeing up student leaders to come to a full day seminar class each week, some of the school building principals objected. They felt that the seminar program was pulling some of the most positive and influential leadership from the schools. As a result, a compromise was struck. High schools were asked to send not only their most "positive" leaders, but also some of their most "negative." That is, students ranged from mainstream achievers to radical, anti-establishment critics. By this process, principals were willing to support the program proposal. Through persistence and negotiation, we were able to overcome initial structural problems in order to provide the opportunity for such a course of study.

SCHEDULING FORMAT

During the first year, the entire class met for one full school day every Monday of every school week. The problem we ran into the first year was basic: the students simply lost too much time from their regular school tasks. In addition, the

responsibilities of the seminar were too much to add on a weekly basis to the already full responsibilities of the environmental education staff members, instructors for the seminar. We compromised, and decided to meet one class day every other week. This is the format we have now used for the past ten years. Through participation in this seminar throughout a school year, students are able to earn one full academic credit—usually in Science, and occasionally in Social Studies and Language Arts, depending on the nature of an individual student's project work in the seminar.

INDIVIDUAL STUDENT PROJECTS

Each student in the course is required to do an individual study project of some significance during the year. The project should in some way relate to their expression and interest in the environment. Over the years, these projects have ranged widely—from anthologies of poetry, to original albums of songs on endangered species and energy topics, to water quality surveys of canal systems, to surveys of manatees in a river. Most of the projects have made significant contributions to the body of knowledge and environmental literacy in this community.

CLASS PROJECT

The entire class must select by consensus a community issue or problem that involves elected leaders at some level. The group generally makes a selection by late fall. As a group, the students must design a plan for either resolving or contributing to the resolution of the community problem or issue they have identified, and in which they have become interested, by the end of the school year. The rationale behind this requirement: Many of these students are proficient in working at individual study projects and very specific smaller scale activity projects within their school environment. However, most of these students have not worked on a community action project of major significance. The class projects for the seminar require interacting with elected officials, using organization and stamina to work within committee structures, and working through the frustration and difficulties of the human problems encountered in accomplishing large group kinds of activities. The purpose of this class requirement then is to force students into a situation where they must learn to organize themselves; to deal with the issues of those who carry through with their work and those who fail to carry through; to address questions of emerging leadership; and to discern questions of responsibility as well as rights. These become primary issues that must be addressed by each individual as the class works to resolve the inevitable string of dilemmas that emerge in the process of completing the annual project.

ADDITIONAL ASSIGNMENTS

A third student requirement usually involves a series of smaller assignments in the class period. These smaller assignments have ranged from writing television scripts for the local affiliate of a major network to air on the Sunday evening news broadcast, to reviewing local zoning cases and taking a position on whichever sides of the issue they felt their values most aligned.

CRITERIA FOR GRADING

Students' grades in this class are based on three criteria:

1. **Their participation in class,** since their one-class participation every other Monday is the equivalent of two weeks of regular school in any given subject that they have, as well as additional time spent on class project work beyond meeting hours;

2. **The amount of input and quality of work** that they perform in their individual study project, which is determined in conference between the course instructor and the students; and

3. **The level of input and responsibility** they assume in working with the large group project, with that level of performance reviewed between the individual student and the instructor.

Grades are determined through mutual consensus and discussion between the instructor and each student, in line with the abilities of the student and the responsibilities to which the student has made a commitment within the ground rules of the class.

GETTING UNDERWAY

Early in the first semester of the course—particularly during September, October, and early November—the primary objective is to expose the class members to as many of the local environmental resources and issues as possible. So, students have waded swamps and through mangroves; they've walked beaches and they've been through the Sewage Treatment Plant, the Power Plant, and the Mosquito Control facilities. They are literally immersed in looking at and thinking about the southwest Florida community in which they have a real stake.

Remember that this class is comprised of "negative" and "positive" leaders. Over the years, we've learned that it is very difficult to maintain the so-called dis-interested learners who are there in the class because they generally have taken up negative leadership roles in their school. These students have tended to drop out of this voluntary program by the second month. We searched for ways to minimize this drop-out phenomenon, and struck upon a way that has been successful over the past ten years in bringing the group together as a community.

We have established a procedure that is initiated within the first month of the class operation. The strategy is to take students on a residential camping trip. In our case, more often than not, we go to the Ocala National Forest. Here, students get to work together as a community with a primary emphasis on each student's personal development. Each student's sense of personal responsibility is nurtured as each is respected as a whole and valuable human being. Activities include some values clarification kinds of experiences, canoeing, camping, New Games, interactive kinds of skill-building, and listening to some people who are personally involved as leaders in the state of Florida in environmental issues and problems. We've found that this experience helps to weld the group together into a community. It allows students time to sort one another out—not on the basis of their academic skills and achievement, but on the basis of their skills as human beings. Consequently, when they return from this trip, they are usually prepared to identify and agree upon a significant community problem that will serve as the focus of the group's efforts during the school year. And, the initial purpose for this outing has been served—successfully minimizing student drop-out from the program.

UNDERLYING COURSE OPERATING RULES

The fundamental basis for the class is a set of operating rules. These operating rules have been established over the years and have become the byline for the class operation. The rules are basic, and they apply to instructors as well as students.

The course is premised on helping students understand **natural models**: the principles of diversity, change, interdependence, and the **interrelationships of all things on the planet,** including the ways matter cycles and energy flows, making those cycles possible over and over again. As students understand these basic and fundamental concepts concerning how the universe works, a set of operating rules for their personal working is overlain.

Instructors are facilitators. They must continually make absolutely sure that **students have equal time access to all viewpoints and positions on all issues they encounter in class.** Balance in viewpoint is a key, rather than any form of advocacy that manipulates students.

An overlying premise of this entire course of study is that it must be experiential. The students **must do, rather than simply be told.**

The basic components for this set of rules: **truth, honesty, consistency.** These are key factors in building long-term trust and credibility in the class group as well as the community. So, for example, if you don't know, say so! It is very important to be consistent with all people encountered, and to be consistent with basic values when formulating positions on issues.

Here are the operating rules, addressed to the students who participate in the class.

Positive Viewpoints The first of these rules is that we will only accept positive viewpoints in this class. If you are against something, if you don't like something, or if you don't want something to happen, then you must turn it around. You must be **for** something, you must **want something to happen,** you must have a wish. In the class, we make it the norm to establish and express that positive wish—what it is you want to see happen. (Students are always in a posture of being for something that they care deeply about, rather than against something.)

Homework The second of the rules: You have to do your homework. You must research the background information. You must know the topic as well as anyone in the community. You must become an expert on the data and knowledge base relative to the topic for which you are interested in becoming an advocate. Doing your homework means applying the range of academic skills to find out what the issues are, the background information, and the technical data that are available in order to find out as much about that topic as you can. You become your own expert.

Persistence The third rule is: persistence. For years, that word was displayed as a three-foot-high motto statement over the door in the classroom. In environmental matters, there rarely is closure. They tend never to be resolved; they simply go through varying stages of semi-closure. Therefore, one must be persistent if he or she is going to succeed in the long haul. Persistence is a critical behavioral factor in anyone interested in effecting change in a democratic society.

Force Field A fourth consideration is what we have for years called the force field. The force must be with you if you're going to succeed in a democratic society. The force field phenomenon requires you to analyze those groups and individuals who support your position, and to seek out and find those who might not agree with your position. In force field, we try to take that positive energy from those who agree with us and support our views, and try to at least neutralize those who do not agree with us so that their energy is not counter to ours as we try to implement solutions. In other cases, force field knowledge enables one to be centered to opposing energy, and thereby gracefully to let it pass on its own path.

In working with the force field, **extreme or radical views are not viable.** Those in decision-making roles cannot be threatened by being faced with making very rapid, widespread, or radical departures from the norm. A series of small steps is what is necessary in order to effect change in this culture. The combined impact of these small steps leads to the desired major change in behavior.

Individual The fifth basic rule: everyone needs to be treated as an individual. Everyone is a human being of supreme moral worth, and while you may not agree with him or her, or you may not personally like to spend time with that person, that person is a human being and deserves every bit of the respect with which you would wish to be honored. Each person is thus to be treated as an individual, both in the class, and in the community.

No Stereotyping A sixth rule: no stereotyping allowed. Even when we treat people as individuals, it is still too easy to think of them as part of a stereotypic group. He or she is a "developer" or an "environmentalist" or a "politician." Stereotypes get in people's ways, very often preventing folks from seeing one another as individuals, and thereby preventing any real understanding—mutual understanding—as individuals. So, a critical rule in this seminar: stereotypes are not acceptable at any time, and certainly not when attempting to work with the community.

Recycle A seventh rule: if you've done your homework and followed all those previous rules, and you fail to accomplish what it is you set out to accomplish, then you must recycle. You failed because something didn't happen that needed to happen. So, you must recycle yourself through the process again and find out what it was that you did not succeed in doing effectively enough the first time.

No Scapegoating This is the final rule: no scapegoating. If, in fact, you need to recycle, and you didn't succeed the first time, scapegoating is not an acceptable way of transferring the responsibility for your lack of success to some external source. It is easy to transfer your lack of success to bureaucrats who are unresponsive, or to other stereotypic groups. In fact, however, what generally has happened is that somewhere along the line, you missed a step, as a class group. You missed resolving a need of some group or individual who was in a decision-making role. Missing that step ultimately prevented you from succeeding in implementing your solution. So it's very important that you analyze. Go back and find where that spot was. Was there a glitch in your media campaign? Was there a gap in communicating with some of the agencies or organizations or individuals? Did you neglect to get proper approval or sponsorship from key individuals or groups?

This package of premises and rules is the foundation for the operation of this class. It provides the students with an operating framework for acquiring and developing real skills based on real problems of concern to them in their own community. They are in the position to be always for something, and not against something. It gives them the responsibility for their own success. It gives them the tools so that success is virtually assured, if they are, in fact, realistic—and have done their "homework."

EXAMPLES OF MAJOR CLASS PROJECTS

The Environmental Seminar classes have successfully accomplished a number of projects over the years. The following are examples.

Project RAP: Communication with County Commissioners

The first year project was called Project RAP. In this case, the students felt that the County Commissioners were not responsive to high school students' needs and community interests. The students conducted a three-month-long survey involving almost every high school student in Lee County. They asked students to prioritize the things to which they thought the Lee County Commissioners ought to pay more attention—especially those concerns of particular interest to students in the county. The students then compiled the results, condensed them, and presented them in individual lobbying sessions with each Commissioner. Then they asked the County Commissioners if they would be willing to come to a full day meeting. The format the students recommended was to break into small, round-robin discussion groups, with a Commissioner and a half-dozen representative students at a time, to discuss those priorities that students in the district had identified as needing more communication. This, in fact, did happen. The students held Project RAP in a local park, and the County Commissioners participated. Among the results: two students were placed on the County Parks and Recreation Advisory Board; students had better communication with the Sheriff's Department; and students were given a desk and office in the Planning Department as a home base for their input and operation, as well as in the Department of Transportation. The County Commissioners increased their understanding of students in the community, and these students in turn began to understand the multiplicity of problems that a County Commissioner faces.

Purchase and Protection of a Six Mile Cypress Swamp

A second major project undertaken by students in this project resulted in the acquisition of the Six Mile Cypress—a 2,500 acre cypress strand that flows through the eastern boundary of the City of Fort Myers, becoming the urban shaper as Fort Myers grows into Lee County. The swamp had been proposed for public acquisition under federal acquisition lists. It also had been designated as a potential state park area, but after years of sitting on lists, it had moved no closer to purchase. Students who had waded through the swamp as part of the Seminar class experience felt that it was too unique to see chopped up into short-term-use farm fields and real estate development. They were concerned about overdrainage conditions and general degradation due to lack of any kind of coordinated planning or protection for the swamp.

After considerable research, the students determined that the state and federal government would not be able to buy the swamp. They conducted a biological survey, an ownership survey, a geological survey, a hydrological survey, and a land use survey. All their information was compiled into a booklet on Six Mile Cypress Swamp. This was the project for one year's class group: the compilation of an extended knowledge base about Six Mile Cypress Swamp.

Since juniors and seniors are selected to participate in this course, many of the same students who had worked on compiling the booklet continued from their junior year into their senior year. Their leadership in the next year's class group was instrumental. The students decided that the Six Mile issue was very important to them, and their major project for that year would be to try to get a public referendum on the ballot to allow citizens to acquire Six Mile through a local tax referendum. The students prepared their ballot presentation. They did their homework. They lobbied with each individual County Commissioner using teams, and proceeded to work throughout the year in trying to get the Six Mile Cypress issue placed on a referendum ballot. After having lobbied individually with the five County Commissioners, the students found they had the support of four. With what they thought were four votes in place, the students presented their plan to the County Commission at an open public meeting. Much to the students' surprise, the County Commissioners turned them down three to two, on the issue of placing the referendum on the ballot for the voters.

Following the rules of the class, the students came back, recycled, mumbled a bit, and immediately started to work to figure out how to overcome that negative vote. They were successful. The students worked to meet all the tenets the County Commissioners had placed in objection. Within one week, a new vote of the County Commissioners on this issue was held, and the five Commissioners unanimously supported placing the referendum on the ballot for the public to vote in the following November. The students were also able to influence the wording of the ballot for the referendum. They were the ones to select at what public ballot, timing-wise, the issue would be placed before the voters. They were intimately involved in the critical political decisions affecting this referendum issue.

The following year's group—the third year of the Six Mile Project—had the problem of coming in as a new group with some members who had carried over from the previous year's junior population. The third-year-group decided to stick with the project, and found themselves having to sell this project to the voters in a community where one-third of the population are retirees on fixed incomes. Between September 15th and November 5th, students had to carry on a campaign that literally had no budget attached to it. They needed to sell a referendum for an increase of one-half mill of taxation for two years. Lee County voters were being asked to tax themselves to buy the Six Mile Cypress Swamp.

The election was held in November. The voters overwhelmingly approved the referendum—in the highest plurality ever given to a tax issue in Lee County. The process of purchasing the swamp has been underway since that time, proceeding smoothly through the tax monies generated in that referendum.

The next year's Seminar class took a look at the Six Mile Cypress project, and decided all the work was not done—even though the swamp was now to be purchased and protected. The students were heartened by the public's approval of the acquisition of Six Mile Cypress—but they discovered that the Lee County Parks and Recreation Department had no staff with professional training in park planning. Not one of Lee County's regional parks had a master plan established for it. So, in this fourth year of the Six Mile project, the class group made it their project to establish a Park Master Plan for the Six Mile Cypress Swamp and became the technical assistance arm for the Lee County Parks and Recreation master plan group. They also assisted in establishing guidelines for the county's acquisition of Six Mile Cypress, negotiating a contract with The Nature Conservancy to assist in that acquisition.

Manatee Survey

Another major project that students worked on in ensuing years was a survey of the manatee population in the Orange River. That survey led to the group interacting during a controversy between the Environmental Protection Agency (EPA) and the Florida Power and Light Company. The Environmental Protection Agency had discovered that Florida Power and Light, at its local generating plant—in drawing water from the Caloosahatchee River and discharging into the Orange River—had created a delta-t block in the Orange River. A temperature gradient barrier was created that prevented the manatees from migrating up into the headwaters of the Orange River to reach their nursery and spawning grounds. The Environmental Protection Agency had provided an injunction to Florida Power and Light to redesign their canal discharge system and redirect it into the Caloosatchee River.

Such a project would have cost millions of dollars and consequently placed a great burden on local rate payers. Florida Power and Light requested that the Seminar class review the situation, with the hope that they would support Florida Power and Light's position.

Remember that one of the guiding principles of the Seminar is that in all endeavors students are always exposed to both sides of any issue, or as many sides of an issue as are plausible. Con-

sequently, students were given an opportunity to interact with the officials and biologists from Florida Power and Light, and they were then also given the opportunity to interact with the officials of the Environmental Protection Agency in Atlanta, who had placed this injunction on Florida Power and Light. The students concluded that the EPA rules were excellent and well-founded. The students also decided, after having done much homework, that there were extenuating circumstances in the Orange River that perhaps overshadowed the intent of the EPA injunction. That is, they discovered that the key index species of manatee that the EPA was concerned about were no longer able to reproduce significantly or carry on nursery functions in the Orange River because previous development in the headwaters of the Orange River had already altered that system. Secondly, they discovered that the manatee population in the Orange River was far greater than anyone had anticipated or counted previously. Consequently, their logic was that if the canal system were shifted from the Orange River into the Caloosahatchee River, those manatees—an endangered species—would be placed in further jeopardy of their ultimate survival. The students' legal research indicated this to be contrary to both the Marine Mammals Protection Act and the Endangered Species Act, and thereby created an illegal situation. The EPA could not, as a federal agency, create a new condition that would further threaten an endangered species. In concert with Florida Power and Light, the students requested a public administrative hearing. EPA granted that hearing, and the students testified on behalf of Florida Power and Light, also strongly expressing the view that the EPA policies and regulations which guided the injunction in the first place were excellent. The students emphasized that this case in Lee County should in no way weaken those regulations. They emphasized the unusual nature of the extenuating circumstances of upland development in the river system and, more specifically, of the unique manatee population that had come to winter in the Orange River complex due to the power-heated effluent.

This was thus a classic case of a group of high school students reviewing all sides of an issue, resulting in their being able to contribute to the resolution of a community problem of economic, political, and ecological significance. As a result of their also recognizing the lack of protection for manatees in the Orange River, the students proceeded to work with the county commissioners to post signs in the Orange River. The students raised funds. They had signs warning people with boat traffic at every marina, cautioning about manatee in order to protect them. In addition to signs on the Orange River, they had signs at every marina on the Caloosahatchee River and the adjacent tributary streams where manatees are known to spend time. The students got Lee County to post the park that is adjacent to Florida Power and Light effluent canal, heavily used by winter fishermen, warning people of the manatees in that canal system and of the penalties for harassing or harming the manatees in any way. This action was the forerunner of Florida's state manatee laws—supported by another Seminar student group two years later, as the laws were being created by the Florida state legislature.

Park Management

Another class group of students worked trying to resolve a conflict between Lee County and the state of Florida over management questions on a 640-acre county park called Cayo Costa Park. Students were able to move both parties to a position where an agreement was established for management responsibility in the ultimate future of that park system.

Southern Bald Eagles

A recent Seminar group project focused on the southern bald eagle population in Lee County. Students discovered that Lee County has one of the largest wintering southern bald eagle populations in the United States. The southern bald eagle is an endangered species. The students found that the future prognosis for this animal in Lee County is growing dimmer. The preponderance of eagle's nests in the county exists on land that is suitable for development. One by one, those eagle's nests are gradually being crowded out as development moves into the coastal plain and the coastal zone, along the feeding and nesting zones for the southern bald eagle. Students researched federal and state policies and regulations that protect the bald eagle. They researched the Lee County Comprehensive Plan and discovered that the policy statements whereby Lee County Commissioners take a strong stand toward protecting eagles actually provide no specific mechanisms for doing do. So, students have worked with scientists, public officials, developers, and others to establish a set of proposed new regulations to guide the protection of the bald eagle as development takes place in and around Lee County. These development regulations have been proposed for adoption as a part of Lee County's Comprehensive Plan. Such adoption is under consideration at the present time.

SUPPORTING THE POSSIBLE

Lee County's Environmental Education Seminar Program takes interested students from five public high schools and one private high school, and mixes them together into a group of students with high potential for leadership. These are students who are likely to be change agents in their communities in the future. This program gives them an opportunity to practice their leadership through experience with real-life situations. They gain skills for political effectiveness in order to become more effective leaders. They are supported and prepared for becoming leaders who understand their community, understand many community relationships, and know how to effect change which they believe is desirable and needed for a healthier, happier, wiser, more loving, more ecologically sound community. They are whole human beings who know how to accomplish such change—all within the operations of a democratic society.

PROJECT EVALUATION

Project WILD has undergone thorough evaluation of a variety of forms. The purpose has been to develop as well-conceived and tested a supplementary instructional resource as possible.

Expert Review

All of the instructional activities in Project WILD, as well as the conceptual design reflected in the Curriculum Framework, have been reviewed for educational soundness, balance, and content accuracy. The initial instructional activities were written primarily by classroom teachers. Reviewers throughout each stage of the project's development have included classroom teachers, university faculty, resource agency personnel, wildlife biologists, representatives of private conservation groups, school administrators, curriculum developers, environmental education specialists, representatives of private industry, citizen volunteers, and others. Results of this review process were used in editing and improving the Project WILD instructional materials throughout the program's development.

Pilot Test

Of the literally hundreds of instructional activities developed for possible use in Project WILD, a core group was selected and refined for use in the preliminary pilot test version of the materials. Each of the instructional activities which appears in the final Project WILD materials was tested by classroom teachers to ensure its quality and appropriateness. Some revisions—from major to minor—were made in each of the activities, and a few were discarded entirely. This entire process was developed and implemented by a respected team of researchers.

Field Test

Following the year of the pilot test, a major field test was designed and conducted to determine the effectiveness of the materials when used by teachers with their students. Again, this study was developed and implemented by a knowledgeable and esteemed team of researchers.

The field test was conducted in three states, in three demographic areas (urban, suburban, and rural), and across all elementary and secondary grade levels during one full school year. Two hundred fifty-nine teachers and more than 6000 students were involved.

The results indicate that Project WILD has a definite impact on teachers and students. Students showed significant gains in learning, and developed attitudes toward wildlife that are consistent with the goals of Project WILD. Teachers generally found the activities stimulating and worthwhile in their classes, and were able to integrate them into their curricula. A direct relationship was evidenced between the number of Project WILD instructional activities used by the teachers and student gains in knowledge and attitudes. Project WILD was effective in urban, suburban, and rural areas.

Continuing Evaluation

Project WILD will be monitored and evaluated on an on-going and long-term basis, in order to ensure its quality and effectiveness as well as to make revisions and additions to the program as needed.

ACKNOWLEDGEMENTS

Project WILD is made available as the result of the concerned and dedicated efforts of literally thousands of people.

It is not possible to individually thank and credit all of those who have assisted—including the thousands of students in kindergarten through high school classrooms who participated in the pilot and field test stages of the project's development.

We would like to make special mention of the contributions of the American Forest Institute, cosponsors of Project Learning Tree with the Western Regional Environmental Education Council. Project Learning Tree's record of quality and success led directly to the development, and subsequent availability, of Project WILD.

We would also like to acknowledge the generous support made possible through the contributions of the International Association of Fish and Wildlife Agencies, as well as the other Associate Sponsors and Contributors to the Project.

With chagrin and apologies as we recognize that we will inadvertently omit the names of many for whom we would wish acknowledgement, we would like to thank the following.

Project WILD Steering Committee Kerry Baldwin, Chairman; William F. Hammond; William R. "Bob" Hernbrode; Dr. Richard Kay; Joanna P. Lackey; Dolores Moulton Larson; Dr. Don Lundstrom. Ex Officio: Cliff Hamilton, Fiscal Manager, Western Regional Environmental Education Council. Former Members: Edward Eschler (Chairman); Dr. Tom Fitzgerald (Ex-Officio); Cliff Hamilton; Dr. Lewis Nelson, Jr.; Rudolph J. H. Schafer (Chairman); Dr. Jerry Tucker.

WREEC Members and Former Members Kerry Baldwin, Meyer Bogost, Bob Briggs, Tom Cates, Bill Dillinger, George Ek, Edward Eschler, Dr. Bill Futrell, John Gahl, John George, B. K. Graham, Dr. Gary Hall, Cliff Hamilton, John Hawkins, Dick Hess, Dr. Richard Kay, David A. Kennedy, Joanna P. Lackey, Don MacCarter, Carl Masaki, Susan McLane, Jennifer Meyer, Dolores Moulton Larson, Stu Murrell, Dr. Mary Jo Lavin, Dr. Richard Peterson, Dr. Al Ramirez, David Rice, Ray Remund, Rudolph J. H. Schafer, Bud Smith, Ray Thiess, Vince Vandre, Joe Vogler, Chris Williams, Vince Yannone.

Associate Members: Dr. Cheryl Charles, Dr. John Disinger, Jim Graban, Bob Hernbrode, June McSwain, Dr. Lew Nelson, Dr. Dave Phillips, Dr. Darleen Stoner.

Reviewers of Project WILD Curriculum Framework The Project WILD Curriculum Framework was reviewed by hundreds of individuals, representing a range of organizations including conservation groups, natural resource agencies, private industry, public education, and private education. We regret not being able to list these many individuals and organizations by name, but appreciate their substantial contributions to the overall accuracy and quality of the framework which formed the basis for the development of the Project WILD instructional materials.

We would like to especially acknowledge Mr. Cliff Hamilton of the Oregon Department of Fish and Wildlife and member of the Project WILD Steering Committee for his exceptional effort and skill in serving as general editor of the final framework.

Project WILD Writing Conference Participants
Alaska: Dolores Moulton, Edward Eschler, Lew Nelson, Kris Kantola, Sue Matthews, Paul Arneson, Eric Morris, Wendell Shiffler, Nancy Murphy, Peter Buck, Sue Quinlan, Walter Suomela, Hal Neace, Sister Bridget M. Connor, Judy Hauck, Cheryl Charles; *Arizona:* Rosemary Elkins, Jean Fields, Patty Horn, Cleo Scheyli, Eloise Babcock, Valerie Davison, Ann Motley, Peggy Griego, Judith Enz, Kitty Fischer, Mary Howell, Dean Holland, Bob Hernbrode, Kerry Baldwin, Joanna Lackey, Jerry Tucker, Wendy Greenberg, Cheryl Charles, Gerry Hernbrode, Jim Hudnall, Tanna Baldwin; *California:* Rudy Schafer, Augie Scornaienchi, Larry Rose, Anne Namolis, Evelyn Cormier, Phyllis Shuck, Molly Whiteley, Carolie Sly, Marlynn Kaake, Jan Rensel, Bob Flasher, Steve Wilkes, Martin Abrams, Otis McCain, John Mackenzie, Juanita Gex, Olina Gilbert, Mary Rodgers, Susan de Treville, Dolores Moulton, Cheryl Charles, Rocky Rohwedder; *Colorado:* Russell Skillings, Glenn McGlathery, Paul Bauman, Jeff Brigham, Sue Miller, Evaline Olson, Carol Bergevin, Kathy Williams, James Jackson, Cheryl Charles, Kerry Baldwin, Bud Smith, Gene Carroll, Jack Anderson, Helen Davis, Cliff Hamilton, Roxy Pestello, William Turner, Stu Murrell, John Ernst, Kris Gabrielson, Robin Hernbrode, Joanna Lackey, George Ek, Sandy Sanborn, Dave Perry, Bill Huntley, Dr. Norma Livo, Kathy Kelley, Bill Haggerty; *Idaho:* Marjorie Reinecker, Nancy Christensen, Royce Williams, Glendon Jones, Bob Humphries, Mary Lynn Popplewell, Begie Hatmaker, Joanna Lackey, Bob Hernbrode, Cheryl Charles, Jerry Tucker, Lewis Nelson, Cliff Hamilton, Edward Eschler, Richard Kay, Ray Remund, Stu Murrell, Ben Peyton, Harry Mills, Bob Nisbitt, Lea Williford, Shelley Davis, Creed Noah, Dennis Cartwright, Cindy Teipner, Joe Vogler, Connie Gilman, Lyn Fleming.

Field Test Teachers and Administrators Teachers, administrators, and students in school districts in the states of Colorado, Virginia, and Washington assisted in the formal field testing of the Project WILD materials. The confidentiality of the testing process requires that we not identify the participating personnel and districts. We extend our grateful thanks to all of those involved for their assistance.

Pilot Teachers, Students, and Administrators
Teachers, administrators, and students in school districts in the states of Washington and Arizona assisted in the formal pilot testing of the Project WILD materials. We thank each of these people for their dedicated and generous assistance. In particular, we would like to acknowledge the coordination and support provided by Lynn Olson, Principal, La Center, Washington; and Dick Clark, Science Supervisor, Washington Public Schools, Phoenix, Arizona. In addition, we would like to thank the following individual teachers for providing a wealth of valuable information that was used to improve and revise the Project WILD materials: Becky Staley, Jacque Sniffen, E. Helledy, Nancy Schmidt, M. Little, Virginia Barton, Bonnie Lock, M. Bruder, Robert Ryan, Sandy Mraz, Kitty Whitlaw, Gary Wallace, Karen Atkins, M. Balkenbush, M. Dollar, Mr. Gissell, Brenda Pierce, Charri Strong, Albert L. Pitzer, Tom Lutz, J. Gallagher, M. Kelbourn, M. Mitchell, Mary Anne French, Mr. Allison, Mr. Schoenborn, Mary Cowan, Diana Smiley, Tom Kennedy, Lea Hamlet, M. Russell, M. Christofanelli, K. Klaas, M. Bergmann, W. Hart, M. Pruitt, Doris Rankin, Mary Flanders, T. Kreuser, Shirley Corn, B. Charles Dorsey, Lydia Whitey, Sandy Stanley, M. Schmidli, Linda Lee Tatro. If we have inadvertently omitted anyone who assisted, please let us know, and we will make the appropriate corrections in the next printing of these materials.

Special Personnel and Materials Assistance:
Alameda County Office of Education (California), Alaska Department of Fish and Game, American Humane Association, Arizona Department of Game and Fish, Boulder Valley Public Schools (Colorado), California Department of Game and Fish, Colorado Department of Education, Colorado Division of Wildlife, Defenders of Wildlife, Hawksong Associates, Idaho Department of Game and Fish, Montana Office of the Superintendent of Public Instruction, National Audubon Society, National Wildlife Federation, New Mexico Department of Game and Fish, Ohio Department of Natural Resources, Oregon Department of Fish and Wildlife, Pennsylvania Game Commission, U.S. Forest Service, U.S. Fish and Wildlife Service, Utah Department of Natural Resources, Virginia Commission of Game and Inland Fisheries, Virginia Department of Education, Washington Department of Game, Washington Office of the Superintendent of Public Instruction, Wyoming Department of Game and Fish.

Principal Contributing Editors and Authors, in Addition to Writing Conference Participants Kerry Baldwin, Liz Caile, Dr. Cheryl Charles, Judy Dawson, Lyn Fleming, Dr. Gary Hall, Cliff Hamilton, Bob Hernbrode, Dr. Richard Konicek, Dr. Ben Peyton, Joanna Prukop Lackey, Dr. Don Lundstrom, Ernie McDonald, Dolores Moulton, Dr. Lew Nelson, Jan Rensel, Bob Samples, Rudy Schafer.

Evaluation Pilot Testing: Dr. Ben Peyton, Principal Investigator; Lyn Fleming, Associate; Field Testing: Lyn Fleming, Director; Dr. Rick Kroc, Dr. Ben Peyton, Dr. Norris Harms, Contributing Consultants; Dr. Gene Glass, Dr. Mary Lee Smith, Dr. Kenneth Hopkins, Technical Assistance.

Additional Special Assistance Tom Charles, Harry Mills, Tony Angell, Donna Szuhy, Dale Crider, Linda Crider, Dick Draney, Bob Flasher, Marlynn Kaake, Jim Gladson, Jim Graban, Bill Hammond, Tex Hawkins, John Herrington, Dick Hess, Larry Littlebird, June McSwain, Dr. Jake Nice, Jim Phillips, Augie Scornaienchi, Jan Rensel, Bob Samples, Robin Hernbrode, Chris Wille, Irene Shelver, Bill Shelver, Stician Samples, Dr. Tom Fitzgerald, Perl Charles, Mattie Charles, Teresa Auldridge, George Ek, Dave Boynton, Dr. Judith Enz, Dr. Jon Hooper, David A. Kennedy.

Reviewers of Pilot Materials Carlton Owen, June McSwain, Lester DeCoster, Rocky Rohwedder, Bob Flasher, Dore Zwingman, Janet Sheldon, Bev Wu, Larry Malone, Linda DeLucchi, Bill Bolar, Kerri Lubin, Joy Crupper, Dr. Jim Armitage, Phyllis Clarke, Tina Yeager, Wanda Headrick, David Yeager, Tiajuana Cochnauer, Shirley J. Wright, Dana Bowyer, Dean Williams, Ron Hamilton, Nancy Christensen, Pam Aikins, Jim Carlson, Ernie McDonald, Bob Samples, Dr. Gary Hall, Cliff Hamilton, Bob Hernbrode, Dr. Lew Nelson, Dr. Ben Peyton, Vince Vandre.

Copy Editing Assistance and Additional Technical Review Dick Hess; Chief, Information and Education, Colorado Division of Wildlife

Principal Editor Dr. Cheryl Charles

Production

Word Processing for Typeset Telecommunication: Cheryl Charles, Judy Dawson, Jan Rensel.

Telecommunication to Graphic Directions: Oli Duncan, Sharon Andriola.

Graphic Design: Cheryl Charles and Bob Samples, Hawksong Associates.

Layout and Pasteup: Cheryl Charles, Bob Samples, Bardet Storyk, and Judy Dawson.

Artwork: All drawings are by Bob Samples unless otherwise acknowledged.

Photos: Photographs remain the property of the contributing photographer. All photographs are by Bob Samples and Cheryl Charles, with the following exceptions.

Arizona Game And Fish Department—p. 47 (Jerry Day), p. 105, p. 124 (Pat O'Brien), p. 127 (Pat O'Brien), p. 130 (David Daughtry), p. 142 (David Daughtry), p. 164 (Kerry Baldwin).

California Department of Fish and Game—p. 24 (Paul Wertz), p. 57 (Trey Bonetti), p. 131 (Paul Wertz), p. 147 (Norman Underwood).

Florida Department of Environmental Services—p. 18, p. 129.

Idaho Department of Fish And Game—p. 125 (Stu Murrell).

New Mexico Game and Fish Department—facing p. 1, p. 80.

Oregon Department of Fish and Wildlife—p. 19, p. 30, p. 106.

Pennsylvania Game Commission—p. 5 (J.E. Osman), p. 132 (J.E. Osman), p. 172 (J.E. Osman).

United States Fish and Wildlife Service—p. 53 (W.H. Julian).

Wyoming Game and Fish Department—p. 44, p. 143, p. 153.

Dr. David E. LaHart, p. 40.

Printing: Johnson Publishing Company; Don Caven, Sales Manager.

CODE OF PRACTICE ON ANIMALS IN SCHOOLS

Position statement of the
National Science Teachers Association,
Washington, D.C.

This code of practice is recommended by the National Science Teachers Association for use throughout the United States by elementary, middle/junior high, and secondary school teachers and students. It applies to educational projects involving live organisms conducted in schools, or in school-related activities, such as science clubs, fairs, competitions, and junior academies.

The purpose of these guidelines is to enrich education by encouraging students to observe living organisms and to learn proper respect for life. Study of living organisms is essential for an understanding of living processes. This study, however, must go hand-in-hand with observation of humane principles of animal care and treatment which are described below. These principles apply to both vertebrates and invertebrates.

A. A teacher must have a sure understanding of and **strong commitment to responsible care of living creatures** before making any decision to use live organisms for educational purposes. Preparation should include acquisition of knowledge on care appropriate for that species, as well as housing and other equipment needs and food, and planning for care of the living creatures after completion of study.

B. Teachers should try to assure that live organisms entering a classroom are **healthy and free from transmissable diseases** or other problems that may endanger human health. Not all species are suitable. Wild animals, for instance, are frequent carriers of parasites and disease and generally are not appropriate.

C. Of primary importance is **maintenance of good animal health and provision of optimal care** based on an understanding of the life habits of each species. Animal quarters shall be spacious and avoid overcrowding, and be sanitary. Handling shall be gentle. Food shall be palatable to the species and of sufficient quantity and balance to maintain a good standard of nutrition at all times. No animal shall be allowed less than the optimum maintenance level of nutrition. Clean drinking water shall always be available. Adequate provision shall be made for the animal's care at all times, including weekends and vacation periods.

D. **Experimental procedures conducted on vertebrate animals shall include only those which do not involve pain** or discomfort to the animal.

E. All aspects of animal care and treatment shall be **supervised by a qualified individual** who will ensure that proper standards are maintained.

F. Supervisors and students should be familiar with appropriate **literature on care and handling** of living organisms. Practical training in learning these techniques is encouraged.

G. Adequate plans should be made to **control possible unwanted breeding** of the species during the project period.

H. Appropriate plans should be laid for **what will happen to the living creatures at the conclusion of the study.** Sometimes it may be possible to find a comfortable home for an animal with a responsible person.

I. As a general rule, **laboratory-bred or non-native species should not be released into the wild.** For instance, in some climates *Xenopus* frogs, or gerbils, if released, can disturb the normal ecosystem or become pests.

J. On rare occasions it may be appropriate to sacrifice an animal for educational purposes. This shall be done in an approved humane (rapid and painless) manner by a person experienced in these techniques and it should **not** be done in the presence of immature or young students who may be upset by witnessing such a procedure. Maximum efforts should be made to study many biological principles and **utilize as many body tissues as possible from a single animal.**

K. **The procurement, care, and use of animals must comply with existing local, state, and federal regulations.**

EXPERIMENTAL STUDIES

1. In biological procedures involving living organisms, **species of plants, bacteria, fungi, protozoa, worms, snails, insects, and other invertebrate animals should be used wherever possible.** Their wide variety, ready availability, and simplicity of maintenance and subsequent disposal make them especially suitable for student work.

2. **Some sample plant, protozoan, and/or invertebrate projects include:** field studies and natural history (life cycles, incidence in nature, social structures, etc.); germination; genetics; reproduction; effect of light, temperature, other environmental factors, and hormones on growth and development; feeding behavior; nutritional requirements; circulation of nutrients to tissues; metabolism; water balance; excretion; movement; activity cycles and biological clocks; responses to gravity and light; perception to touch, humidity and vibration; learning and maze running; habituation; communication; pheromones; observations of food chains and interdependence of one species on another.

3. **No experimental procedures shall be attempted on mammals, birds, reptiles, amphibians, or fish that cause the animal pain** or distinct discomfort or that interfere with its health. As a rule of thumb, a student shall only undertake those procedures on vertebrate animals that could be done on humans without pain or hazard to health.

4. Students shall **not perform surgery** on vertebrate animals.

5. **Examples of non-painful, non-hazardous projects on some vertebrate species** (including, in some instances, human beings) include some already mentioned under item (2) and also: group behavior, normal growth and development; properties of hair, pulse rate and blood pressure; various normal animal behaviors such as grooming, and wall-seeking; reaction to novelty or alarm; nervous reflexes and conditioned responses; special senses (touch, hearing, taste, smell, and proprioceptive responses); and respiration. None of these projects requires infliction of pain or interference with normal health.

6. **Experimental procedures shall not involve** use of microorganisms which can cause diseases in humans or animals, ionizing radiation, cancer-producing agents, or administration of alcohol or other harmful drugs or chemicals known to produce toxic or painful reactions capable of producing birth defects.

7. **Behavioral studies should use only reward** (such as providing food) and not punishment (such as electric shock) in training programs. Food, when used as reward, shall not be withdrawn for periods longer than 12 hours.

8. **Diets deficient in essential nutrients are prohibited.**

9. **If bird embryos** are subjected to invasive or potentially damaging experimental manipulations, the embryo must be destroyed humanely two days prior to hatching. If normal embryos are to be hatched, satisfactory humane provisions must be made for the care of the young birds.

10. On rare occasion it may be appropriate to **pith a live frog** for an educational demonstration. Correct procedure is rapid and virtually painless, and the animal should never recover consciousness. However, if done incorrectly, this procedure can cause pain. The technique should be learned initially using dead animals. Pithing live animals should only be undertaken by a person knowledgeable in the technique.

(CAUTION: Pithing, shocking, experimental medication, and other activities may be illegal in your state; they are, for example, in California. Please check local, state, and federal regulations involving use of wildlife in instructional settings.)

For conservation reasons, efforts should be made to protect depleted animal species such as *Rana pipiens*. Similar educational objectives can frequently be achieved using alternative species, or pursuing alternative methods of study.

11. **Protocols** of extracurricular projects involving animals **should be reviewed in advance** of the start of work by a qualified adult supervisor. Preferably, extracurricular projects should be conducted in a suitable area in the school.

12. High school students may wish to take assistant positions with professional scientists working in established USDA-registered research institutions.

*Reprinted from **The Science Teacher.** Washington D.C.: National Science Teachers Association, September 1980.*

ALPHABETICAL
LISTING